A Study Book for the
NEBOSH National Diploma

in Occupational Health and Safety Practice

Managing Health and Safety

RMS Publishing Limited
Suite 3, Victoria House
Lower High Street
Stourbridge
DY8 1TA

© ACT Associates Limited.
First Published April 2005.
Second Edition August 2006.
Third Edition August 2008.
Third Edition April 2009 (reprint).

Cover design by Graham Scriven.
Printed and bound in Great Britain by CPI Antony Rowe.

ISBN-13: 978-1-906674-02-1

Editor's Notes

Diagrams and photographs

A number of the diagrams included in the Study Book for the NEBOSH National Diploma in Occupational Health and Safety Practice have been produced in hand-drawn format. In particular these are diagrams that students studying for NEBOSH examinations may be required, or find it helpful, to produce by hand at the time of examination. They are provided to help the student to get an impression of how to do similar drawings of their own. I hope that these diagrams show that such drawings are achievable by hand and also assist in illustrating a standard that might be expected in examination.

We have taken particular care to support the text with a significant number of photographs. They are illustrative of both good and bad working practices and should always be considered in context with supporting text. I am sure that students will find this a useful aid when trying to relate their background and experience to the broad based NEBOSH National Diploma syllabus. They will give an insight into some of the technical areas of the syllabus that people have difficulty relating to when they do not have a strong technical background.

Where diagrams/text extracts are known to be drawn from other publications, a clear source reference is shown and ACT wish to emphasise that reproduction of such diagrams/text extracts within the Study Book is for educational purposes only and the original copyright has not been infringed.

Legal requirements

Legislation is referred to in context in the various elements that comprise the study book. This reflects the interest of the NEBOSH National Diploma syllabus and requirements to study new/amended legislation under the rule from NEBOSH that it has to have been in force for six months before it becomes examinable. In addition, the essential points of legislation relevant to this Unit of the Diploma syllabus are contained in the section of the study book under Relevant Statutory Provisions.

Case law, as specified by the NEBOSH National Diploma syllabus, is referred to in the Hazardous Agents in the Workplace Study Book. It is important to note that these cases are examined in the NEBOSH National Diploma. Additional cases may be referred to in the same element. Though they are not referred to specifically in the syllabus it is useful to be aware of them as they have an influence on the workplace and showing knowledge of them at time of examination may emphasise a greater depth of understanding of the topic. Further information on other significant cases can be found in the other two RMS Publishing Study Books in the series for the NEBOSH National Diploma.

The NEBOSH National Diploma examinations do not assess the students' knowledge of section numbers of the Health and Safety at Work Act or knowledge of regulation numbers in an unhelpful way. Instead questions ask the student to explain something about a section number, or significant regulation, by giving the number and the purpose of that section or regulation. In addition, it should be remembered that the student might choose to refer to a section number when answering a question that requires a broad knowledge of law. Knowledge of significant section and regulation numbers is important when answering the questions for the Diploma examinations. Section and regulation numbers are referred to in the Study Books in order to differentiate different components of the law and to aid the student in referencing legislation in the workplace, if required by their work or Unit D assignment.

Syllabus

Each element of the Study Book has an element overview that sets out the learning outcomes, the contents, the relevant statutory provisions and any connected sources of reference. The Study Book reflects the order and content of the NEBOSH National Diploma syllabus and in this way the student can be confident that the Study Book reflects the themes of the syllabus. In addition, the syllabus, and therefore this study book, is structured in a very useful way; focusing on hazards, their control and core management of health and safety principles which would be useful as reference for any health and safety practitioner.

Higher Level Qualifications

The structure, level and content of this study book is appropriate for those involved in study of health and safety at university level, particularly if the course is one that is accredited by the Institution of Occupational Health and Safety (IOSH).

National Vocational Qualification

We are confident that those working to national vocational qualifications in occupational health and safety will find this Study Book a useful companion. For students working towards the S/NVQ Level 4 in Occupational Health and Safety Practice they will find a good correlation between the scope of the Study Book series for NEBOSH National Diploma and the domain knowledge needs at that level.

Relationship to other RMS Study Books

This study book content is built on the foundation knowledge contained in the RMS Publishing Study Books for Certificate level and should be read in conjunction with them, in particular the study book for the NEBOSH National General Certificate in Occupational Health and Safety.

Acknowledgements

Managing Editor: Ian Coombes CMIOSH - Managing Director, ACT; member of NEBOSH Council, past NEBOSH Board member and NEBOSH examiner; Chairman of IOSH Initial Professional Development Sub-Committee.

RMS Publishing and ACT Associates Ltd wish to acknowledge the following contributors and thank them for their assistance in the preparation of the Unit A Study Book for the NEBOSH National Diploma: Nick Attwood, Nicola Clarke, Kris James, Dean Johnson, Geoff Littley, Janice McTiernan, Barrie Newell, Clive Raybould, Robert Sannwald, Gordon Self and Julie Skett.

NEBOSH Study Books also available from RMS:

Publication	Edition	10-digit ISBN	13-digit ISBN	EAN
The Study Book for the NEBOSH General Certificate	Fifth	1 900420 97 X	978-1-900420-97-6	9781900420976
The Study Book for the NEBOSH International General Certificate	First	1 900420 90 2	978-1-900420-90-7	9781900420907
A Study Book for the NEBOSH Certificate in Fire Safety and Risk Management	Second	1 900420 88 0	978-1-900420-88-4	9781900420884
The Study Book for the NEBOSH National Certificate in Construction Safety and Health	Second	1 900420 89 9	978-1-900420-89-1	9781900420891
The Study Books for the NEBOSH National Diploma in Occupational Safety and Health:	A series of three study books, including this study book.			
■ (Unit B) Hazardous Agents in the Workplace	Third	1 900420 98 8	978-1-900420-98-3	9781900420983
■ (Unit C) Workplace and Work Equipment	Third	1 906674 01 9	978-1-906674-01-4	9781906674014

Contents

Figure List (including tables and quotes)

List of abbreviations

LEGISLATION

CAWR	Control of Asbestos at Work Regulations 2006
CDGUTPER	Carriage of Dangerous Goods and Use of Transportable Pressure Group Regulations 2004 (as amended 2005)
CDM	Construction (Design and Management) Regulation 2007
CHIP	Chemicals (Hazard Information and Packaging for Supply) Regulations 2002
CHPR	Construction (Head Protection) Regulations 1989
CIMAH	Control of Industrial Major Accident Hazards Regulations 1984
CLAW	Control of Lead at Work Regulations 2002
CLER	Classification and Labelling of Explosives Regulations 1983
COER	Control of Explosives Regulations 1991
COMAH	Control of Major Accident Hazards Regulations 1999 (as amended 2005)
CNWR	Control of Noise at Work Regulations 2005
CoPA	Control of Pollution (Amendment) Act 1989
COSHH	Control of Substances Hazardous to Health Regulations 2002 (and as amended 2004)
CVWR	Control of Vibration at Work Regulations 2005
CPA	Consumer Protection Act 1987
CSR	Confined Spaces Regulations 1997
DDA	Disability Discrimination Act 1995
DSEAR	Dangerous Substances and Explosive Atmospheres Regulations 2002
EESR	Electrical Equipment (Safety) Regulations 1994
EIA	Environmental Impact Assessment Regulations 1999
ENVA	Environment Act 1995
EPA	Environmental Protection Act 1990
ESQCR	Electricity Safety, Quality and Continuity Regulations 2002
EWR	Electricity at Work Regulations 1989
FAR	Health and Safety (First-Aid) Regulations 1981
HASAWA	Health and Safety at Work etc Act 1974
HSCER	Health and Safety (Consultation with Employees) Regulations 1996
HSMAR	Health and Safety (Miscellaneous Amendments) Regulations 2002
HSOA	Health and Safety (Offences) Act 2008
HWR	Hazardous Waste Regulations 2005
IER	Health and Safety Information for Employees Regulations 1989
IRR	Ionising Radiations Regulations 1999
LOLER	Lifting Operations and Lifting Equipment Regulations 1998
LoWR	List of Wastes (England) Regulations 2005
MHSWR	Management of Health and Safety at Work Regulations 1999
MMHSPR	Mines Miscellaneous Health and Safety Provisions Regulations 1995
NIHHS	Notification of Installations Handling Hazardous Substances Regulations 1982
NOMAS	Dangerous Substances (Notification and Marking of Sites) Regulations 1990
OFAR	Offshore Installations and Pipeline Works (First-Aid) Regulations 1989
OLA	Occupiers' Liability Acts 1957 and 1984
OLSA	Occupiers' Liability (Scotland) Act 1960
PER	Pressure Equipment Regulations 1999
PPER	Personal Protective Equipment at Work Regulations 1992
PSSR	Pressure Systems Safety Regulations 2000
PUWER	Provision and Use of Work Equipment Regulations 1998
QR	Quarries Regulations 1999
RIDDOR	Reporting of Injuries, Diseases and Dangerous Occurrences Regulations 1995
RRFSO	Regulatory Reform (Fire Safety) Order 2005
RTA	Road Traffic Act 1999
SMSR	Supply of Machinery (Safety) Regulations 1992
SRSC	Safety Representatives and Safety Committees Regulations 1977
SPVSR	Simple Pressure Vessels (Safety) Regulations 1991
SSAA	Social Security Administration Act 1992
SSACPR	Social Security Act (Claims and Payments) Regulations 1979
SSIDPDR	Social Security (Industrial Diseases) (Prescribed Diseases) Regulations 1985
SSSR	Health and Safety (Safety Signs and Signals) Regulations 1996
WAH	Work at Height Regulations 2005
WHSWR	Workplace (Health, Safety and Welfare) Regulations 1992

GENERAL

ACOP	Approved Code of Practice
ADR	Alternate Dispute Resolution
AFCI	Arc-Fault Circuit Interrupter
AITT	Association of Industrial Truck Trainers
AWS	Automated Warehousing Systems
AZDN	Azodiisobutyronitrate

BASEEFA	British Approvals Service for Electrical Equipment for Flammable Atmospheres
BATNEEC	Best Available Techniques Not Entailing Excessive Cost
BAT	Best Available Techniques
BCEC	British Crane and Excavator Corporation Ltd
BLEVE	Boiling Liquid, Expanding Vapour Explosion
BPEO	Best Practicable Environmental Option
BP	British Petroleum
BS	British Standards
CA	Competent Authority
CAT	Cable Avoidance Tool
CCF	Common Cause Failures
CCTV	Closed Circuit Television
CE	Conformité Européene
CENELEC	European Committee for Electro-technical Standardisation
CEN	European Standardisation Committee
CFC	Chlorofluorocarbons
CITB	Construction Industry Training Board
CNC	Computer Numerically Controlled
CPR	Cardio Pulmonary Resuscitation
DTI	Department of Trade and Industry
EA	Environmental Agency
EC	European Community
EEA	European Economic Area
EEBAD	Earthed Equipotential Bonding and Automatic Disconnection
EEC	European Economic Community
EHSR	Essential Health and Safety Requirements
EMA	Employment Medical Adviser
EN	European Standards
ESD	Electrostatic Discharge
EU	European Union
EWC	European Waste Catalogue
FEAB	Fartygsentreprenader AB
FID	Flame Ionisation Detector
FKAB	Fartygskonstructioner AB
FLT	Fork Lift Truck
GB	Great Britain
HAZOP	Hazard and Operability Studies
HBC	High Breaking Capacity
HCFC	Hydrochlorofluorocarbons
HSC	Health and Safety Commission
HSE	Health and Safety Executive
IBC	Intermediate Bulk Container
IDLH	Immediately Dangerous To Life or Health
IEE	Institute of Electrical Engineers
IPC	Integrated Pollution Control
IPPC	Integrated Pollution Prevention and Control
IP	Index of Protection
ISO	International Organisation for Standardization
LAAPC	Local Authority Air Pollution Control
LAPPC	Local Air Pollution Prevention and Control
LCA	Life Cycle Assessment
LEFM	Linear Elastic Fracture Mechanics
LEL	Lower Explosive Limit
LEV	Local Exhaust Ventilation
lm	Lumen
LPG	Liquefied Petroleum Gas
LPI	Liquid penetrant inspection
MAPP	Major Accident Prevention Policy
MATTE	Major Accidents To The Environment
MEGC	Multiple Element Gas Containers
MEL	Maximum Exposure Limit
MEWP	Mobile Elevated Work Platform
MIC	Methyl Isocyanate
NO_x	Nitrogen Oxide
MSDS	Material Safety Data Sheet
MSW	Municipal Solid Wastes
mV	Milli Volts
NDT	Non-destructive Testing
OES	Occupational Exposure Standard
OCPD	Overcurrent Protective Device
PE	Photo-electric
PES	Programmable Electronic Systems

PPE	Personal Protective Equipment
RID	International Carriage of Dangerous Goods by Rail
RPE	Respiratory Protective Equipment
RTITB	Road Transport Industry Training Board
SADT	Self Accelerating Decomposition Temperature
SCBA	Self-Contained Breathing Apparatus
SELV	Separated Extra Low Voltage
SEPA	Scottish Environmental Protection Agency
SO_2	Sulphur Dioxide
SSW	Safe Systems of Work
SWL	Safe Working Load
SWR	Steel Wire Rope
UV	Ultra Violet
VDU	Visual Display Unit
VOC	Volatile Organic Compounds
WAC	Waste Acceptance Criteria
WRA	Waste Regulatory Authorities

Element

A1

Principles of health and safety management

Learning outcomes

The intended learning outcomes are that the student will be able to:

A1.1   explain the moral, legal and economic reasons for a health and safety management system

A1.2   discuss the principles of an effective health and safety management system with reference to appropriate examples

A1.3   outline the requirements, role, structure (implementation and monitoring) of an effective health and safety policy

A1.4   outline the role and responsibilities of health and safety specialists

Contents

Relevant statutory provisions

Management of Health and Safety at Work Regulations (MHSWR) 1999 - Regulations 3, 4, 5 and 7

Health and Safety at Work etc Act (HASAWA) 1974 - Section 2

This page is intentionally blank

ELEMENT A1 - PRINCIPLES OF HEALTH AND SAFETY MANAGEMENT

A1.1 - Reasons for managing health and safety

The reasons for risk management may be based on moral, legal, and economic considerations.

Moral

DUTY OF REASONABLE CARE

The common law duty of care is the duty on an individual to take reasonable care of those affected by what he does or doesn't do. This reflects the moral duty to take reasonable care to not hurt each other by one's actions.

UNACCEPTABILITY OF PUTTING HEALTH AND SAFETY OF PEOPLE AT RISK

It is unacceptable in our society to put the health and safety of people at risk, especially for one's own profit, if there are reasonable ways of reducing that risk to acceptable or tolerable levels. As an employer or manager, we would feel morally responsible if someone we had set to carry out a task suffered an injury as a consequence.

Considerations should include: the general well being of employees; the interaction with the general public who either live near the organisation's premises or come into contact with the organisation's operations - e.g. transportation, noise, effluent discharges etc. and the consumers of the organisation's products or services, who ultimately keep the organisation in business.

SOCIETY'S ATTITUDE TO MORAL OBLIGATIONS

The attitude of society changes through time and can put pressure on the way an employer conducts his business. The public outrage at rail, sea and air disasters shows that if the risk impinges on the general public, they are less likely to accept it as being part of life. Society sees the employer as owing a moral obligation to the society in which he conducts his business. This is a long way from the attitude in the Industrial Revolution, where it seemed as though society was grateful for the chance to work and the prosperity an employer could bring, rather than having a moral duty to conduct a business safely. Generally speaking, decisions in common law and changes in statute reflect the increasing awareness of society's attitude to moral obligations.

Legal

The moral obligation for taking reasonable care of persons at work and those affected by work is not just reflected in common law, but also in statute law and is criminally enforceable. Health and safety legislation in most cases goes beyond taking reasonable care and may place duties of absolute, practicable or reasonably practicable care.

Considerations should include possible consequences of failing to comply with health, safety and environmental legislation, approved codes of practice, guidance notes and accepted standards, plus other relevant legislation concerning fire prevention, pollution, and product liability. Loss may result from the preventive (by enforcement notices), punitive (through criminal sanctions), and compensatory effects of law.

Failure to manage health and safety does not necessarily have to result in an accident to attract punitive measures. Notices and prosecutions can result from breaches of the law which have not caused a loss.

Where a loss has occurred, claims for compensation may be made for a breach of statutory duty and/or negligence.

PREVENTIVE (BY ENFORCEMENT NOTICES)

The enforcers have the power to issue Improvement Notices for breaches of the law and Prohibition Notices where they feel that there is a risk of serious personal injury. The issue of notices is to prevent situations from occurring that may result in loss. Failure to comply with the notices may result in criminal prosecution, in addition to prosecution for the original breach of law, for which the notice was issued.

PUNITIVE (THROUGH CRIMINAL SANCTIONS)

Prosecution in the criminal courts is meant to be a punishment for not complying with the law of the land. For health and safety breaches, this may be fines, rarely imprisonment or sometimes both. The individual prosecuted may be an individual employer or a corporate body, and/or an individual within the organisation, which may be a director or similar officer, manager, supervisor or worker.

COMPENSATORY EFFECTS OF LAW

Where an individual suffers a quantifiable loss due to a workplace accident, that person may sue in the civil courts for compensation. The individual may sue for a breach of a certain statute and/or someone's failure to fulfil a common law duty. Generally, the insurers under Employer's Liability Compulsory Insurance or Public Liability Insurance pay compensation. Compensation claims can cause an increase in the insurance premiums.

Economic

Moral, legal and economic reasons for managing health and safety are closely linked. An organisation that loses money through poor management of health and safety will have to answer to the board and shareholders eventually as to where this loss is occurring. A small company may lose much of its profits and not be able to break even, possibly going out of business. Economic reasons are considered to be powerful motivators.

Considerations should include the financial impact on the organisation of the costs of accidents, the effect on insurance premiums, possible loss of production / service and the overall effect on the 'profitability' of the organisation. Costs may be direct and indirect.

ACCIDENTS - DIRECT COSTS

- Insurance cover increased.
- Compensation payments.
- Fines.

- Damage to the equipment, materials, property and environment.
- Lost time of injured person and continued employment payments for employee.

ACCIDENTS - INDIRECT COSTS

- Time due to interference with service/production, failure to fill orders on time, loss of bonuses, penalty schemes and similar causes.
- Lost time by other employees who stop work or suffer reduced performance: out of curiosity; out of sympathy; weakened morale.
- Lost time by supervisor or other managers.
- Assisting injured employee.
- Investigating the cause(s) of the accident.
- Arranging for the injured employee's work to be continued by some other employee.
- Selecting, training, and/or induction of a new employee to replace injured employee.
- Preparing accident reports, attending hearings, inquests courts etc.
- Time and skill of specialists for:

1. First aid / fire fighting / spill control.
2. Clean up / salvage / recovery.
3. Detailed investigation.
4. Legal advice / defence.
5. Customer / supplier / public confidence.

A1.2 - Introduction to health and safety management

Definitions

HAZARD

Hazard may be defined as: "the ability of something to cause harm (loss)", e.g. electricity, trailing cables, working at height.

Through hazard identification it is possible to establish the level of risk. The presence of hazards at a given level of risk may not be a cause for immediate concern. However, some situations may exist or arise where there is a potential for loss.

RISK

Risk may be defined as: "the likelihood of a given loss occurring in defined circumstance", e.g. electrocution through contact with a damaged conductor, tripping over equipment left in walkways, falling from a height without edge protection.

The level of risk depends on a number of factors: the likelihood of the hazard causing harm, the severity of that harm and the people involved.

DANGER

Danger may be defined as: "imminent contact with a hazard."

SUITABLE AND SUFFICIENT

Suitable and sufficient is not defined in law, but in terms of risk assessment is defined in the Management of Health and Safety at Work Regulations (MHSWR) 1999 Approved Code of Practice and can be summarised as follows - the risk assessment will be suitable and sufficient if:

- The risk assessment identifies the risks from, or in connection with, work and the details are proportionate to the risk.
- It takes account of non-routine operations.
- All persons affected by the undertakings are considered.
- It is appropriate to the nature of the work.
- It identifies the period of time it is likely to remain valid.

Suitable and sufficient, as used elsewhere in regulations, for example Regulation 25 of the Workplace (Health, Safety and Welfare) Regulations (WHSWR) 1992, the provision of "suitable and sufficient" rest facilities, can be defined using similar criteria to that of risk assessments: rest rooms shall be suitable and sufficient if they include, e.g. suitable arrangements to protect non-smokers from discomfort caused by tobacco smoke, (considers all persons affected).

Outline of management models

Health and safety management systems are a formal and logical way of planning and controlling management of risk in an organisation. The models can be based on the HSE's model in the guidance HSG65 or the environmental model BS EN ISO 14001.

Explanation of health and safety management systems

HSG65

HSG65 - 'Successful Health and Safety Management' was first prepared by the HSE's Accident Prevention Unit in 1991 and a second edition was published in 1997. The original 5 steps model is unchanged; however, a three component framework is advocated.

This consists of:

1. Management arrangements - essentially the management system.
2. Risk control systems (RCS) - to make sure workplace precautions are implemented and kept in place.
3. Workplace precautions - to prevent harm at the point of risk.

Management arrangements

This consists of the original '5 steps' approach i.e.

- Set your policy.
- Organise your staff:
  - Competence.
  - Control.
  - Co-operation.
  - Communication.
- Plan and set standards.
- Measure your performance.
- Audit and review.

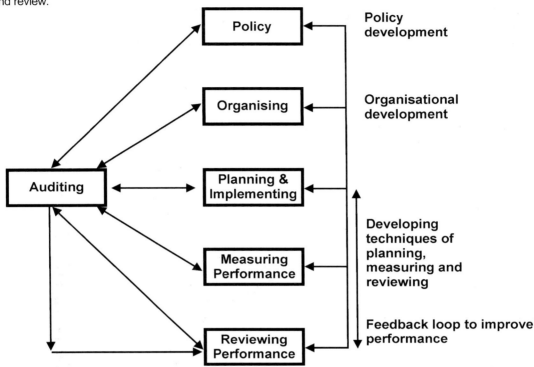

Figure A1-1: Key elements of successful health and safety management.   *Source: HSG65.*

Risk controls

Measures to ensure workplace precautions are implemented and in place.
- Input controls such as purchasing and recruitment.
- Process controls such as maintenance and change management.
- Output controls such as product packaging/labels and disposal.

Workplace precautions

Measures to control hazards
- Local exhaust ventilation.
- Machine guarding.

BS 8800

BS 8800:1996 - 'Guide to Occupational Health and Safety Management systems' is based on two alternative approaches. Organisations can base their occupational health and safety management system (OHSMS) on:

- HSG65 Successful Health and Safety Management Systems for those who wish to base their approach on the HSE model (model is shown above).
- Or: BS EN ISO 14001 for those who wish to base their management system on the environmental systems standard. *(The model is shown later in this Element).*

It should be noted that BS 8800 is a guide rather than a standard that can be assessed and certified. Thus words like "should" rather than "will" or "must" are used. For example, under 4.2.3 of BS8800 HSG65 option - OH&S documentation includes the paragraph:

The organisation should maintain any records necessary to demonstrate compliance with legal and other requirements.

Figure A1-2: Requirement for OH&S document   *Source: BS8800 - HSG65 option - ref 4.2.3.*

OHSAS 18001

Neither of the models in BS8800 are standards, containing as they do the word "should" and not "shall" or "will". This means that there is not a British or European occupational health and safety management system (OHSMS) standard against which an organisation's management system can be assessed and certified. In response to a demand for such a system, the OHSMS specification, Occupational Health and Safety Assessment Series (OHSAS) 18001 and the accompanying OHSAS 18002, Guidelines for the implementation of OHSAS 18001 have been developed. OHSAS 18002 has a similar relationship to OHSAS 18001 as an approved code of practice has to regulations.

In OHSAS 18001, the word "shall" is used throughout. This means there is no choice in the matter, therefore when the organisation's OHSMS is assessed it can clearly be measured against the requirements.

OHSAS 18001 has been developed to be compatible with ISO 9001 (Quality) and ISO 14001 (Environmental) management systems standards in order to facilitate the integration of quality, environmental and occupational health and safety management systems by organisations, should they wish to do so.

The OHSAS specification will be reviewed or amended when considered appropriate. Reviews will be conducted when new editions of ISO 9001 or ISO 14001 are published, to ensure compatibility.

BSI, who owns and publishes OHSAS 18001, says it will be withdrawn on publication of its content in, or as, an international standard.

The extract below is representative of the style and content of this management system.

1.3.1 Planning for hazard identification, risk assessment and risk control

The organisation shall establish and maintain procedures for the ongoing identification of hazards, the assessment of risks, and the implementation of necessary control measures. These shall include:
> Routine and non-routine activities;
> Activities of all personnel having access to the workplace (including sub-contractors and visitors);
> Facilities at the workplace, whether provided by the organisation or others.

The organisation shall ensure that the results of these assessments and the effects of these controls are considered when setting its OH&S objectives. The organisation shall document and keep this information up to date.

The organisation's methodology for hazard identification and risk assessment shall:
> Be defined with respect to its scope, nature and timing to ensure it is proactive rather than reactive;
> Provide for the classification of risks and identification of those that are to be eliminated or controlled by measures defined in 4.3.3 and 4.3.4 *(OHSAS 18001)*;
> Be consistent with operating experience and the capabilities of risk control measures employed;
> Provide input into the determination of facility requirements, identification of training needs and/or development of operational controls;
> Provide for the monitoring of required actions to ensure both the effectiveness and timeliness of their implementation.

Figure A1-3: Extract from 18001.

Source: BSI - 18001.

Quality management systems

BS EN ISO 9000 SERIES

Early in the twentieth century, the method for ensuring delivery of quality products to the customer was based on what was known as quality control. This meant that a number of people stood at the end of a factory production line and weeded out the products that did not meet customer requirements. Towards the middle of that century, a standardisation system called quality assurance was developed. This involved establishing procedures to manage everything that affected the quality of the manufactured product. The first quality assurance standards were published by the British Standards Institution (BSI) in 1979: the BS 5750 series. They enabled organisations to become certified and display a mark of registration issued by the body that carried out the assessment.

In 1987 the International Organisation for Standardisation (ISO) based their ISO 9000 family of standards on BS 5750. The EU adopted the standards, as did the UK, and they became known as BS EN ISO 9000.

The standards, having been identified as being suitable for organisations delivering services as well as for those manufacturing products, required some adaptations. In 1994 they were revised to make them more user-friendly for service industries, and by the year 2000 a major revision was completed creating the current standard series.

There are four core standards and a series of supporting standards.

The standards are based on eight quality management principles, which can be used by senior management as a framework to guide their organisations towards improved performance. The principles are as follows:

- Principle 1 Customer focus.
- Principle 2 Leadership.
- Principle 3 Involvement of people.
- Principle 4 Process approach.
- Principle 5 Systems approach to management.
- Principle 6 Continual improvement.
- Principle 7 Factual approach to decision making.
- Principle 8 Mutually beneficial supplier relationships.

```
┌─────────────────────────────────────────────────────────────────────────────┐
│                          ISO 9000: 2000 -                                     │
│                     Quality Management Systems                                │
│                     Fundamentals and Vocabulary                               │
│                                                                               │
│   ┌───────────────────────────────┐   ┌───────────────────────────────┐      │
│   │       ISO 9001: 2000 -        │   │       ISO 9004: 2000 -        │      │
│   │     Quality Management        │   │     Quality Management        │      │
│   │     Systems Requirements      │   │     Systems Guidance          │      │
│   └───────────────────────────────┘   └───────────────────────────────┘      │
│                                                                               │
│           ┌───────────────────────────────────────┐                          │
│           │          ISO 19011: 2000 -            │                          │
│           │         Quality Management            │                          │
│           │         Systems Auditing              │                          │
│           └───────────────────────────────────────┘                          │
│                                                                               │
└─────────────────────────────────────────────────────────────────────────────┘
                    ┌───────────────────────────────────────┐
                    │              ISO 10000 -              │
                    │            Series of QMS              │
                    │          supporting standards         │
                    └───────────────────────────────────────┘
```

Figure A1-4: Quality management systems - four core standards and supporting standards.   *Source: BS EN ISO 9000 series.*

An example of the benefits derived from the use of the standards and of actions that managers typically take in applying the principles to improve their organisations' performance is shown below and taken from the ISO document, "Quality Management Principles 2004".

Principle 2 Leadership

Leaders establish unity of purpose and direction of the organisation. They should create and maintain the internal environment in which people can become fully involved in achieving the organisation's objectives.

Key benefits:

> People will understand and be motivated towards the organisation's goals and objectives.
> Activities are evaluated, aligned and implemented in a unified way.
> Miscommunication between levels of an organisation will be minimised.

Applying the principle of leadership typically leads to:

> Considering the needs of all interested parties including customers, owners, employees, suppliers, financiers, local communities and society as a whole.
> Establishing a clear vision of the organisation's future.
> Setting challenging goals and targets.
> Creating and sustaining shared values, fairness and ethical role models at all levels of the organisation.
> Establishing trust and eliminating fear.
> Providing people with the required resources, training and freedom to act with responsibility and accountability.
> Inspiring, encouraging and recognising people's contributions.

Figure A1-5: Quality management systems - principle 2 leadership.   *Source: Quality Management Principles 2004.*

There are many different ways of applying these quality management principles. How they will be implemented will depend on the nature of the organisation and the specific challenges it faces.

Total quality management

Total quality management (TQM) was devised in the 1930s - 40s by an American statistician, Dr. W. Edwards Deming. It was virtually ignored by USA industry, but was adopted by the Japanese as they worked to re-build their industry after WW II. For them it led to tremendous success, and it has become steadily more popular in the West since the 1980s.

TQM is generally defined as:

Total	=	*Quality involves everyone and all activities in the company.*
Quality	=	*Conformance to requirements; meeting customer requirements.*
Management	=	*Quality can and must be managed.*
TQM	=	*A process for managing quality; it must be a continuous way of life, a philosophy of perpetual improvement in everything we do.*

Figure A1-6: Definition of total quality management.   *Source: amazon.com.*

TQM is customer driven quality with strong leadership and commitment from the top. It involves the attitude, culture and organisation of a company with an emphasis on getting things right the first time and eradicating defects and waste from the operations. It involves continual improvement in everything.

THE TEN STEPS TO TQM ARE AS FOLLOWS

1. Pursue new strategic thinking.
2. Know your customers.
3. Set true customer requirements.
4. Concentrate on prevention not correction.
5. Reduce chronic waste.
6. Pursue a continuous improvement strategy.
7. Use structured methodology for process improvement.
8. Reduce variation.
9. Use a balanced approach.
10. Apply to all functions.

AND THE PRINCIPLES OF TQM ARE AS FOLLOWS

1. Quality can and must be managed.
2. Everyone has a customer and is a supplier.
3. Processes not people are the problem.
4. Every employee is responsible for quality.
5. Problems must be prevented, not just fixed.
6. Quality must be measured.
7. Quality improvements must be continuous.
8. The quality standard is defect free.
9. Goals are based on requirements, not negotiated.
10. Life cycle costs, not front end costs.
11. Management must be involved and lead.
12. Plan and organise for quality improvement.

TQM is very difficult to achieve and surveys by consulting firms have found that only 20 -36% of companies undertaking it have seen improvements. This has made many people sceptical about it. However, there is a higher percentage of successful TQM implementation amongst successful companies.

Figure A1-7: About total quality management.   *Source: J. S. Associates, 2004.*

Environmental management systems

BS EN ISO 14000 SERIES

Environmental management systems (EMS) seek to integrate environmental responsibility into every day management practice within all types of organisation. They may be described as: the organisational structure, responsibilities, practices, procedures, processes and resources for implementing and maintaining environmental management.

Environmental management systems standards are the formal requirements, which those seeking certification must achieve. Environmental management system standards have been developed in a number of countries including the UK, France, Ireland, Spain, and South Africa. In addition to these national standards two international management systems and standards have been developed. In the European Union it is the Eco - Management and Audit Scheme, and worldwide, the ISO 14000 series of standards being developed by the International Standards Organisation.

ISO 14001 sets out the general requirements that an organisation needs to have in place for an environmental management system. This covers the following areas:

Policy: Top management are required to define the organisation's environmental policy.

Planning: The environmental management system must be properly planned. To do so knowledge is needed of environmental aspects and impacts, legal and other requirements, objectives and targets for the company in terms of its environmental performance and an environmental management programme to implement its objectives and targets.

Implementation and Operation: This requires that roles, responsibilities and authorities are defined and documented in order to facilitate effective environmental management. Training awareness and competence must also be considered for the positions within the management system. Communication, documentation and documentation control must also be considered. The standard also requires examination of operational control and emergency procedures.

Checking and Corrective Action: The organisation is required to establish and maintain documented procedures to monitor and measure on a regular basis the key characteristics of its operations and activities. Non-conformance and corrective action procedures are also required together with records. Periodically, audits must be carried out.

Management Review: The top management are required to review the performance of the system on a periodic basis to ensure its continuing suitability, adequacy and effectiveness.

ISO 14000

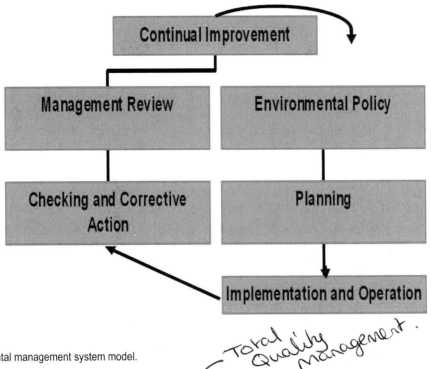

Figure A1-8: Environmental management system model.

Source: ISO 14000.

Arguments for / against integration of management systems

Looking at the management systems above: quality: TQM, environmental and health and safety, it would appear that, in structure, they are very similar. The models have the same general requirements, and in some cases, they only need a word replacement to be the same, e.g. change "Environmental Policy" in BS EN ISO 14000 to "set the Policy" in HSG65. They all require strong leadership and commitment, worker participation, reduction of waste, reduction of errors, etc.

Recognition of the sameness of the basic requirements has led many people to believe that an integration of quality, environment and health and safety as one management system is the way ahead.

The Japanese tend to put all aspects under the quality heading and say that any deviation, such as a minor injury accident, is a quality failure. The TQM approach they favour requires that they strive for no deviations, including those that could cause an injury.

An area of concern for health and safety specialists is that health and safety is often assumed to follow from other controls without being specifically addressed. For example, employees will be highly trained in all aspects of the operation and therefore guarding dangerous parts of machinery may not be seen as necessary as "a highly trained operative would not put their hand in the dangerous parts of a machine". The health and safety specialist would consider what a machine operator may do when distracted, such as put their hand where they normally would not. The practitioner would require such danger to be guarded.

For some, the problem with an integrated system is that whoever manages it may have a vested interest in one area over the others. Many people believe that quality puts the product before the employees and others believe that health and safety issues slow the job down and get in the way of production. Environmental issues may take a secondary position to health and safety, for example, where a hazardous airborne substance is vented to atmosphere. Conversely, an environmentally hazardous substance may be replaced by one that is more harmful to health, for example, trichloroethylene instead of 1.1.1.trichloroethane, now banned because it depletes the ozone layer.

Complete segregation of quality, environment and health and safety could result in one problem being tackled in three separate ways, e.g. controlling noise, and some problems not being accepted as belonging to anybody, e.g. poor leadership. A health and safety manager could recommend changing to plastic for milk bottles instead of glass to solve a noise problem, while the environmental manager recommends biodegradable cartons and the quality manager says the customer prefers glass.

It could be argued that in many cases, the lack of belief in integration can be put down to anecdotal evidence and a poor understanding of the management systems. As in many cases, a compromise could be the answer. A standard way of managing the systems with standardised monitoring, review and audit methods could be utilised. Many of the general requirements are the same and would only become specific at the basic level. For example, employee commitment and participation would be an over-riding requirement with training being one way to help achieve this. The training itself would be specific to needs.

An integrated approach to disparate issues is a principle in all management systems.

Influence of the Turnbull Report on health and safety management

There has been increasing awareness at the corporate level throughout the nineties and into the new century of the need for risk management. This awareness can be linked to the increased focus on "Corporate Governance", which followed a series of high profile (financial) corporate disasters and controversy over directors' pay. These issues instigated debate on the need for tighter controls within publicly listed companies. The findings and recommendations of the Cadbury Committee (1991), the Greenbury Report (1995) and the Hampel Committee (1998) became consolidated into a code on corporate practice known as the Combined Code. This Code places a mandatory requirement on listed companies to make an annual disclosure statement, setting out how it has applied the principles of the Code and also if it has complied with the provisions of the Code, giving reasons for any non-compliance.

The Code contained principles, for example, "the board should maintain a sound system of internal control to safeguard shareholders' investments in the company's assets".

It also contained provisions, for example, "The directors should, at least annually conduct a review of the effectiveness of the group's system of internal controls and should report to shareholders that they have done so. The review should cover all controls, including financial, operational and compliance, and risk management".

There was guidance for financial controls, but no formal guidance for the other aspects of internal control. The Institute of Chartered Accountants in England and Wales (ICAEW) set up a working party, the Turnbull Committee, to provide guidance for directors on the implementation of the internal control recommendations of the Code.

The principal aim of internal control is the management of risks and the responsibility of internal control lies with the most senior managers - the board of directors. There is also a role identified for less senior managers and other employees for risk control within their sphere of activity.

- The board of directors is responsible for the system of internal control. It should set policies on internal control and seek regular assurance on system effectiveness.
- Managers should have responsibility for implementing policies. They should also be responsible for identifying and evaluating risk.
- All employees have some responsibility for achieving objectives. They require knowledge, skill and authority.

The report identifies those factors that should be considered by the board when determining its policies on internal control:

- The nature and extent of the risks facing the company.
- The likelihood of risks materialising.
- The ability to reduce the incidence and the impact of risk.
- The "risk appetite", which will vary, i.e. a higher risk of failure when developing new products.
- Cost benefit analysis of the proposed risk control systems.

Points made in the Turnbull Report include:

- Systems for internal control should be part of the company's management systems and culture. They should be "embedded".
- Risk identification and evaluation should be a continual process.
- All news, bad as well as good should be reported to the highest levels. The internal system should prevent bad news being filtered out by managers before it reaches the board. The company should be committed to learning from its past mistakes rather than hiding or denying them.
- A member of the board should be responsible for ensuring that information on health and safety is passed on to the other members.

Although the Combined Code and the Turnbull Report are focused on listed companies, the principles they contain represent good management practice and as such apply equally to the public sector, unlisted companies and other organisations.

Effective management of health and safety includes the allocation of resources and responsibilities, setting performance standards and the provision of information and training in order to minimise loss. This requires, first of all, a commitment from the most senior managers in the company. They have the power, and the responsibility, to write the company's policy, state that there will be management of health and safety and that it will involve continual improvement. Whatever OHSMS is chosen, the persons involved with its management must receive training, generally on managing health and safety, and specifically on the OHSMS to be used. A genuine commitment to managing health and safety must be backed up by appropriate resources; not just the allocation of money, although that is very important, but adequate time in order to carry out the necessary tasks of training, meetings, risk evaluation, etc.

Performance standards must be, at the very least, the legal requirements, with the aim of increasing over time to best industrial practice.

Information and training provided for all employees will show that the commitment must also come from all levels in the organisation. This will also have the effect of improving the company's health and safety culture.

Effective management of health and safety can make an organisation self-regulating, where any shortfalls in the system will be picked up and put right without the need of the enforcers. There will also be fewer accidents, which is morally, legally and economically beneficial.

Effective management of health and safety

APPROPRIATE ALLOCATION OF RESOURCES AND RESPONSIBILITIES

In order to effectively manage health and safety there needs to be an appropriate allocation of resources: money set aside for training of staff, purchase of suitable equipment and any other necessities; time allocated for the planning and implementation of strategies, e.g. time to carry out risk assessments and for carrying out inspections. Individuals should know and accept their responsibilities, and be competent to carry them out, e.g. who will organise the emergency response and who is responsible for monitoring the practice drills.

SETTING AND MONITORING PERFORMANCE STANDARDS

In the first instance, performance standards should be set at the basic legal requirement. Monitoring those standards will be the check to ensure they are being achieved. With continual improvement, the standards can be raised when they are comfortably being achieved. The standards may be set at industry standards, which will either be equal or better than the legal standards. Monitoring may be active (before loss occurs) or reactive (after loss has occurred).

SYSTEMS FOR FEEDBACK AND IMPLEMENTATION OF CORRECTIVE ACTION IN ORDER TO MINIMISE LOSS

Within the HSMS there should be systems for ensuring feedback from the monitoring goes to the right person who can arrange for corrective action to be taken. The corrective action may come from feedback from an inspection or from the recommendations following an accident investigation. Further control measures will help to prevent loss or minimise it to an acceptable level.

A1.3 - Health and safety policies

Role of the health and safety policy

With the creation of The Health and Safety at Work etc Act (HASAWA) 1974 came an obligation to manage the risks that organisations create. A cornerstone of this was seen to be the establishment of an active health and safety policy. This has been consistently misunderstood and underestimated by many over the years since the HASAWA came into force. With the introduction of the Management of Health and Safety at Work Regulations this has received a fresh focus. Without active management any attempt at organised accident prevention will be restricted and predominantly reactive.

The health and safety policy is central to the Health and Safety Management Systems (HSMS) as it shows the intention of the employer (organisation) to managing health and safety, those who are responsible for carrying through that intention and how that intention is to be fulfilled. It is meant to demonstrate clear commitment to the requirements of the HSMS. Communication of the policy statement is a legal requirement so it will be used to give employees and other interested parties information on all areas that affect them. For example, at induction for new employees, they can be told the intention of the company regarding health and safety and the names of the persons with responsibility. Once working, they can be given the information on the arrangements for their particular tasks, i.e. the safe systems of work, permits to work and the relevant training. In this way, the health and safety policy is the overall control document and the vehicle for communication.

Legal requirements for a written health and safety policy and for recording arrangements

HASAWA 1974 ACT - SECTION 2(3)

Section 2 (3) of the HASAWA 1974 requires all employers, except for the smaller organisations (currently those with fewer than five employees) to:

- Create a written health and safety policy statement.
- State the organisation and arrangement for bringing the statement into effect.
- Bring the policy to the attention of employees.
- Revise the policy as necessary.

MANAGEMENT OF HEALTH AND SAFETY AT WORK REGULATIONS 1999 - REGULATION 5 (HEALTH AND SAFETY ARRANGEMENTS)

Appropriate arrangements must be made for the effective planning, organisation, control, monitoring and review of preventative and protective measures (implicit for the management of health and safety). Employers with five or more employees must have their arrangements in writing.

General components of a health and safety policy document

STATEMENT OF INTENT

Overview

A particularly effective way of demonstrating management philosophy and commitment to health and safety is by communicating a policy statement. In order to accentuate this commitment the statement should be signed and dated by the most senior member of the management team. Lack of firm management commitment of this kind leads to the belief that health and safety is not equal to other organisational goals.

It, and its revisions, must also be brought to the attention of employees, particularly as they are involved in making it work.

Safety goals and objectives

Goals are seen to be long-term outcomes of an organisation's actions. Objectives are the steps necessary to reach that goal and tend to be shorter time based. Though they may be described as short, medium or long term objectives they remain steps towards the goal. The statement should establish health and safety as a significant goal of the organisation. The extent of the goal should be well communicated and include health and safety, not just safety.

The statement should establish a summary of the objectives that must be fulfilled to meet the goals. Often objectives are summated as being to prevent all accidents. This may be confusing, as this is better seen as a goal, rather than an objective. Objectives should include key management activities: plan, organise, control, monitor, and review.

ORGANISATION

It is usual to express how the organisation is organised by showing an organisational chart, allowing reporting/communication structures of line and function staff to be depicted. This is supported by clear depiction of responsibilities of management and supervisors at all levels, duties of workers and the role and functions of health and safety professional staff. Setting out organisation for health and safety will include:

- The unbroken and logical delegation of duties through line management to first line managers (supervisors) who operate where the hazards arise.
- The identification of the key managers, who are accountable to top management for ensuring that detailed arrangements for safe working are drawn up, implemented and maintained.
- The definition of the roles/function of line and functional management.
- Defining adequate support by all relevant functional management, not only by the health and safety practitioner, but also, according to need, by the medical staff (doctor and nurse), engineers, designers and chemists.
- Defining key employees to assist with health and safety arrangements.
- Defining the responsibilities of employees and others.
- Stating employee involvement through representatives, briefing systems and committees.
- The nomination of persons with the authority and competence to monitor health and safety performance; both individually and collectively, by unit, by site or by department.

Job descriptions (or similar) should be drawn up to identify specific roles/functions and to avoid expensive and potentially dangerous overlapping. An involvement in health and safety should be seen as an essential part of good management. The responsibility for taking direct action lies with line management, rather than with the health and safety practitioner. The practitioner's role includes monitoring the effectiveness of the health and safety policy and the provision of information for senior management.

Duties and responsibilities in relation to health and safety

Duties placed on people, in order for the organisation to meet its objectives, must be clear and understood. Duties placed on subordinates do not remove the responsibility of the senior person to ensure that duties and the related actions are carried out. Indeed it is a primary duty of the senior to ensure that subordinates carry out their duties. Each person assigned duties is accountable for them being carried out. It follows therefore that a senior is accountable for the duties they assign as well as their own.

It is important for managers to ensure the proper allocation of resources to health and safety because they can now be more easily held accountable in law for deficiencies within their area of control. Failures cannot be readily ascribed to 'circumstances beyond control'. The director or manager's job is to be in control. Duties and responsibilities should be defined for the following people:

- The Senior Manager of the organisation.
- The Senior Managers that report to the Senior Manager.
- The Senior Manager nominated to deal with health and safety matters.
- Middle Managers.
- First Line Managers.
- Functional staff, in particular the Health and Safety Practitioner.
- Employees.

Organisational structure in relation to health and safety

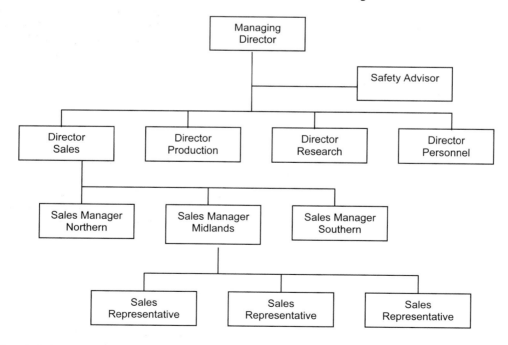

Figure A1-9: Organisational structure example.

Source: ACT.

Organisational structure in relation to health and safety

This should clearly show who is responsible to whom and the nature of the responsibility, line or functional responsibility. This can be visually presented by the use of a management structure diagram(s). This then summarises and supports the written definition of duties and responsibilities.

Key people

The organisation should define the key people who will assist with the carrying out of specific health and safety arrangements, for example:

- First Aiders.
- Fire Wardens.
- Risk Assessors - general risks and specific risks such as: substances, manual handling.
- Employee Representatives or structure for communication on an individual basis.

ARRANGEMENTS

Scope

The scope of arrangements made by an organisation, and depicted in the policy, is dictated by the nature of the organisation (i.e. its hazards and controls). In summary, these tend to fall into two categories, general and specific arrangements. General arrangements will have an influence on a variety of hazards (e.g. accident investigation, induction training, and first aid arrangements). Specific arrangements will be established for specific hazards (e.g. electricity, noise, manual handling, and display screen equipment). Arrangements to control a particular hazard will comprise of a blend of technical, procedural and behavioural arrangements.

Extent

The extent that arrangements reach to, and are depicted in, the policy will be influenced by the level of risk arising from a hazard or the benefit gained from a particular general control measure. Inevitably the arrangements of an organisation are not necessarily set out in a single document. It is quite acceptable for the primary policy document to refer to other documents which depict these arrangements. These connective documents are often known by a variety of names e.g. standing instructions, safe working practices, and safe systems of work, rules, and procedures.

Systems

Systems of work may be very general or specific and can be written in such a way as to make them advisory to work situations or very prescriptive. The formality of a system tends to be dependent on the level of risk arising from the work, perhaps the most formal being a permit to work system.

Rules

Rules are created to remind people of the correct (safe and healthy), mandatory behaviour expected of them. Rules should be written to avoid ambiguity and should not be confused with guidance. The clearest rules are those that can have the words 'always or never' in front.

Procedures

Procedures formalise the actions necessary within a work activity that will ensure health and safety. They tend to be written in the order that the actions are likely to be carried out. Procedures formalise and bind arrangements in place. If something needs to be done in a particular way the procedure would help to ensure it is done. They may be used during training or monitoring exercises. Procedures should set clear standards of performance and apply to:

- People selection, training and supervision.
- Equipment and substances - purchase, supply, transport, storage and use.
- Products and services - design, delivery, transport and storage.
- Environmental and place of work control.
- Management actions and the way work is done.

Standards

Standards help to build a positive culture and control risks. They should identify who does what, where, when, how and with what results. Above all the standards must be: measurable, achievable and realistic.

Statements such as "staff must be trained" are difficult to measure if it is not known exactly what "trained" means and who is to do the work. Many industry-based standards already exist and they can adopt, where applicable. In other cases advice will have to be taken in order to set standards applicable to the organisation. Standards should be specific enough to enable them to be measured, referring to numbers, quantities, levels and timing. For example:

- Specifying levels of waste, effluent or emissions that are acceptable.
- Methods and frequency for checking guards on machines.
- Specific levels and content of training.
- Manuals.

Cross-reference to key documents

The health and safety policy of an organisation (statement of intent, organisation, arrangements) may be substantial. The documentation to depict this may also be extensive. It is usual to establish a system of manuals that depict and control the policy. The actual system used will depend on the organisation, but a primary document (manual) should contain all three of the above policy items, including any references to other documents that give additional information.

The purpose of the manual is to provide control of management actions and would therefore be made available or provided to them. Employees would usually gain access to the manual through a request system or library point and be provided with a summary of the main points of the manual. This includes a full copy of the statement, summary of the organisation and arrangements and reference to manuals. A leaflet or a booklet might achieve this.

Communication

The effective communication of the policy is important. It must be understood by all those affected by it. In order to achieve this a good deal has to be done. Merely posting or distribution of a copy to employees is not enough. Training and briefings will be necessary, as a minimum, to ensure effective communication. For new employees this is often done as part of the induction process.

The format, complexity and language(s) used should be considered. Experience shows that no one form of document is adequate to meet everyone's needs, therefore the document is usually produced in at least a summary and a detailed format. If it is likely to be revised frequently, a loose-leaf scheme will be advisable for the detailed version. This is especially true when the names and contact telephone numbers of staff are included. Arrangements must be put in place to enable revisions to be communicated effectively.

A1.4 - Role and responsibilities of health and safety practitioner

Role of health and safety practitioners

ROLE (AND FUNCTION) OF HEALTH AND SAFETY PRACTITIONERS

The role of the health and safety practitioner is to support line management in meeting their responsibilities by:

- Providing information and advice.
- Supporting line management with the co-ordination of health and safety effort.
- Monitoring the effectiveness of actions to meet responsibilities.

The function of the health and safety practitioner includes:

- Identify problems (including hazards).
- Assess the need for action.
- Assist with the assessment of risks.
- Design and develop strategies and plans.
- Advise on relevant current best practice for prevention.
- Present themselves and their advice in an independent manner.
- Promote and communicate health, safety and welfare advances and practices.
- Assist with the implementation of these strategies and plans.
- Evaluate their effectiveness.
- Maintain key records relating to health and safety performance.

MANAGEMENT OF HEALTH AND SAFETY AT WORK REGULATIONS - REGULATION 7 (HEALTH AND SAFETY ASSISTANCE)

The regulation places an absolute duty on the employer to take the following actions:

- Appoint one or more competent persons to assist with compliance with health and safety legislation.
- Make arrangements for the persons to co-operate.
- Ensure the number of people appointed, time available, means at their disposal are adequate. Consider size of organisation, risks and distribution of the risks.
- Persons appointed that are not employees are provided with information.
- Persons appointed are informed of any person working under a fixed-term contract or employed in an employment business.

The regulations state that competence means having sufficient training and experience or knowledge and other qualities. The approved code of practice (ACOP) says employers should consider:

- Knowledge and understanding of work involved.
- Principles of risk assessment and prevention.
- Current health and safety applications.
- Capacity to apply to tasks required.
- Identifying problems.
- Assessing the need for action.
- Designing and developing strategies and plans.
- Implementing these strategies and plans.
- Evaluating their effectiveness.
- Promoting and communicating health, safety and welfare advances and practices.
- Understanding of relevant current best practice.
- Awareness of own limitations.
- Willingness and ability to supplement existing experience and knowledge.
- Membership of a professional body or similar.
- Holding competence based qualification (NVQ).

The regulations do not require the self employed, who are themselves competent, to appoint anyone.

The regulations do not require individuals in business partnership to appoint a person if one of them is competent.

DESIGN OF HEALTH AND SAFETY MANAGEMENT SYSTEMS

The first decision to be made is which model to use for the HSMS. Once that is done, each part should be dealt with accordingly, e.g. who will be the co-ordinator and who will control the planning. The health and safety practitioners involved in the health and safety management system (HSMS) will vary according to the organisation. Generally, there should be an overall manager of the system who will be able to make decisions. Input will be required from the health and safety practitioner and advice sought from quality and environmental practitioners, who have had many years of experience of management systems. Exactly what will be required at each stage will depend on the nature of the organisation.

IMPLEMENTATION OF HEALTH AND SAFETY MANAGEMENT SYSTEMS

Under regulation 7 of the MHSWR 1999, the employer must appoint one or more competent persons to assist him in complying with the legal obligations imposed on the undertaking. The number of persons appointed depends on the size of the establishment and the range and severity of the risks.

If more than one competent person is appointed, then arrangements must be made for ensuring adequate co-operation between them. The competent person(s) must be given the necessary time and resources to fulfil their functions. This will depend on the size the undertaking, the risks to which employees are exposed and the distribution of those risks throughout the undertaking. The employer must ensure that competent persons who are their employees are informed of the factors known (or suspected) to affect the health and safety of anyone affected by business activities. This requirement is to enable the planning and implementation of the HSMS. Competent people are defined as those who have sufficient training and experience or knowledge and other qualities to enable them to perform their functions. These functions may involve carrying out risk assessments to help the employer fulfil his regulation 3 duties under MHSWR 1999, which is the planning stage of the HSMS, and regulation 4, putting control measures in place, which is the implementation stage.

EVALUATION OF HEALTH AND SAFETY MANAGEMENT SYSTEMS

Once the controls are in place, competent persons are required to evaluate the HSMS. This may be done internally by trained, in-house auditors or by external auditors. Eventually, when the requirements of OHSAS 18001 become a British Standard that HSMS will be externally accredited in the same way as quality and the environmental management systems.

MAINTENANCE OF HEALTH AND SAFETY MANAGEMENT SYSTEMS

Where failures to achieve the standards are highlighted, they should be remedied. People should be given the responsibility of ensuring this is done. This may require the health and safety specialist involving the expertise of others, such as electrical/mechanical/chemical engineer, to improve the systems in their specialist area. The occupational health specialists should be involved to ensure the commitments to health issues are maintained. Also, it should be noted that HSMS require a commitment to continual improvement.

Need for health and safety practitioners to evaluate and develop their own practice

Health and safety practitioners need to keep abreast of new developments such as changes in the law and new technical developments, for example, in guarding. In order to evaluate and develop their own practice, they could devise a personal development plan stating their aims and objectives and how they plan to achieve them. For example, a health and safety advisor could decide that he should find out about the "Work at Height Regulations" and plan to attend a seminar on that subject. A continuing professional development portfolio is a useful way to formalise this, where copies of course programmes and learning outcomes may be held.

Continuing professional development (CPD) points are awarded for attendance at health and safety seminars, for training courses and for other development programmes. They are a requirement for membership of the professional body for health and safety specialists, e.g. IOSH. Failure to keep up to date with changes and failure to develop one's own knowledge and expertise could result in the advisor giving wrong information or not using the best controls to reduce risk. These failures have moral, legal and economic implications.

This page is intentionally blank

Loss causation and incident investigation

Learning outcomes

The intended learning outcomes are that the student will be able to:

A2.1 explain the theory of loss and causality, their quantitative analysis, limitations of their application, and their presentation in numerical and graphical form

A2.2 explain the statutory and internal reporting and recording systems for loss events (injuries, ill-health, dangerous occurrences) and near misses

A2.3 describe loss investigations; the requirements, benefits, the procedures, the documentation, and the involvement of and communication with relevant staff and representatives

Contents

Relevant statutory provisions

Reporting of Injuries, Diseases and Dangerous Occurrences Regulations (RIDDOR) 1995

Social Security Act (Claims and Payments) Regulations (SSACPR) 1979

Social Security Administration Act (SSAA) 1992

Social Security (Industrial Diseases) (Prescribed Diseases) Regulations (SSIDPDR) 1985

This page is intentionally blank

A2.1 - Loss causation and analysis

Losses result from lack of control and are revealed by loss causing events. These events may be known by a variety of names, the most common of which is 'accident'. There are many different definitions for the term accident, ranging from simple to complex. A useful definition of an accident is:

> An unplanned, uncontrolled event which led to, or could have led to injury to persons, damage to plant or some other loss to the company.

Figure A2-1: Definition of an accident. *Source: ACT.*

This definition encompasses events that result in a wide range of losses and has, for a long time, helped to provide a good perspective of events with different outcomes. This has assisted greatly in encouraging people to learn from events and the subsequent prevention of accidents. The definition therefore, includes 'near misses', i.e. where no injury or damage etc. occurs. It is important not to think of injuries, damage and other losses as accidents, but rather as the **results** of accidents.

The following accident model is offered to illustrate the above statement: a spanner falls from a height. The following consequences could result:

1. The brick falls into a pile of sand and there is no damage or injury.
2. The brick hits an item of equipment, resulting in damage, but no injury.
3. The brick strikes a person causing a cut and bruising to the hand, this is an injury accident.
4. The brick strikes a person working directly underneath causing a fatality.

Figure A2-2: Accident.   *Source: HSG245.*   Figure A2-3: Near miss.   *Source: HSG245.*

The difference between a near miss and a fatal accident in terms of time and distance can be very small indeed. It is therefore clear that the damage to persons or property is not the accident, but part of the effects of the accidents (i.e. the result or consequences).

An old adage says never waste an accident. Apart from being unpleasant and perhaps very costly, every accident constitutes an opportunity to correct some problem. For this purpose, a near miss which has the potential to cause loss is just as important as a serious injury/damage, in fact even more important if we are to avoid a future loss incident, a golden opportunity not to be missed.

In the HSE Guidance Document HSG245 "Investigating accidents and incidents", the HSE refers to an 'Adverse Event'. An adverse event includes:

- Accidents.
- Incidents.

The term 'adverse event', as used by the HSE is similar to the term 'accident' used in figure A2-1 above and encompasses events that have a wide range of outcomes. The HSE reserve the term 'accident' for events that involve harm to people.

The HSE define an Accident as:

> An event that results in injury or ill-health.

Figure A2-4: Definition of an accident. *Source: HSE. HSG245.*

The HSE states that an incident includes a:

- Near miss.
- Undesired circumstance.

The HSE considers a 'Near Miss' to be: an event that, while not causing harm, has the potential to cause injury or ill-health. They take the term near miss to include dangerous occurrences specified in the Reporting of Injuries, Diseases and Dangerous Occurrences Regulations (RIDDOR) 1995.

In the view of the HSE the term incident includes 'Undesired Circumstance', which they take to be: a set of conditions or circumstances that have the potential to cause injury or ill-health, e.g. untrained nurses handling heavy patients i.e. the potential for back injury.

The HSE have set out an interesting perspective in their guidance document HSG245, which will generate some debate. Some practitioners may feel a definition of accident that limits itself to outcomes that harm people to be too narrow, others may find it useful to have a focused definition, for reporting and analysis purposes. It is important to remember that HSG245 is a guidance document and carries no direct legal duty to follow or use the definitions contained in it.

Loss causation

DOMINO AND MULTI-CAUSALITY THEORIES

The Domino Theory

HW Heinrich, an American safety engineer, proposed one of the first coherent theories of accident causation in the mid 1920s. He suggested that accidents were not 'acts of God' but were caused by the failures of people. His domino theory suggested that the series of events, which led to an injury or some other loss, were a succession of events which followed a logical pattern.

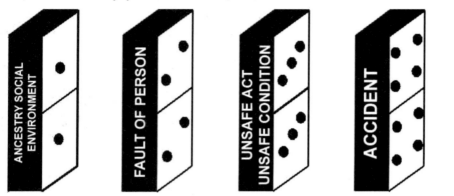

Figure A2-5: Accident causation domino.   *Source: H.W. Heinrich.*

Further research by the International Loss Control Institute (ILCI) into accident causation led them to put forward a modified domino theory.

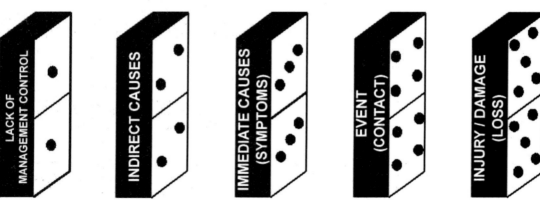

Figure A2-6: Accident causation domino.   *Source: Frank Bird - ILCI.*

Considering each stage of the Frank Bird - ILCI domino separately:

"Loss"

This is the consequence of the accident and can be measured in terms of people (injuries), property (damage) or loss to the process (failed telecommunication) or the potential for any of these (near miss) and hence loss of profit.

"Event (accident or incident)"

The event producing the loss involving contact with a substance or source of energy above the threshold limits of the body or structure.

"Immediate (direct) causes"

These are the substandard (unsafe) acts (e.g. using tools and equipment for tasks they were not designed to do) and substandard (unsafe) conditions (e.g. a trailing telephone cable in an office) which gives rise to an accident. These are symptoms which can be observed. Whilst these symptoms cannot be ignored, action solely at this level will not, by itself, ensure that recurrence is not prevented. Unsafe acts and conditions may be considered as workplace hazards.

Underlying (indirect or root) causes

These are the underlying or root causes of accidents. Identifying these causes will explain why the substandard act happened or the condition arose. They are not always easy to identify. Underlying causes fall into three major categories:

- Organisational Factors   (Procedural).
- Job Factors   (Technical).
- Personal Factors   (Behavioural).

Organisational factors	*Job factors*	*Personal factors include*

Organisational factors
- Work standards and procedures.
- Communication.
- Co-ordination.
- Supervision.

Job factors
- Design of equipment and layouts.
- Maintenance.
- Purchase of materials and equipment.

Personal factors include
- Physical capability.
- Mental capability.
- Physical stress.
- Mental stress.
- Knowledge.
- Information.
- Skill.
- Motivation.

"Lack of management control"

This is the initial stage centred on the management functions of:

- Policy.
- Planning.
- Organising.
- Controlling.
- Monitor.
- Review.

In the HSE's guidance document on the investigation of accidents and incidents, HSG245, they set out their perspective of the domino theory. "Each domino represents a failing or error which combine with other failings and errors to cause an adverse event. Dealing with the immediate cause (B) will only prevent this sequence. Dealing with all causes, especially root causes (A) can prevent a whole series of adverse events." This is an important aspect of loss causation / prevention which is why thorough investigation to determine root causes is necessary.

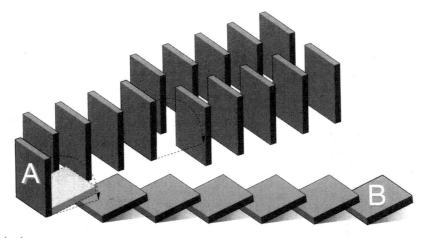

Figure A2-7: Sequence of dominoes. *Source: HSG245.*

In this guidance document the HSE explain their view on what is an immediate, underlying and root cause, HSG245 should be read with care as some of the data on what is meant by these different causes appears in more than one place and is contradictory. The meanings that follow good practice conventions have been selected from the document and set out below.

"Immediate cause: the most obvious reason why an adverse event happens, e.g. the guard is missing"

"Underlying cause: the less obvious 'system' or 'organisational' reason for an adverse event happening, e.g. pre-start-up machinery checks are not carried out by supervisors"

"Root cause: an initiating event or failing from which all causes or failings spring. Root causes are generally management, planning or organisational failings."

Multiple accident causes

It should be remembered that accident investigation experience confirms that there is usually more than one causative factor, therefore each of the multiple causation factors may be seen as one domino in its own line of dominoes (just as the roots of a tree branch out).

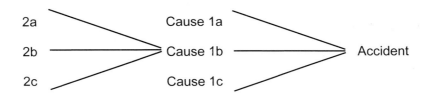

Figure A2-8: Multiple accident causes. *Source: ACT.*

For example - consider a tired gas fitter; he does not check his work equipment before leaving home and is delayed by heavy traffic on his way to work. On arrival at work, he finds a co-worker has not arrived on time, so starts a two-man job on his own. The work is to be carried out at height. On checking, he finds that his ladder is not on his van, so uses a drum for access to a high level pipe, slips and injures his leg.

ACCIDENT RATIO STUDIES AND THEIR LIMITATIONS

Some years ago, a study of 1,750,000 accidents, in 21 industry sectors, led by Frank Bird, showed that there is a fixed ratio between losses of different severity (and accidents where no loss occurred, i.e. near misses).

This can be demonstrated with a pyramid model:

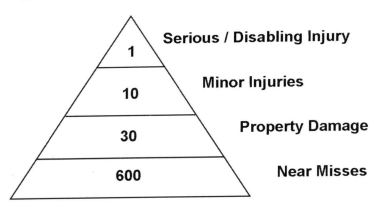

Source: Frank Bird.

Figure A2-9: Accident ratio study.

There have been several versions of the accident pyramid, with some in HSE publications, e.g. HSG 96 "The Costs of Accidents at Work".

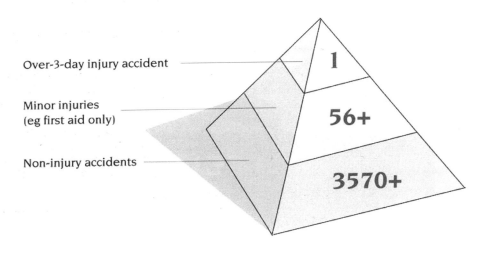

Source: HSG96 the costs of accidents at work.

Figure A2-10: Accident ratio pyramid.

These results show that Bird's findings are not uniform throughout industry and in fact differ from industry to industry. This may be mostly due to the range of risk involved, but there could also be cultural differences, and the level of reporting.

The accident ratio studies may not necessarily show the extent of the loss to the organisation. For example, the "property damage" category may include extensive damage to large plant and equipment. Also, shown from Bird's and HSE's examples, there are no universally agreed definitions of each subset of accident type.

Analysis

METHODS OF CALCULATING INJURY RATES FROM RAW DATA

ACCIDENT FREQUENCY RATE

Frequency rate = accidents compared with time =

$$\frac{\text{Number of accidents in the period}}{\text{Total hours worked during the period}} \times 1,000,000$$

This uses the '1,000,000' multiplier that the HSE and International Labour Office (ILO) use. In the UK organisations frequently use multipliers of 100,000 or less, in order to bring the numbers to a manageable size, and the USA use 200,000. Care should be taken that the multiplier is specified when making comparisons.

ACCIDENT INCIDENT RATE

Incidence rate = accidents compared with number of people =

$$\frac{\text{Number of accidents in the period}}{\text{Average number employed during the period}} \times 10,000$$

ACCIDENT SEVERITY RATE

Severity rate (average number of days lost compared with hours worked) =

$$\frac{\text{Total no. of days lost}}{\text{Total no. of man hours worked}} \times 1,000$$

These calculations are made from the actual numbers of accidents, hours worked, numbers employed and days lost. In order for the result to be a meaningful number, a large multiplier is included in the equation. The injury rates themselves only mean something if they are compared to other injury rates and to be used to show trends. They may be compared to rates from previous years, to rates from other departments in the company, to other companies or to rates in a particular industry.

The definition of all of these factors must be agreed in order to make comparisons. It is only meaningful to compare like with like. For example, accident may mean any period of "lost time" to some organisations, but to others a lost time accident is a "RIDDOR reportable" accident which is greater than 3 days. The number of people employed in a given period may or may not include part-time workers and/or contractors, agency staff, other temporary workers. Calculating the hours worked may be inaccurate depending on where the figures come from. The finance department may give the paid hours rather than the actual hours. If workers get double time for overtime, this can skew the figures.

If a fatality occurs, it will not show up in the severity rate, as it will not be possible to say how many days have been lost. With the severity rate being low, it will appear that the accidents that have occurred have been minor.

If all rates are used together and compared with rates using the same definitions they will be valid.

If the rates rise, it does not necessarily mean that there has been no improvement. It could mean that the reporting procedures are better and an improved health and safety culture means more people are willing to report. As with all statistical data, injury rates must be carefully analysed.

APPLICATION OF STATISTICAL AND EPIDEMIOLOGICAL ANALYSES IN THE IDENTIFICATION OF PATTERNS AND TRENDS

The statistics collected on injuries, ill health and other losses such as property damage can help to identify patterns and trends. These data can be collected in-house or by the enforcing authority from RIDDOR reports. Statistics collected on, for example, respiratory tract ill-health associated with a new process where a certain chemical is used could be used by the HSE to recommend the chemical being included in EH40 under a new or revised category.

Injury statistics may show a certain type of injury in a certain industry. For example, there was a trend for head injuries in the construction industry that resulted in the Construction (Head Protection) Regulations (CHPR) 1989. In-house, a company could find that there is a pattern of manual handling injuries on the night shift. Absenteeism in the office may show a pattern that is seasonal. Seeing patterns and trends is much easier if the statistics are shown in some type of graphical or numerical format.

How to present and interpret loss event data

GRAPHICAL AND NUMERICAL FORMAT

Histogram

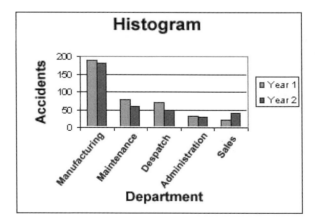

Figure A2-11: Histogram.   *Source: ACT.*

The above diagram is a histogram. In this particular histogram, the scale on the y-axis (vertical) shows the number of recorded accidents and the x-axis shows a comparison between two years in each department.

Where the scale is on the x-axis this type of histogram is known as a bar chart.

Pie chart

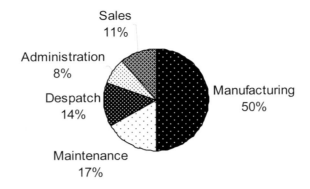

Figure A2-12: Pie chart.   *Source: ACT.*

The pie chart shows the pie as the whole amount being considered and the slices as ratio parts of that whole. The above pie representation could be representative of accidents in the different departments. It is easy to see at a glance where most of the accidents are.

Cusum chart

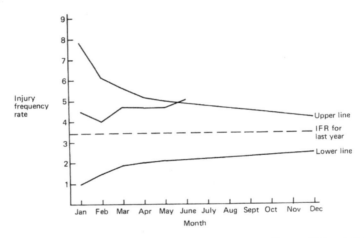

Figure A2-13: Cusum chart.   *Source: Ridley, J; Safety at Work; Fourth Edition; 1994.*

A cusum chart is a cumulative sum chart, like the one above, which shows the cumulative injury frequency rate. Month by month the frequency rates are added and each is plotted on the graph. The upper and lower limits are drawn in and are decided by a calculation based on a random difference from the previous year's frequency rate. If the line being plotted goes outside these lines then it is outside the random difference, is statistically significant and should be investigated.

Line graphs

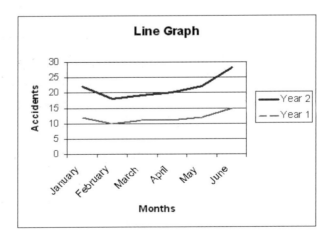

Figure A2-14: Line graph.   *Source: ACT.*

Line diagrams, such as the simple one above can show at a glance, accidents over a period, but not in much detail.

Normal distribution

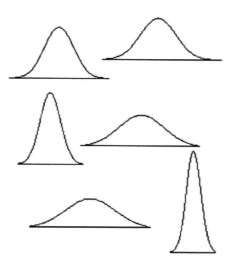

Figure A2-15: Normal distribution.
Source: http://davidmlane.com/hyperstat/A15211.html Normal distribution.

The normal distribution curve above can show the normal or most frequent occurrence of a single variable. A simple example is looking at the height of people in the workplace. There will be a range of heights that the majority of people fit into, but there will be some small and some tall at each end of the curve. The normal range of anything can be seen by this when looking for an average range that most people will fit into, e.g. buying a selection of safety boots for visitors' use.

Poisson distribution

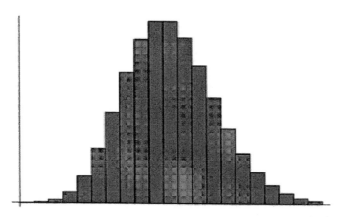

Figure A2-16: Poisson distribution.
Source: http://mathworld.wolfram.com/PoissonDistribution.html Poisson distribution.

When looking at the distribution of accidents over a group of people in a department, it is usual that most of the group have no accidents, some have one and a few individuals have four or more. This variation may be chance or it may be for reasons that require investigation. The Poisson distribution allows the expected distribution to be found and the actual distribution to be calculated, thereby allowing a comparison to be made. If there is a significant difference then it is not chance, but something that needs further investigation.

A2.2 - Reporting and recording of loss events (injuries, ill-health and dangerous occurrences) and near-misses

Statutory reporting requirements and procedures

The legal requirements for recording and reporting accidents, diseases and dangerous incidents at work are laid down in the Social Security Act (Claims and Payments) Regulations (SSACPR) 1979, the Social Security Administration Act (SSAA) 1992 and the Reporting of Injuries, Diseases and Dangerous Occurrences Regulations (RIDDOR) 1995. RIDDOR reports are sent to the relevant authority and are used to compile statistics to show trends and to highlight problem areas in particular industries or companies.

The social security legislation referred to above sets out requirements on employers to confirm whether a claim for 'industrial injury benefit' made to the social security department by an employed earner relates to an accident at work. The request for confirmation of circumstances is initiated by the social security department, following a claim by an employed earner. The legislation places duties on the employer and the employed earner, to enable this process to take place.

The employed earner who suffers personal injury for which benefit may be payable must give 'notice' to the employer in writing or orally as soon as practical after it happens. Notice can be given to the employer directly or to someone supervising the work of the employed earner at the time of the injury. This can be done by someone acting on the employed earner's behalf.

If the employer occupies specified premises then an accident book (BI 510), or other means of holding a record of the same data, must be kept at the location.

Specified premises are:

- Every factory, mine and quarry.
- Works or premises where the factories Act 1961 applies.
- Any premises where or about ten or more people are employed at the same time.

Particulars to be given of accidents are:

(1) Full name, address and occupation of injured person.

(2) Date and time of accident.

(3) Place where accident happened.

(4) Cause and nature of injury.

(5) Name, address and occupation of person giving the notice, if other than the injured person.

The means of recording, e.g. the accident book, must be easily available at all reasonable times.

An entry of the appropriate particulars of the accident in a book or similar, if made as soon as practicable after the accident, will be considered sufficient notice.

When notified, the employer has a duty to investigate the cause of the injury. If the employer finds anything different from what was recorded in the accident book this must be noted. Records must be kept for three years.

The Social Security (Industrial Injuries) (Prescribed Diseases) Regulations (SSIIPDR) 1985 list those diseases that are prescribed for the purpose of payment of disablement benefit.

A prescribed disease is defined in the Social Security Act (SSA) 1975 as:

- A disease that ought to be treated, with regard to its causes, incidence and other relevant considerations, as a risk of occupation and not a risk common to everyone.
- Such that, in the absence of special circumstances, the attribution of particular cases to the nature of the employment can be established with reasonable certainty.

Schedule 1 to the regulations classifies prescribed injuries or diseases as:

- Conditions due to physical agents - such as cataract from an occupation involving frequent or prolonged exposure to radiation from red-hot or white-hot material.
- Conditions due to biological agents - infection by leptospira from an occupation involving work in places liable to be infested with rats, field mice, or voles; work at dog kennels or handling of dogs; contact with bovine animals or pigs or their meat products.
- Conditions due to chemical agents - Anaemia with a haemoglobin concentration of 9g/dL or less, and a blood film showing punctuate basophilia from an occupation involving the use or handling of, or exposure to the fumes, dust or vapour of, lead.
- Miscellaneous conditions - Diffuse mesothelioma (primary neoplasm of the mesothelium of the pleura or of the pericardium or of the peritoneum) from an occupation involving exposure to asbestos at a level above that commonly found in the environment at large.

Some of the prescribed diseases carry a specification of how much harm has occurred, e.g. a 50dB reduction in hearing in both ears, this level of harm is required before benefit is payable. These regulations were amended in 2006, modifying some of the criteria for certain prescribed diseases.

The Reporting of Injuries, Disease and Dangerous Occurrences Regulations (RIDDOR) 1995

RIDDOR covers the requirement to report certain categories of injury and disease sustained at work, along with specified dangerous occurrences and gas incidents, to the relevant enforcing authority. These reports are used to compile statistics to show trends and to highlight problem areas, in particular industries or companies.

THE MAIN POINTS OF RIDDOR

Reporting

1) When a person **dies or suffers any major injury** specified in Schedule 1 **(Reporting of Injuries)** and Schedule 2 **(Reporting of Dangerous Occurrences)** a responsible person is to notify by the quickest possible means (usually by telephone) the enforcing authorities and must send them a written report within 10 days (F2508).

2) In cases of diseases which are linked to work activities listed in Schedule 3 **(Reporting of Diseases)** a responsible person must notify by the quickest possible means (usually by telephone) the enforcing authorities and must send them a written report forthwith (F2508A).

3) If personal injury results in **more than 3 days incapacity** from work which they might reasonably be expected to do in the normal course of their work, but does not fall in the category of "major injury", the written report alone is required. The day of the accident is not counted, but any days which would not have been working days are included.

4) The enforcing authority is either the Health and Safety Executive or the Local Authority. The approved form for reporting is F2508 for injuries and dangerous occurrences and F2508A for diseases.

Accident

'Accident' includes:

- An act of non-consensual physical violence done to a person at work.
- An act of suicide which occurs on or in the course of the operation of a relevant transport system.

Responsible person

Reportable event	To	Responsible person
Death, Major injury, over 3 day injury, disease	Employee	Employer
	Self-employed person working in someone else's premises	Person in control of the premises: At the time of the event and In connection trade, business or undertaking
Major injury, over 3 day injury, disease	Self-employed in own premises	Self-employed person or someone acting for them
Dangerous occurrences - general		Person in control of the premises where, or in connection with the work going on at which, the dangerous occurrence happened: At the time of the event and In connection trade, business or undertaking

Road traffic accidents

Road traffic accidents only have to be reported if:

- Death or injury results from exposure to a substance being conveyed by a vehicle.
- Death or injury results from the activities of another person engaged in the loading or unloading of an article or substance.
- Death or injury results from the activities of another person involving work on or alongside a road.
- Death or injury results from an accident involving a train.

Non employee

The responsible person must not only report non-employee deaths, but also cases that involve major injury or hospitalisation.

Employee death

Where an employee dies as a result of a reportable injury, within one year of the date of the accident, as soon as the employer knows the employer must inform the enforcing authority in writing of the death.

Gas incidents

Specified gas incidents are notified 'forthwith' and reported within 14 days to the Health and Safety Executive.

Injury under medical supervision

If a person is injured as a result of an accident arising directly from the conduct of an operation, examination or other medical treatment whilst under the supervision of a registered medical practitioner or dentist the injury does not need to be reported.

Self-employed people

If a self-employed person suffers a major injury while working at their own premises they do not need to notify the enforcing authority immediately. However, they or someone acting for them must report the injury within 10 days.

Recording

In the case of an accident at work, the following details must be recorded:

- Date.
- Time.
- Name.
- Occupation.
- Nature of injury.
- Place of accident.
- Brief description of the event.

Copies of F2508 or suitable alternative records must be kept for at least 3 years. They may be held electronically provided they are printable.

Defences

A person must prove that he was not aware of the event and that he had taken all reasonable steps to have such events brought to his notice.

MAJOR INJURIES (RIDDOR 1995 - SCHEDULE 1)

The list of major injuries includes:

- Any fracture, other than the finger or thumbs or toes.
- Any amputation.
- Dislocation of the shoulder, hip, knee or spine.

- Permanent or temporary loss of sight.
- Chemical, hot metal or penetrating eye injury.
- Electrical shock, electrical burn leading to unconsciousness or resuscitation or admittance to hospital for more than 24 hours.
- Loss of consciousness caused by asphyxia or exposure to a harmful substance or biological agent.
- Acute illness or loss of consciousness requiring medical attention due to any entry of substance by inhalation, ingestion or through the skin.
- Acute illness where there is a reason to believe that this resulted from exposure to a biological agent or its toxins or infected material.
- Any other injury leading to hypothermia, heat-induced illness or unconsciousness requiring resuscitation, hospitalisation greater than 24 hours.

DISEASES (RIDDOR 1995 - SCHEDULE 3)

Conditions due to physical agents and the physical demands of work, e.g.

- Inflammation, ulceration or malignant disease of the skin due to ionising radiation.
- Decompression illness.
- Subcutaneous cellulitis of the hand (beat hand).
- Carpal tunnel syndrome.
- Hand-arm vibration syndrome.

Conditions due to chemicals and other substances e.g.

- Arsenic poisoning.
- Ethylene Oxide poisoning.
- Cancer of a bronchus or lung.
- Folliculitis.
- Acne.
- Pneumoconiosis.
- Asbestosis.
- Occupational dermatitis.

Infections due to biological agents, e.g.

- Anthrax.
- Hepatitis.
- Legionellosis.
- Leptospirosis.
- Tetanus.

DANGEROUS OCCURRENCES (RIDDOR 1995 - SCHEDULE 2)

Dangerous occurrences are events that have the potential to cause death or serious injury and so must be reported whether anyone is injured or not. Examples of dangerous occurrences which might take place in general workplaces that must be reported are:

- The failure of any load bearing part of any lift, hoist, crane or derrick etc.
- The failure of any pressurised closed vessel.
- The failure of any freight container in any of its load bearing parts.
- Any unintentional incident in which plant or equipment either:
  - Comes into contact with an uninsulated overhead electric line, or
  - Causes an electrical discharge from such an electric line by coming into close proximity to it.
- Electrical short-circuit or overload attended by fire or explosion which results in the stoppage of the plant involved for more than 24 hours.

Schedule 2 contains requirements to report specific dangerous occurrences for the following workplaces:

- Mines.
- Quarries
- Transport systems.
- Offshore.

Note: This information is a brief summary only. For full details consult HSE document L73 A Guide to RIDDOR 95.

When notifying and reporting the responsible person is at liberty to use the Incident Contact Centre (ICC), instead of contacting the relevant enforcing authority direct. The ICC can be contacted by telephone; this will satisfy the notification requirement of RIDDOR 1995. The ICC will also fill the appropriate report form in and send a copy for the responsible person's record. In addition, they will send the report to the correct enforcing authority, dealing with the reporting requirement of RIDDOR 1995.

An alternative to contacting the ICC by telephone is to report by accessing the ICC website, www.riddor.gov.uk. This method satisfies RIDDOR 1995 requirements for reporting.

INTERNAL REPORTING AND RECORDING SYSTEMS

Relevant report forms

A number of report forms are utilised to identify and inform that accidents and ill-health have occurred, these include:

- Accident book, in the form of BI 510. This accident book has been revised to take into account the Data Protection Act (DPA) 1998. Completed accident records should be detached from the book, passed to the nominated person and stored securely, for example in a lockable cabinet.
- First aid treatment reports.
- Medical treatment reports.

- Medical (doctor) reports of ill-health.
- Sickness absence reports.
- Event (accident) reports.
- Event (near miss) reports.
- Maintenance/repair reports.
- Insurance reports.
- Reporting Injuries, Diseases and Dangerous Occurrences Regulations (RIDDOR) 1995 reports - F2508, F2508A.

Investigation report forms

Investigation report forms vary in design, layout and content. Many organisations recognise that a different report form may be necessary for first line managers' initial investigations (a level 1 report) and those done by other managers and health and safety professionals (a level 2 report). The main difference is the section relating to causes of the accident. The version used by other managers and professionals often has more analysis in this area and causes greater investigation of underlying causes. In the same way, reports prepared by an investigation team would not tend to be on a pre-printed format, but would be designed around agreed headings and the content/extent of the report would depend on the matter being investigated and findings (a level 3 report).

Common structure of a report tends to determine:

- What happened - the loss.
- How it happened - the event.
- Why it happened - the causes.
- Recommendations - remedial (and preventive) action.

The report is usually supported by drawings, photographs and statements as appendices.

Reporting routes

Reporting of an accident or ill-health may be by a number of means and includes:

- Person suffering harm.
- Person causing loss.
- Person discovering loss.

Person suffering harm

This person is often the source of first reporting of less serious events. The reporting system must make available to them the means to make a report. They have a right to report in an 'accident book' BI 510 (or equivalent) any event that may cause them to claim Social Security benefit. This might be fulfilled by using: a copy of the BI 510 book or first aid/medical treatment documents/event report forms that are adapted to contain the same data. These reports should be under the control of a responsible person who would then initiate an investigation which would usually require the completion of an event (e.g. accident) report.

Person causing loss

This person would be expected to bring the loss to the attention of a line manager who would fill in the appropriate event (e.g. accident) report and initiate an investigation to complete the remainder of the report that the person reporting the loss may not be able to do.

Person discovering the loss

If this person is not the manager responsible for the location in which the loss took place they would have to bring the loss to the attention of a line manager, as above. If the person is the line manager they would initiate an investigation and report on the appropriate event form.

Copies and distribution of reports

Reports from first line managers may be copied to the next line manager (middle manager), health and safety professional and employee representative. It is important that the originator retains a copy till action to prevent re-occurrence is complete. This will help to encourage ownership and continued involvement. The copy passed to the next line manager is usually seen as the primary document. The manager confirms/adds to the investigation, retains a copy and passes the report to a central record point. Clearly this may be done in part or whole as a computerised or paper system.

Records held by the line manager/health and safety professional may be held for varying periods depending on their role. Central records should be under the control of the responsible person and are usually maintained in accordance with the organisation's own practices. A minimum period is usually 3 years for accident (in order to respond to civil claims) and 40 years for events resulting in ill-health (in order to deal with the long lived nature of the problem).

Follow-up

This virtually finishes the work of the investigator, but management is still responsible for seeing that the necessary remedial actions are implemented, and monitored to ensure that the causes are satisfactorily controlled. The line manager, health and safety professional and health and safety committee/members will monitor these actions.

Action following a fatal accident

Reporting a death at work following an accident should include informing:

- Enforcing authority.
- The senior manager.
- Health and safety specialist.
- Coroner.

- Next of kin.
- Employee representatives.
- Other employees.
- Insurance company.

A2.3 - Investigation of loss events

IMPLIED LEGAL REQUIREMENTS

It is not overtly stated in law that accidents must be investigated. However, the implication is there in statute. The Health and Safety at Work etc Act (HASAWA) 1974 states that the employer must ensure so far as is reasonably practicable the health, safety and welfare of employees at work. This implies that should an accident occur, he should find a way of preventing it happening again. In order to do this he needs to investigate the accident, find out what caused it and put further measures in place to prevent a recurrence.

The Management of Health and Safety at Work Regulations (MHSWR) 1999, regulation 5, requires the employer to put arrangements in place for the preventive and protective measures, with one of the arrangements being for monitoring. The ACOP talks about monitoring as including "adequately investigating the immediate and underlying causes of incidents and accidents to ensure that remedial action is taken…" Therefore, although not stated in the legislation itself, in order to comply with legislation, accident investigation should be carried out.

Also, following the Woolf Report on civil action, full disclosure of the circumstances surrounding the accident to the person(s) considering legal action is required. Conducting a prompt investigation will enable this obligation to be met. In addition, carrying out a full investigation and taking remedial action will show the court that the employer has a positive attitude to health and safety.

The results of the investigation will also be essential information for the insurers in the event of a claim.

HSE GUIDANCE

'Successful health and safety management', HSG65 is a practical guide for those with responsibility for health and safety to improve health and safety within their organisations. It was first prepared by HSE's Accident Prevention Advisory Unit. In the section on 'monitoring', there is information on reactive monitoring, which includes accident investigation. There is advice on the level and nature of investigation, collecting the data from immediate and underlying causes and analysing it. This should be followed by recommendations and actions to prevent recurrence. Following HSG65 will ensure compliance with the legal requirements.

Further guidance is provided by HSE in the document HSG245 'Investigating accidents and incidents'. It takes a step-by-step approach to investigations:

Step 1: Gathering the information - the where, when and who of the adverse event. The information gathered will include results of interviews, photographs of the equipment involved and the area in which it was positioned at the time, sketches of the workplace layout, weather conditions, etc.

Step 2: Analysing the information - the what happened and why stage. Analysing the information to find the immediate, underlying and root causes. At this stage it should be considered if human error is a contributory factor. This can be cross-referenced with HSG48 'Reducing error and influencing behaviour'. Job factors, human factors and organisational factors can all influence human behaviour and will all need to be considered in the analysis.

Step 3: Identifying suitable risk control measures. Possible solutions can be identified. This will involve looking at the technical, procedural and behavioural controls, with the technical or engineering risk control measures being more reliable than those that rely on human behaviour.

Step 4: The action plan and its implementation - which risk control measures should be implemented in the short and long term? This is the risk control action plan, which should have *smart* objectives, i.e. Specific, Measurable, Agreed and Realistic, with Timescales. This will also state which risk assessments need to be reviewed and which procedures need to be updated; any trends that need further investigation; and what the adverse event cost.

HSG245 contains some useful investigation forms that could be used and developed for individual companies. It also has examples of simple, but effective investigation tools such as the accident/incident investigation tree.

Purposes of investigation

The purposes of investigation includes:

- Discovery of underlying causes.
- Prevention of recurrence.
- Establish legal liability.
- Data gathering.
- Identification of trends.

The purpose of an investigation of this nature should never seek to blame any individual or group of individuals.

If human error is believed to be a significant cause, the reasons for this must be investigated. Lack of knowledge, training or unsuitability for the job may be the causes of this error. These are management and not operator failings. Only when these have been evaluated can the conclusion of wilful and intentional acts or omissions be considered.

DISCOVERY OF UNDERLYING CAUSES

Accident investigation should identify both immediate and underlying causes, including the design of appropriate Risk Control Systems (RCSs).

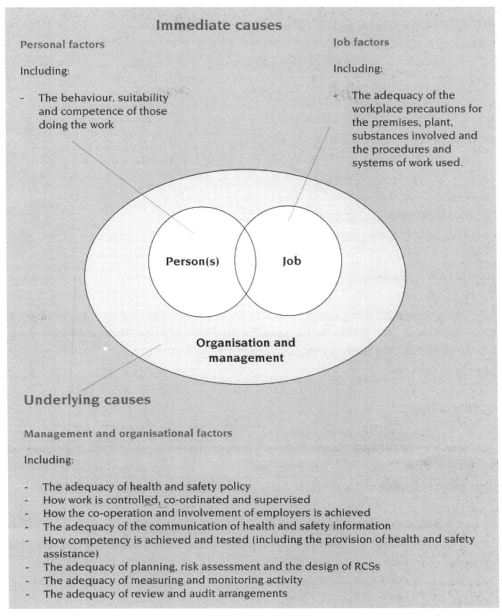

Immediate causes

Personal factors

Including:

- The behaviour, suitability and competence of those doing the work

Job factors

Including:

- The adequacy of the workplace precautions for the premises, plant, substances involved and the procedures and systems of work used.

Person(s)   Job

Organisation and management

Underlying causes

Management and organisational factors

Including:

- The adequacy of health and safety policy
- How work is controlled, co-ordinated and supervised
- How the co-operation and involvement of employers is achieved
- The adequacy of the communication of health and safety information
- How competency is achieved and tested (including the provision of health and safety assistance)
- The adequacy of planning, risk assessment and the design of RCSs
- The adequacy of measuring and monitoring activity
- The adequacy of review and audit arrangements

Figure A2-17: Discovery of underlying causes.   *Source: HSG65 Successful Health and Safety Management.*

PREVENTION OF RECURRENCE

The main purpose of accident investigation is to find out what has gone wrong and put further controls in place to prevent that accident happening again. It is not to find someone to blame, although the person's actions may well need to be changed as part of the range of control measures. The further controls therefore will be taken from technical, procedural and behavioural issues.

LEGAL LIABILITY

Part of accident investigation is to highlight where there are any breaches of the law and make sure they are dealt with. If there is any legal action, the accident investigation report may be asked for and a prompt, thorough report could help to show the organisation has a good safety culture and is committed to improving standards. It may be used in a criminal court as mitigation as part of a defence if a guilty plea has been lodged. It may be used as a defence in civil court if someone is claiming compensation. Investigation of an accident does not indicate that the employer accepts legal liability for the accident; since it might have been unforeseeable. Investigation shows commitment to managing health and safety.

DATA GATHERING

The investigation will enable data to be collected. These data may be numbers of incidents involving a certain type of work equipment, injuries occurring in a certain department and/or problems during a certain time of the shift. Records of interviews will be compiled together with related procedures and instructions and relevant training. This is important to determine any flaws in the system of work, rather than to focus on individual failure alone. At first the data may be too insignificant to do anything with, but it will be available should there be other investigations etc.

IDENTIFICATION OF TRENDS

Where the data is sufficient, it may be possible to identify trends. These may be cut fingers or slips and trips; they may be accidents occurring in a particular department; at a certain time of day; involving certain individuals; or particular tasks. Once a trend is noted, resources can be directed to that area.

Investigation procedures and techniques

Ideally all accidents should be investigated. A study of minor injuries and near misses can often reveal a major hazard, as the occurrence and severity of injury is a random happening. The depth of investigation should depend on the severity of actual or potential loss, whichever is the greater. The procedure should follow guidelines similar to those below:

- The scene of the accident may still be highly hazardous. Anyone wishing to assist the injured party must take care, so that they too do not become victims.
- The investigation must begin as soon as possible after the accident.
- Consider the people, equipment, materials, environment, task, position (location), time and paper evidence.
- Take photographs, do sketches, measurements and note the people involved.
- Keep the objective clearly in mind. (This is, of course, to discover the causes in order to initiate remedial action, not to find a scapegoat).
- Identify the underlying causes of the accident, not just immediate ones.
- Conclusions must be translated into effective action.

INCIDENT REPORT FORMS

Investigation report forms vary in design, layout and content. Many organisations recognise that a different report form may be necessary for first line managers' initial investigations (a level 1 report) and those done by other managers and health and safety professionals (a level 2 report).

GATHERING RELEVANT INFORMATION

Information can be gathered from photographing or sketching the scene of the accident, eye witness accounts, a variety of documents: risk assessments, safe systems of work, maintenance records, training records, inspection reports, technical files; previous investigation reports.

INTERVIEWING WITNESSES

- Put the person being interviewed at ease. The witnesses may be on guard and very defensive, feeling that blame could be directed their way, it is important to state that the purpose of the interview is to help determine the facts to prevent a re-occurrence.
- Record details: names of the interviewers and interviewee; place, data and time of the interview; and any significant comments or actions during the interview.
- Conduct the interview in private with no interruptions.
- Do not interview more than one person at a time.
- Protect the reputation of the people you interview.
- Set a casual, informal tone during the interview to put the individual at ease.
- Ask probing questions. (These should not put words in the witnesses' mouth).
- Avoid jumping to conclusions.
- Approach the witness with an open mind.
- Notes should be taken, so that the investigator is not relying on memory.
- Summarise your understanding of the matter.
- Express appreciation for the witnesses' information.

ANALYSIS OF INFORMATION

There are a number of computerised analysis programmes available, from health and safety publications or exhibitions, which can help to analyse the collected data to highlight common features and underlying causes.

INVOLVEMENT IN THE INVESTIGATION PROCESS

First line manager (supervisory) investigations

As the person in immediate operating control of an area or activity, it is logical to expect the first line manager to gather information on all accidents that happen in their sphere of responsibility. This investigation is normally all that is necessary for the majority of accidents. It should result in swift remedial actions being implemented, and underlines the first line manager's responsibility for health and safety, on a day to day basis. In some cases this is seen as only the initial investigation, further investigation taking place by another party.

Employee involvement in investigations

Involvement can bring a useful perspective and go some way towards acceptance of the changes that may have to be put into place following an accident. Asking the union appointed Safety Representative or the non-union Representative of Employee Safety to work with the group or individuals conducting the investigation can do this. The other forum for employee involvement may be through health and safety committee meetings or briefing groups that might be asked to consider a particular accident and its underlying causes.

Health and safety professional investigations

The health and safety professional will observe and evaluate the events reported and decide what is considered to be noteworthy, but not warranting a formal investigation team. These events will then be investigated by the health and safety professional to a greater depth. Ill-health events may require involvement of other specialists with a medical background or environmental workplace assessment.

Manager investigations

Organisations that encourage management involvement identify events that warrant further investigation by a nominated manager. A manager, independent of the line managers where the event occurred, may be required by the Senior Manager of an organisation to conduct a more in depth (detailed) investigation. They would take advice, including that from the health and safety professional, as appropriate.

In some cases Middle Managers who receive reports of initial investigations conducted by First Line Managers may decide that a more in-depth investigation is required. This may be in order to gain a better understanding of the underlying causes of the accident, something that may be outside the perspective of the First Line Manager.

Formal investigation team

In some cases a formal investigation team will be convened to take the information gained by the First Line Manager, in the initial stages, and conduct an investigation which is independent from line managers. This is often conducted in situations where a significant loss has resulted (e.g. those that result in a major injury). Organisations with a more developed health and safety programme will also use a team to investigate events that have a high potential for loss, e.g. a significant near miss.

The team size should be kept small in number and could include the following people:

- A senior manager to sit as chair person.
- A manager at a lower level than the chair person e.g. supervisor/team leader.
- A health and safety professional.
- An employee representative.
- As necessary, a person competent to give technical advice e.g. an electrical engineer in the case of electrocution.

Any person whose responsibilities or actions may have been involved in the incident being investigated should be excluded from sitting on the committee, but would, of course, be valuable witnesses.

Use of failure tracing methods as investigative tools

Fault Tree Analysis (FTA) and Event Tree Analysis (ETA) are failure tracing methods that can be used as tools for investigating the causes of loss. They show in graphical format what could be the possible causes of the loss (FTA), or the possible outcomes from a series of problems (ETA).

FAULT TREE ANALYSIS

FTA is a logic based assessment process used to identify and analyse the events, which can lead or contribute to accidents. The procedure was developed by Bell Telephone Laboratories for the US air force for use with the Minuteman ICBM system (Intercontinental Ballistic Missile) to determine the sequence or combinations of events, which could lead to an unauthorised launch of the weapon.

FTA describes sequences of events, either human failure or equipment malfunctions, by working downwards from a Top Event or undesired occurrence, e.g. explosion of a flammable gas. The FTA is constructed by using this reverse logic to establish the relationship between cause and event. It is easy to follow the flow of events and sub events in each particular failure and also indicates where the placement of sensors or controls will have maximum impact on the progression from cause to effect. Graphical representation can show at a glance what the basic events could be that could lead to the loss.

FTA has three key aspects:

1. Problem formulation.
2. Key definitions.
3. Graphical representation.

EVENT TREE ANALYSIS

Unlike fault tree analysis, event tree analysis is a "forward thinking" process, that is, the analyst begins with an initiating event and develops the resulting sequences of events that describe potential accidents, accounting for both the successes and the failures of the safety functions as the accident sequence progresses. They are binary in form, each stage requiring a yes or no, success or failure answer.

Event trees provide a methodical way of recording the accident sequences and defining the relationships between the initiating events and the subsequent events that combine to result in an accident. They are an element of safety management much favoured by the Health and Safety Executive.

Event trees are valuable in examining the consequences of failure, because these are greatly influenced by factors such as operator intervention and weather conditions, which can be expressed more readily in event tree form.

See also - Failure tracing methods - Element A3

This page is intentionally blank

Identifying hazards, assessing and evaluating risk

Learning outcomes

On completion of this element, candidates should be able to:

A3.1 outline hazard identification using appropriate techniques

A3.2 describe how to use internal and external sources of information in the identification of hazards and the assessment of risk

A3.3 explain how to evaluate and prioritise risk using qualitative, semi-qualitative and quantitative methods

A3.4 describe the principles and techniques of failure tracing methodology

Contents

Relevant statutory provisions

Management of Health and Safety at Work Regulations (MHSWR) 1999 - Regulation 3

This page is intentionally blank

A3.1 - Hazard identification

Hazards identification techniques

HAZARD IDENTIFICATION

Regulation 3 of the Management of Health and Safety at Work Regulations (MHSWR) 1999 places an absolute duty on the employer to make a suitable and sufficient assessment of the risks to health and safety of his employees at work and to non-employees who are affected by his undertaking. The self-employed similarly have an absolute duty to assess the risks to themselves and to others they may affect.

The first step in assessing risks is to identify the hazards that can create a risk.

A hazard can be defined as "the ability of something to cause harm (loss)".

Successful Health and Safety Management, HSG65, defines a hazard as:

"the potential to cause harm, including ill-health and injury, damage to property, plant, products or the environment, production losses or increased liabilities".

For example, a substance would be a hazard in a particular way depending on the properties of the substance: a strong acid would present a corrosive hazard.

There are many ways hazards can be identified. The methods used will need to be reviewed in order to use the most suitable so that all the hazards associated with a task can be identified. For complex activities it may be necessary to break the activity down into its component parts by, for example, task analysis.

TASK ANALYSIS

For example, when dealing with a large machine, this could mean looking at a number of various tasks:

- Installation.
- Normal operation.
- Breakdown.
- Cleaning.
- Adjustment.
- Dismantling.

The hazards associated with each part could then be identified more easily and thoroughly.

It is necessary to identify contingent hazards which can arise from system, component, checking or maintenance failures, as well as continuing hazards, i.e. those present continuously, e.g.:

- Mechanical hazards.
- Electrical hazards.
- Thermal hazards.
- Noise and vibration.
- Radiation.
- Toxic materials.
- Ergonomic design.

CHECKLISTS

Checklists are useful in conjunction with carrying out an inspection. They can list the variety of hazards that are possible in an area. They can jog the memory and help prevent the competent person failing to perceive hazards in an area he is familiar with. They may have a space on the form where hazards not listed can be added for future reference.

OBSERVATION

Hazard identification can be carried out by observation of the activity and noting the hazards as they occur in the actual work setting. This is seen to have advantages over carrying out a desktop exercise using the safety manual for the use of a machine, for example, as the operator may have developed his own method of working, contrary to instructions and training.

INCIDENT REPORTS

Hazards may also be identified during accident investigation. An accident will often highlight previously unforeseen hazards. Accident statistics from internal and external sources can also be used for hazard information.

A3.2 - Sources of information

Incident data and rates

INCIDENCE, FREQUENCY, SEVERITY

Information used in evaluating risk may be reactive, after the event. Incident data can show hazards that might not have been identified, either missed or not foreseeable.

The rates can show the number of people who have suffered a certain type of loss, how often they occur and how severe they were. These factors can help evaluate the risk by establishing the likelihood that they will occur and the severity of the loss.

External information sources

Information that can assist in risk evaluation can be sourced from external bodies. These might include trade associations, HSE publications and reference to BSEN standards, for example, guarding and maintenance.

HSE

HSE produce documents including the legal series, guidance notes, information sheets and leaflets. The range available is printed in a free catalogue and may be ordered by phone, fax or e-mail. Information is also available from their web site www.hse.gov.uk.

OTHER RELEVANT GOVERNMENTAL AGENCIES

Information can be sourced from the Environment Agency, the Fire Authority, the Health and Safety Laboratory and the National Radiological Protection Board.

EUROPEAN SAFETY AGENCY

The European Safety Agency was set up by the EU to bring together the vast reservoir of knowledge and information on OSH-related issues and preventive measures.

ILO

The International Labour Organisation deals with labour standards, fundamental principles and rights at work. They have a website and a database of all types of work-related information.

WHO

The World Health Organisation is the United Nation's specialised agency for health and was established in 1948. It has information on health, where health is defined as a state of complete physical, mental and social well-being and not merely the absence of disease or infirmity.

PROFESSIONAL BODIES AND TRADE BODIES

There is a range of professional and trade bodies that can provide information to help with risk evaluation: the TUC, the British Safety Council (BSC), the Institution of Civil Engineers, the Institution of Occupational Safety and Health (IOSH), RoSPA, Faculty of Occupational Medicine, the Institute of Electrical Engineers, CBI, and many more.

USE AND LIMITATIONS

External information sources

- Information from external sources is beneficial inasmuch as it utilises the experience of others.
- One organisation's incident data can enable another organisation to evaluate their risk.
- The wealth of information could not possibly be amassed by just one company.
- It is time consuming and expensive to collect data, so having access to it externally is cost effective.

There are *limitations* to the use of external data:

- There is so much of it; it may be difficult to decide what actually is relevant to a particular situation.
- You have to know what you are looking for or you may become lost within the plethora of detail.
- Although it saves resources in collecting your own data, it may require extensive resources to reach a conclusion from it.

Internal information sources

COLLECTION, PROVISION, ANALYSIS

Damage, injury and ill-health data

The information that is gathered during accident investigation, health surveillance and absence records can provide useful data when evaluating risk. Several cases of dermatitis can show a problem with a particular cleaning fluid, whereas one case, when analysed, may show the problem could have been caused by the person's own individual sensitivity or possibly pursuit of a leisure time hobby.

Near-miss information

Near miss reporting is an important way of finding out where the potential for harm is. The reports can be analysed and show where further investigations are needed. For example, a box falling off the racking and almost hitting an employee passing by may show that the racking is damaged or tilting, or the boxes have been badly stacked. This highlights areas of risk that might be thought to have been dealt with.

Maintenance records

These records show where and when equipment breaks down and therefore can be a source of failure rates and reliability data.

USE AND LIMITATIONS

Internal information sources

- Internal information will be relevant to the issues being considered.
- It will be easy to access and easy to ask questions should clarification be required.

There are also *limitations* to the use of internal data:

- Often data held by the organisation may be statistically too small to be of any use. E.g. one lost time accident in a year is not going to provide enough information to be all that useful.
- Collecting data is time consuming and can easily get mislaid.
- Organising a near miss reporting procedure is often difficult to do as employees sometimes do not see (or have not been trained in) the usefulness of reporting something that did not cause any damage.

A3.3 - Evaluation of risk

Types of risk assessment available and how to carry these out

Once the hazards have been identified, the associated risks can be evaluated. This is done by looking at the likelihood of the hazard being realised, severity of the loss, and the numbers of people who may be affected and the efficacy of the existing controls. The type of method to be used will depend on the level of complexity involved in the task or area under consideration. The methods themselves are also of a type, named according to the level of complexity involved in their calculation. The criteria involved in the separation of the three types of risk assessment methods are open to debate, and frequently are found amongst risk assessment of complex risk.

QUALITATIVE

The qualitative method of risk assessment can generally be viewed as not considering equations based on numbers to evaluate risk. A cable trailing over a walkway may be evaluated as being a "high" risk because it is felt that somebody is bound to trip over it as there are many people using the walkway. The severity of the injury may not even play a part in the decision. The resulting controls could be: removal of the cable or use a cable cover (immediate); provide re-routing for cables or extra electrical sockets (medium term); monitor and review the controls (long term). This seems to be a good solution using a straightforward, relatively subjective method. The lack of complexity in the situation may only warrant this approach.

SEMI-QUANTITATIVE

The semi-quantitative method is half way between the experienced/educated sense approach (as opposed to so called common sense) and the use of probabilities.

Everyone has their own perception of risk as a result of life experiences and background. A method is therefore required in order to have a common approach and attempt to overcome individual differences. We can rate a risk according to the consequence and likelihood of any loss resulting from a hazard. Thus: *risk rating = consequence x likelihood* where the:

Consequence: The degree or amount of any resultant loss.

Likelihood: How likely that this loss will occur.

Risk rating: The severity of the remaining risk after current controls have been taken into account.

Consequence categories

The consequence can be assessed on a scale of 1 to 5.

5.	Major	Causing death to one or more people. Loss or damage is such that it could cause serious business disruption (e.g. major fire, explosion or structural damage). Loss/damage in excess of (£_____).
4.	High	Causing permanent disability (e.g. loss of limb, sight or hearing). Loss/damage in excess of (£_____).
3.	Medium	Causing temporary disability (e.g. fractures). Loss/damage in excess of (£_____).
2.	Low	Causing significant injuries (e.g. sprains, bruises, lacerations). Loss/damage in excess of (£_____) e.g. damage to fixtures and fittings.
1.	Minor	Causing minor injuries (e.g. cuts, scratches). No lost time likely other than for first aid treatment. Loss/damage in excess of (£_____) e.g. superficial damage to interior decorations.

The amounts in each of the above categories will depend on the size and type of organisation. Senior management in each case should decide these figures.

Likelihood categories

5.	Almost Certain	Absence of any management controls. If conditions remain unchanged there is almost a 100% certainty that an accident will happen (e.g. broken rung on a ladder, live exposed electrical conductor, and untrained personnel).
4.	High	Serious failures in management controls. The effects of human behaviour or other factors could cause an accident but is unlikely without this additional factor (e.g. ladder not secured properly, oil spilled on floor, poorly trained personnel).
3.	Medium	Insufficient or substandard controls in place. Loss is unlikely during normal operation; however may occur in emergencies or non-routine conditions (e.g. keys left in fork lift trucks; obstructed gangways; refresher training required).
2.	Low	The situation is generally well managed however occasional lapses could occur. This also applies to situations where people are required to behave safely in order to protect themselves but are well trained.
1.	Improbable	Loss, accident or illness could only occur under freak conditions. The situation is well managed and all reasonable precautions have been taken. Ideally, this should be the normal state of the workplace.

Using the formula stated above (Risk Rating = Consequence x Likelihood) the risk rating can be calculated. It will fall into the range of 1 - 25. This risk rating is used to prioritise the observed risks.

The risk rating is then classified as follows:

Risk Rating	1 - 9	Low
Risk Rating	10-15	Medium
Risk Rating	16-25	High

There are many variations on this method and other variables can be used, which may move it closer to the quantitative method.

QUANTITATIVE

These assessments are for complex risk and are based on equations using probabilities. Two of the techniques that can be used are Event Tree Analysis (ETA) and Fault Tree Analysis (FTA). Estimated failure rates are used in a sequence of events to evaluate the probability of a resultant failure. Hazard and operability studies (HAZOP) can be used to identify the undesired events and the probability of failure rates may be worked out from the reliability rates of the components given by the manufacturer. They may also come from maintenance records of failure, be based on historical data or informed opinion.

ETA is often used for systems that have components that operate in sequence. For example, the risk (probability) of a fire burning out of control, taking into consideration the existing control measures, i.e. a detector, alarm and sprinkler system, can be evaluated using ETA. The reliability data for each component part may come from the manufacturer; therefore the failure rate of each can be calculated.

FTA can be used to show the probability of a top event (risk/loss) occurring by evaluating the risk at each level of the tree. For example an investigation of an explosion following the release of a flammable gas, would consider all the root causes which lead to the release and similarly all the root causes which lead to the presence of a source of ignition.

See also - Failure tracing methods - later in this section.

Factors affecting risk

There are many factors affecting the level of risk that someone may be exposed to. They all need to be taken into account to arrive at a risk rating or an evaluation of the risk.

HAZARD EFFECTS

A hazard is something with the potential to cause harm, e.g. electricity, trailing cables, asbestos. The presence and type of hazards will need to be identified in all situations in any organisation. The effect of a hazard will depend on the likelihood of coming into contact with it and its ability to cause a degree of harm.

ACCIDENT/EXPOSURE OUTCOMES

Being exposed to a defective electrical cable can result in contact with a live conductor and electric shock of varying degrees of harm, or death. The severity of harm depends on a number of factors: the current passing through the body, the length of time the current passes through the body, which part of the body is affected, etc.

Being exposed to a strong acid and making contact will destroy the tissue it comes into contact with and all people will be affected if exposed to the same substance. However, exposure to flour dust will cause a sensitised reaction (asthma) only in certain people. It is difficult to predict who might be affected in such a work group exposed to flour dust.

PERSONS AND NUMBERS EXPOSED

The more people exposed, the greater the probability that someone will be affected. If it were the case that one in fifty people exposed to flour dust developed asthma and one hundred were exposed, then two people could develop asthma.

Also, the potential for loss if three people were exposed and came into contact with a live electrical cable could be three times the amount than if one person were exposed and had made contact.

DURATION OF EXPOSURE

The longer someone spends exposed to a hazard, the greater the chance (the risk) that they will make contact and be harmed. There is a certain degree of what is commonly called luck associated with not making contact when exposed to a hazard of this type, but the longer the exposure to the risk continues, the more likely it is that luck will run out and a fatal electric shock will result.

Some exposures such as inhalation of an airborne substance, will present a risk of injury from initial exposure until the risk is removed. The level of harm will be dependent not only on the quantity, but the time of exposure.

FREQUENCY OF EXPOSURE

A similar argument to that above can be put forward for the frequency of exposure. The likelihood of contact with a hazard increases the more one is exposed to it. There are a number of variables at work to increase the risk, e.g. being exposed to a hazard on a number of occasions and no harm occurring can make people believe that they cannot be harmed or it is not a hazard at all. The more frequent the exposure, the more likely other variables come into play. For example, on one of the exposures the person is distracted and forgets he has been regularly trying to avoid pipework at head height.

Evaluation methods

TASK ANALYSIS

Task analysis is a methodology used in the assessment and reduction of human error. There are a number of methods that can be used of which two are outlined below: Hierarchical Task Analysis and Job Safety Analysis.

The methods generally take into account the structure of the task and the observable operator behaviour in various levels of detail.

Analysing the tasks can highlight where there could be errors and eliminate them before they can occur. They can be used at the design stage and when a system is already running. They can also be used in accident investigation where how the task was carried out can be compared to how the task was supposed to be carried out and identifying the differences. This method is useful in identifying immediate causes of loss.

HIERARCHICAL TASK ANALYSIS

This method looks at the overall objective of the job and then how it is organised to achieve that objective. It is a top down approach that involves looking at all the sub-tasks that need to be carried out in order to achieve the top objective. At each stage it may be necessary to break the sub-task down even further. At each stage the potential for error can be noted. This breakdown of the task can help the assessor decide on the control measures needed to reduce the risk of loss and can then be written into a safe system of work or safe procedure.

Example of application:

Task: Preparing a soft boiled egg

1. Boil water.
2. Place egg in water.
3. Boil for 3/4 minutes.
4. Remove egg from water.

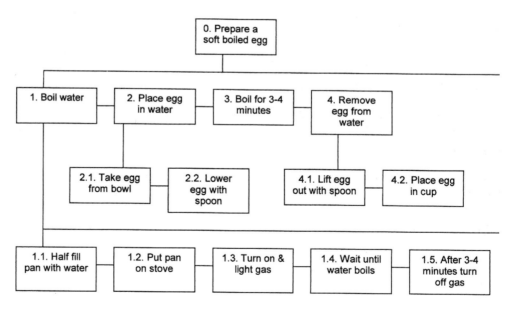

Figure A3-1: Hierarchical task analysis.   *Source: ACT.*

A decision would have to be made as to whether any of the stages need to be expanded, e.g. does there need to be more information at step 1.1 about the size of the pan and the amount of water to be added. Should the water added be cold or hot?

This can make a big difference to the time allowed for carrying out the task. Does step 3 need to expanded? The equipment for timing may have to be provided.

At each of the stages the propensity for error can be noted and this will lead to a decision on the appropriate control measures. For example, what would happen if at stage 1.3 the gas did not stay lit? There is also a potential for scalding at stages 2.2 and 4.1.

The analysis could be followed by a written safe procedure on the preparation of a soft boiled egg.

Of course there are far more onerous tasks than boiling an egg, but the methodology remains the same.

JOB SAFETY ANALYSIS

This is a variation on the method described above. It can be considered looking at the acronym SREDIM:

- Select the task to be analysed.
- Reduce the task to steps.
- Evaluate the risk at each of the steps by identifying the hazards, take into account the existing controls and add in further control measures to reduce the risk.
- Develop a safe system of work.
- Implement the SSW.
- Monitor and review.
- The following example could be expanded in any area thought necessary by the assessor. For example, the existing controls, which are here included in the job step, could be written in a separate column.

Example of the application of job safety analysis

Consider dispensing sulphuric acid from a 200 litre drum:

Job step	Risk factor	Control action
Select drum	Error in selection	Check drum identification and hazard label
Fit eye, hand, body and foot protection	Splash to eyes / face Hands, forearms, body	Select and fit suitable personal protective equipment (PPE) e.g. Chemical goggles / visor, protective suite, gauntlet gloves and boots
Loosen and remove drum dispensing bung	Acid vapour on ventilation	Ensure local ventilation operating Controlled release of bung
Insert closed drum dispensing tap	Poor seal	Align carefully, tighten securely
Locate drum stillage holder	Unstable load	Ensure correct contact
Position drum horizontally	Unstable load	Use kinetic technique
Place drip tray beneath drum dispensing tap	None	None
Release ventilation bung	Acid vapour on ventilation	Controlled release of bung
Position container to receive discharge	Unsuitable container	Acid resistant Suitable opening Correct identification / hazard label
Discharge acid	Risk of splash / overfill	Full attention, regulate discharge
Close discharge valve	None	Clockwise direction
Close ventilation bung	None	Clockwise direction
Check PPE for signs of contamination	Risk of burns when removing	Wash off any contamination with water at safety shower Remove PPE to storage

Figure A3-2: Example of the application of job safety analysis.   *Source: ACT.*

The findings from the JSA should then be developed into a safe system of work, which can then be used in training the operators and as a checklist during the task.

Acceptability/tolerability of risk

ACCEPTABILITY OF RISK

There is risk in all parts of life and everyday risks are generally acceptable. The risk of tripping over your feet as you walk along an obstacle-free surface would be acceptable.

The decision as to whether a risk is acceptable or not is based on legal requirements, industry standards and an organisation's own standards, the latter two being higher than the legal standards. For example, the risk of being entangled in the rotating part of a machine, where access is not required, is unacceptable. This is because regulation 11 of the Provision and Use of Work Equipment Regulations states the absolute duty to safeguard machinery so far as is practicable, with a fixed guard being practicable for parts that do not require regular access.

Where the duty in law is qualified by "so far as is reasonably practicable" the acceptability of risk will depend on the level of risk. The higher the risk the less acceptable it is.

Organisations may set their own levels of acceptable risk using, for example, a risk rating method. If on a scale of 1 to 25, the risk rating is calculated as up to 8, this may be deemed to be acceptable.

TOLERABILITY OF RISK

To say that a risk is "tolerable" does not mean that it is acceptable. Tolerability relates to a person's willingness to accept a risk so that they might gain certain benefits. Thus saying that risks are tolerable does not mean that they are negligible, or not in need of proper control, or something to be ignored. Even tolerable risks need constant review in order to reduce them further if possible.

Individual risk is concerned with the consequences relating to an individual. For example, what is the chance that a person and his/her family might be injured or suffer some other loss through a large-scale accident involving a power station? This is considered by calculating the risk to any individual who lives within a certain radius of the station.

The risks that are regulated by society as a whole must also be considered. Societal risks are based on the concept of securing general benefits for the community. The increased risks posed to people living near a power station, for example, are offset by the benefit that society enjoys through the use of electricity. These risks are still considered or minimised through appropriate controls and the geographical siting of individual power stations. An estimation of societal risks can be measured by considering, for example, the chance of a large accident causing a defined number of deaths or injuries.

The HSE document broadly defines a risk of death of 1 in 1000 per annum as the most that is ordinarily accepted by substantial groups of workers within any industry in the UK. This level is exceeded only by fishermen and small sub-groups such as divers, demolition workers and helicopter pilots. To put this into context, the following table gives some indication of levels of fatal risk:

1 in 100	Risk of death from 5 hours of solo rock climbing every weekend
1 in 1000	Risk of death due to work in high-risk groups within relatively risky industries such as mining
1 in 10,000	General risk of death in a traffic accident
1 in 100,000	Risk of death in an accident at work in the very safest parts of industry
1 in 1 million	General risk of death in a fire or explosion from gas at home
1 in 10 million	Risk of death by lightning

Figure A3-3: Levels of fatal risk (average figures approximated). Source: HSE - "The Tolerability of Risks from Nuclear Power Stations".

Thus it would seem reasonable to say that a risk of death from accidents at work greater than around 1 in 1000 is unacceptable to any other than fairly exceptional groups of workers. Similarly, a risk of death arising from work activities to a member of the public of 1 in 10,000 would be the maximum that should be tolerated. The individual acceptance of these risks depends on a number of factors (e.g. who is in control, who benefits and how much benefit accrues).

RISK RETENTION

As discussed earlier, risk control strategies can be broadly divided into several categories. These are risk: avoidance, retention, transfer and reduction (i.e. through safety and security measures and/or through organisational contingency planning). Risk retention can be sub-divided into with and without knowledge.

With knowledge

Risk retention with knowledge *(active risk retention)* represents a deliberate decision by the organisation to stand either the full or partial amounts of any losses arising from identified risks. This is the result of a conscious evaluation of possible losses and careful consideration of alternative forms of action. In essence this decision may be made when:

- The magnitude of potential losses associated with a particular risk do not justify avoiding it; and
- The costs associated with the transferring of risk (e.g. insurance premiums) over time outweigh the cost of any potential losses; or
- Potential losses are not a significant threat to the financial stability of the business.

Retention may take the form of assuming the risk themselves via a contingency fund (self-insure), or through a captive insurance company (an insurance company owned, or partially owned, by the organisation which has been formed for commercial reasons).

Without knowledge

Risk retention without knowledge *(passive risk retention)* represents a failure on the part of the organisation to identify risks that may lead to loss or to fully appreciate the potential for loss by, for example, inadequate hazard identification or risk assessment. This might occur through neglect or inertia on the part of the organisation. As a result the appropriate controls may be inadequate or non-existent. In effect the organisation will either be under insured, either by failing to appreciate the magnitude of the risk or by failing to adjust the sum assured in line with inflation, or not be insured at all.

Categorisation and prioritisation of risk

Categorisation and prioritisation of risk

The level of risk may be categorised as "high, medium or low", given a number from a risk rating system or be a probability. These levels are generally arrived at by consideration of a number of variables, e.g. likelihood X severity or likelihood X severity X number of persons exposed. The level of risk may be arrived at purely by failure rates, e.g. one component in a system of two may fail with the probability of 1 in 10 or 0.1 and the next with a probability of 1 in 50 or 0.02. Therefore the probability that the system will fail will be 0.1 X 0.05, which is 0.005 or 1 in 200. This result may then be placed in a category of "high, medium or low".

Priority of risk will depend on a number of factors. Risk may be prioritised as needing "immediate, medium or long term attention" because of the category of risk: the higher the category the higher the priority. It may depend on legal compliance, i.e. the risk of injury is low, but the risk of enforcement action is high e.g. failure to have a Health and Safety policy in writing when employing 5 or more persons. Prioritisation may also depend on public acceptability and perception of risk. The risk may be placed in a low category, but the public's view that it is high may give it high priority e.g. the siting of microwave telecommunication repeater aerials on school buildings.

Relativistic methods of risk rating

A relativistic rating system is a qualitative way of evaluating risks in order to allow comparisons between the various risks thereby indicating priorities for management action. Relative rating systems can take the form of a simple category system (high/medium/low) or take the form of a risk ranking system based on a numerical matrix. This allows priorities to be set and can be used to justify the cost of control measures. Once controls have been implemented the approach can be repeated to indicate the effect of the change.

Probabilistic methods of risk rating

Probabilistic method of rating considers the chance of the undesired event arising. This uses mathematical and statistical techniques in order to aid the decision making process. Techniques such as Event Tree Analysis and Fault Tree Analysis can be used to establish a probability figure or failure rate of an undesired event occurring (e.g. a 1 in 10,000 chance of there being an undetected fire in a laboratory in a given year). This has the advantage of being far less subjective than relativistic systems. Probabilistic methods also allow the risk assessor to be more authoritative when justifying the expenditure on controls and can be used to satisfy the enforcing authorities with regard to the control of complex risks. Although statistics and quantitative methods can be invaluable as an aid to improved decision making they should be used with great care. There are several possible drawbacks including the following:

Statistics can be manipulated or interpreted to produce a desired result ("There are three kinds of lies: lies, damn lies and statistics" - Disraeli) or can be misinterpreted through limited knowledge of the subject.

They cannot encompass all the information and variables which must be considered and therefore should not be used as a substitute for executive evaluation and decision making. The most that these techniques can achieve is the narrowing of the range in which subjective judgement must operate.

Statistical information may be difficult or impossible to obtain.

A3.4 - Failure tracing methods

Principles and techniques of failure tracing methods in the assessment of risk

Not every situation can be covered by a general or generic risk assessment. General assessments will not identify failures that may lead to a downstream catastrophe e.g. failure of a signalling circuit that leads to a train derailment. There is always a need for complex analysis, which may be qualitative, quantitative, or a mixture of both.

Many specialist risk assessment techniques have been developed, predominantly within those industries generally regarded as 'high risk' (e.g. nuclear, chemical and petrochemical industries). The effectiveness of these techniques has been demonstrated over the past years and they have moved into the mainstream of safety management techniques. These techniques adopt a structured approach to identify high-risk areas and tasks and those elements of a process that contribute to overall risk.

The main 'advanced' risk techniques, which adopt a failure tracing methodology, are:

- Hazard and operability studies (HAZOP).
- Failure modes and effect analysis (FMEA).
- Fault tree analysis (FTA).
- Event tree analysis (ETA).

These techniques offer significant benefits in all areas of risk management not just health and safety.

HAZARD AND OPERABILITY STUDIES (HAZOP)

HAZOP Studies aim to identify hazards and operability problems that could reduce a plant's ability to achieve its target production in safety. ICI Limited initially developed it for use in their chemical plants and HAZOP is now used as a standard assessment tool in most industries.

HAZOP can be used on new plant, part of the plant or existing facilities, but is always best done at the design stage. Any change or modification to such plant, temporary or permanent must also undergo a HAZOP to ensure plant safety is not jeopardised by the change.

Features of HAZOP

HAZOP is a team-based assessment and a major feature of a HAZOP is the use of a multidisciplinary team of specialists. An experienced facilitator is required to guide the team and ensure that each discipline can make its contribution. A typical team would include a safety specialist, engineering specialists and operational staff; other specialists could be utilised depending on the operation under assessment, e.g. building and services engineers.

The initial efforts of the team are directed towards identifying the deviations from the design intent and establishing solutions and medications. This allows everyone to become familiar with the operation and encourages a free flow of ideas within the team. Checklists are used to maintain the relevance of the process and reduce the opportunity for ideas to be lost or forgotten. The team will identify a range of hazards that vary from little consequence to life or multi-life threatening.

Definitions

The key words used in HAZOP are, "guide words", "study nodes", "intention", "deviations", "causes" and "consequences".

- Guide words - are used to qualify the intention in order to guide and stimulate discussion.
- Study nodes - are defined as the locations on the plant or services at which the process parameters are investigated for deviation from the design intent.
- Intention - describes how the plant is designed to operate.
- Deviation - are the departures from the intention.
- Causes - are the reasons why deviations may occur.
- Consequences - are the results of the deviations.

Example - HAZOP guide words, meanings and applications

Guide Word	Meaning	Parameter	Deviation
No	Negation of the design intent	Flow	No flow
Less	Quantitative Decrease	Temperature	Low Temperature
Reverse	Logical opposite of the intent	Open	Close

Figure A3-4: HAZOP guide words, meanings and applications.   *Source: ACT.*

The steps of a HAZOP

There are ten steps to carrying out a HAZOP:

1. Define objectives and scope

Management should establish these and typical examples would include checking the safety of a proposed plant or equipment changes.

2. Select the team leader

The team leader should be independent and experienced and should be capable of identifying study nodes, problems, and also encourage and support team members.

3. Select the team

The team should be skilled in the disciplines relevant to the operation.

4. Define the physical boundaries

The team should define the precise physical area that the HAZOP will cover.

5. Collect data

Drawings, flow charts, plant layouts, technical drawings, equipment manuals should be collected and identified.

6. Process the data

For some processes the amount of data processed can be quite small. However, for alterations to existing operations the amount can be substantial.

7. Design review

Checklists are applied to the study nodes where the operation has defined design intent. The area between the nodes is considered, as there may be equipment there which changes the conditions between nodes. At each node the guide-words are applied which identify deviations. Guide-words ensure that the design is thoroughly examined. At this stage the study may uncover gaps in the available information or lack of particular knowledge on the part of the team members.

8. Record the results

All ideas must be recorded to ensure a complete record of the discussions of the team resulting in a decision or modification. This is often of immense use in the future in any further modifications.

9. Implement design modifications

The team leader delegates particular modifications to the appropriate team specialist.

10. Reporting

The report should be accurate and identify major deviations from the design intent, recommended modifications and where possible estimates of necessary expenditure.

General comments on HAZOP

HAZOP is a powerful assessment tool detecting deviations through a methodical approach using specialists guided and aided by a formal system. Although formal the approach encourages freethinking among the team members and the freedom to develop new guide words means that the approach can be used in all situations.

The approach requires a team to be gathered and will fail if specialists with the appropriate skills and expertise are not available.

FAILURE MODE AND EFFECTS ANALYSIS (FMEA)

FMEA is a simple yet powerful tool used to improve the quality of products or services by a preliminary failure analysis method. It is used widely in many industries and is a component part of many Total Quality management systems.

To perform a FMEA the assessor must be very familiar with the function of the system, either from their own experience or from manuals and information supplied by the manufacturer. Where this information is not readily available to the assessor specialist assistance should be sought. A critical part of the FMEA is the ability to understand the failure mode or the method by which the system could fail no matter how small the probability of the occurrence.

The analysis must be meticulous and systematic ensuring that the factors that can lead or contribute to failure are identified. The assessor must understand the components of the system and be able to identify any changes that deviate from or are not consistent with normal operation.

Consider the petrol engine of a car. The engine has a fuel system, ignition system, cooling system, lubrication system, all of which have basic components, e.g. fuel pump, filter, pipes, carburettor, tank, battery, alternator, spark plugs, starter motor, fan belt.

Key characteristics of failure

A number of characteristics serve to highlight the presence of failure and can help in its evaluation:

- Loss of operational function, i.e. breakdown.
- Distortion is any change in the shape of the component.
- Discoloration can indicate improper control, corrosion, foreign matter and heating.
- Discontinuity is any break or irregularity in the surface of the component.
- Smell or odour can indicate chemical damage or heating effects.
- Changes in the properties of the material, e.g. loss of elasticity, hardness.
- Foreign matter not part of the designed system, e.g. debris, corrosive accumulations.

The steps of an FMEA

There a five steps to FMEA:

1. Identifying failure modes.
2. Analysing failure modes.
3. Expressing failure modes.
4. Establishing corrective action.
5. Monitoring progress.

FMEA establishes a list of all equipment and systems and the possible failure modes. The assessment should identify immediate and expected effects of failure and the appropriate remedial action.

Example - FMEA worksheet layout

Failure Modes and Effects Analysis of Process / LEV fan motor / Ref. 001 / Date: 06.01.04					
No.	Component function	Failure mode	Failure cause	Failure effect on sub/system	Preventative measures
1	Part description and purpose	Type of failure	Ways of failure including multiple failure	Effects of failure on sub-system, system and plant	Measures to be taken to prevent or mitigate failure
2					
3					

Figure A3-5: FMEA worksheet layout example.   *Source: ACT.*

General comments on FMEA

FMEA is a powerful qualitative tool for the identification of failure in a system and can be used to complement other techniques such as fault tree analysis, but gives no indication of the severity of the failure. However, Failure Modes Effects and Criticality Analysis (FMECA) can give some indication of the critical importance of the failure and, in a similar format to the one above, can include columns for criticality ranking and frequency failure to aid the analyst in decisions to be taken.

FAULT TREE ANALYSIS (FTA)

FTA is a logic based assessment process used to identify and analyse the events, which can lead or contribute to accidents. The procedure was developed by Bell Telephone Laboratories for the US Air force for use with the Minuteman ICBM system to determine the sequence or combinations of events that could lead to an unauthorised launch of the weapon.

FTA describes sequences of events, either human failure or equipment malfunction, by working backwards from a Top Event or undesired occurrence. The FTA is constructed by using this reverse logic to establish the relationship between cause and event. It is easy to follow the flow of events and sub events in each particular failure and it also indicates where the placement of sensors or controls will have maximum impact on the progression from cause to effect.

FTA has three key aspects that differentiate it from other assessment systems:

1. Problem formulation.
2. Key definitions.
3. Graphical representation.

Problem definition

As with many systems of analysis failure to identify the top event accurately allows the analysis to drift from the necessary path of investigation and consequently fails to identify the combinations of causes leading to the undesired event. The top event should be described in terms of:

'what'   'when'   'where'

A fire or explosion is too general a top event, a specific and clear description is required e.g. an explosion occurring during the off-loading of fuel oil from a bulk storage tank.

Key definitions

Design faults and failures. These are equipment failures that occur in the environment for which the equipment was designed and intended. For example; plant such as a pump used for flammable liquids being installed in such a way that there is insufficient access for maintenance or repair; electronic systems such as those utilised for the control of the movement of robotic paint sprayers. If the designer did not take into consideration the effect, for example, of the loss of electrical power, then the robotic arm might not come to rest in a safe position and may malfunction on start up.

Operation faults and failures. An environment for which the equipment was not designed and intended e.g. a conventional smoke alarm may be an unsuitable fire detection device in an area where a corrosive atmosphere is present, whereas a heat sensor might be more suitable because it is less likely to be affected.

Signal faults and failures. Signal faults and failure of protective devices are commonly associated with spurious trips of plant; they may result from the choice at design stage of unsuitable equipment to measure, for example, over pressurisation or over temperature. Often this can result from the use of a single detection device which provides an incorrect reading, leading to unnecessary plant shut down. If two or more detectors arranged in a voting system were used it might reduce the effect of single failure of one detector.

All types of faults and failures appear in a fault tree, since the main aim of a fault tree analysis is to identify the basic contributing failures.

Graphical representation

Symbols fall into two categories, logic symbols and event symbols. These represent the relationships that exist between equipment failures, human errors and a specific accident. There are also OR gates, AND gates, DELAY gates, and MATRIX gates. The two most basic elements of FTA are the AND gate and the OR gate. The AND gate means that all identified inputs are required simultaneously for the end event to occur. The OR gate means that any one of a number of possible inputs can cause an output event.

The most used event symbols are the rectangle, circle and diamond. Rectangles represent a fault event resulting from the combination of more basic faults acting through logic gates. The circle designates a basic system component failure or fault input that is independent of all other events designated by circles and diamonds. The diamond symbol describes fault inputs that are considered basic in a given fault tree; however, this fault tree is not developed further either because current information must be augmented or the consequences are insufficient to warrant further work.

Logic symbols used in fault tree construction

Logic Symbol	Graphical Representation	Description
OR Gate	Output 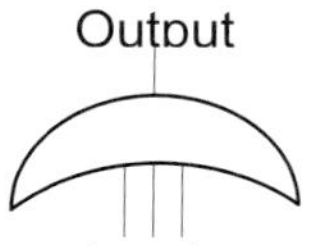 / Inputs	The OR Gate indicates that the output event occurs if any of the input events occur. When calculating probabilities input components to an OR Gate are **added**.
AND Gate	Output 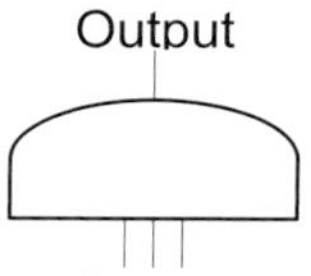 / Inputs	The AND Gate indicates that the output event occurs only when all the input events occur. When calculating probabilities input components of an AND Gate are **multiplied**.

Figure A3-6: Logic symbols used in fault tree construction.

Source: ACT.

Event symbols used in fault tree construction

Logic Symbol	Graphical Representation	Description
BASIC Event	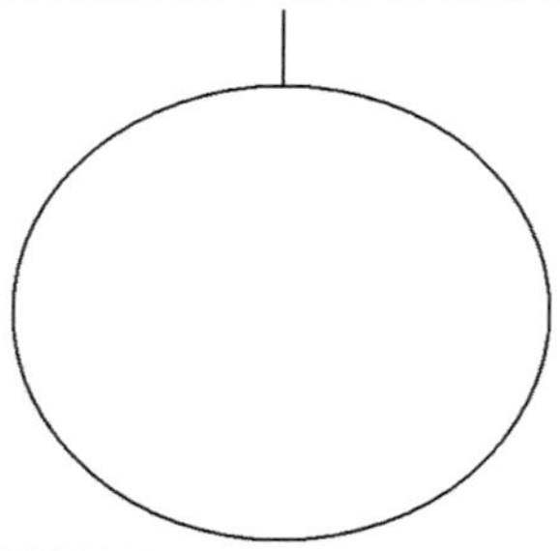	The BASIC Event represents a basic equipment fault or failure that requires no further development into more basic faults or failures.
INTERMEDIATE Event	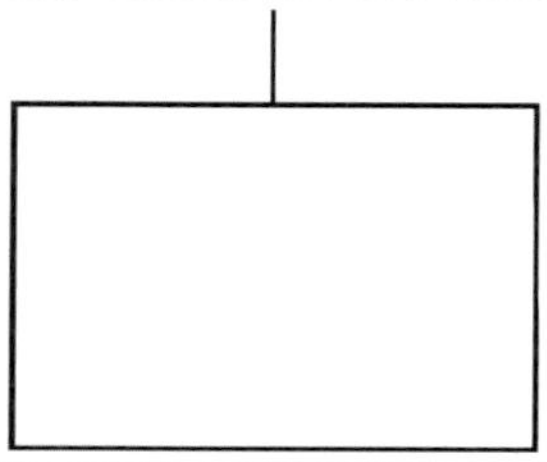	The INTERMEDIATE Event represents a fault event resulting from the combination of more basic faults acting through logic gates.
UNDEVELOPED Event	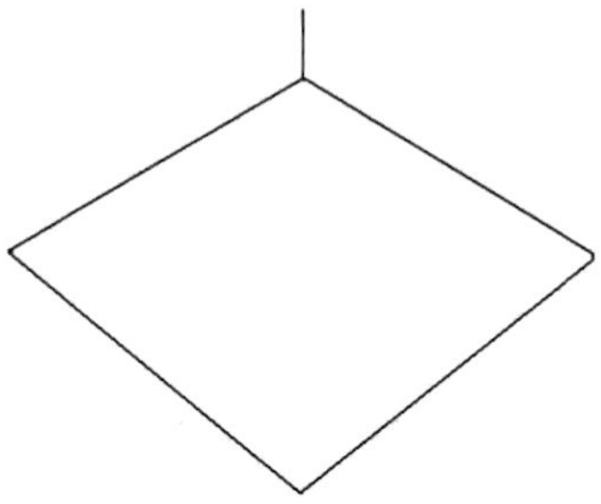	The UNDEVELOPED Event represents a fault tree event that is not examined further because information is unavailable or because its consequence is insignificant.

Figure A3-7: Event symbols used in fault tree construction.

Source: ACT.

The steps of a fault tree analysis

There are nine steps involved in implementing a fault tree analysis.

1. Identify the top event or incident

2. Decide on the level of resolution.

3. Define the analysis boundary conditions.

4. Define the system's physical boundaries.

5. Define the system's initial conditions.

6. Construct the fault tree.

7. Determine the minimal fault tree.

8. Rank the elements.

9. Quantify the fault tree.

Example - fault tree analysis

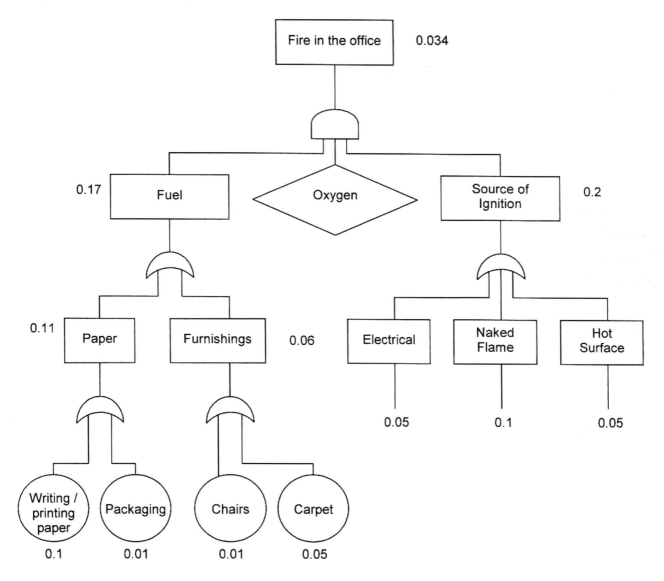

Figure A3-8: FTA example - showing probability figures. *Source: ACT.*

The steps of fault tree analysis

1. Identify the top event (undesirable event)

The top event should be the major failure of the system under consideration (e.g. fires or explosions). The analyst determines the immediate and necessary causes that result in the top event. Normally, these are not basic causes but are intermediate faults that require additional development. If the analyst can immediately determine the basic causes of the top event then the analyst is spending time on an assessment that is too powerful for the problem.

2. Decide on level of resolution

The analyst decides the amount of detail to be included in the fault tree by specifying the level of resolution for the fault tree events. For example, a motor-operated centrifugal pump can be included as a single piece of equipment, or it can be described as several hardware items (e.g. casing, impeller, volute, shaft, packing, etc.).

3. Define the analysis boundary conditions

The analysis boundary conditions describe the system in its normal, successful state. Time should be spent identifying unacceptable events and existing events.

4. Define system physical boundaries

The boundaries of the physical system include the equipment that will be considered in the fault tree and the interaction of the equipment with other processes, utilities and support systems.

5. Define the system initial conditions

The initial equipment configuration and conditions describe the configuration of the system and the equipment that is assumed for the fault tree analysis. The analyst specifies which valves are open and closed, which pumps are on or off, etc. for all equipment within the physical system itself.

6. Construct the fault tree

The starting point in fault tree analysis is to determine whether the fault (or input) has the capacity to act as an AND gate or as an OR gate.

Fault tree construction begins at the top event and proceeds, in a logical approach, level by level, until all fault events have been analysed to their basic contributing causes. The immediate causes of the top event are shown in the fault tree with their relationship to the top event. This has significant similarities to the Domino model of accident causation.

7. Determine the minimal fault tree

The completed fault tree provides useful information by showing the interfaces of equipment failures that could cause an accident. However, except for a simple fault tree, it is necessary to solve the fault tree in order to identify all the combinations of equipment failures that can lead to an accident.

To solve a fault tree means to obtain the minimal development lines for the fault tree.

8. Rank the elements

Ranking the development lines in the FTA is important for setting priorities for designing modifications.

9. Quantify the fault tree

Quantification of the fault tree is carried out by assigning failure data and probability to each event on the tree.

General comments on FTA

FTA is a very useful tool for studying the routes by which a hazard can occur, although its implementation requires skilled analysts and increasingly the use of computers to deduce the development lines. These may also be called 'cut sets'. Quantification of the fault tree depends on the accuracy of the failure data and its availability.

EVENT TREE ANALYSIS (ETA)

Unlike fault tree analysis, event tree analysis is a "forward thinking" process, that is, the analyst begins with an initiating event and develops the resulting sequences of events that describe potential accidents, accounting for both the successes and the failures of the safety functions as the accident sequence progresses.

Event trees provide a methodical way of recording the accident sequences and defining the relationships between the initiating events and the subsequent events that combine to result in an accident. They are an element of safety management much favoured by the Health and Safety Executive.

The steps of an event tree analysis

Five steps are necessary to perform ETA:

1. Identify an initiating event of interest

2. Identify the safety functions or controls designed to deal with the initiating event

The safety functions can be thought of as the plant's defence against the occurrence of the initiating event, and they usually include:

- Safety systems that automatically respond to the initiating event.
- Alarms that alert the operator when the initiating event occurs.
- Operator actions.

The safety systems automatically respond to the initiating event and can shut down the systems. The alarms alert the operator when the initiating event occurs. The operator responds with corrective actions according to laid down procedures or trained for responses.

3. Construct the event tree

The event tree displays the logical progression of an accident. The event tree begins with the initiating event and proceeds through the successes and/or failures of the safety functions that react to the initiating event. Only two possibilities are considered when evaluating the response of the safety functions, quite simply success or a failure.

4. Describe the resulting accident event sequences

The accident event sequences represent a multitude of incidents that can result from the initiating event. One or more of the sequences may represent a back to normal safe operation, some may represent a controlled shut-down and others may result in an accident.

5. The analyst then ranks the accidents based on the severity of their outcomes

Example - event tree analysis

A success of a safety function is defined as its ability to prevent the initiating event from progressing further, thus preventing an accident. The failure of a safety function is defined as its inability to stop the progression of an initiating event or later its course so that other safety functions can respond to it.

Consider the case of a toxic gas escape in a section of a process plant. The relating safety functions are:

- Gas detector.
- Audio alarm.
- An automatic shut down system.

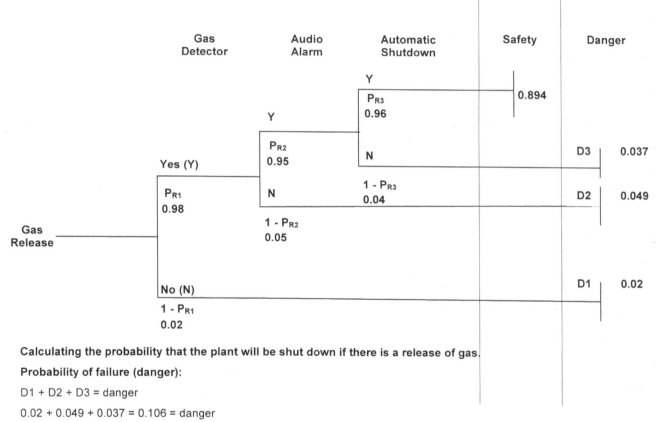

Calculating the probability that the plant will be shut down if there is a release of gas.

Probability of failure (danger):

D1 + D2 + D3 = danger

0.02 + 0.049 + 0.037 = 0.106 = danger

Probability of success (safety):

P_{R1} x P_{R2} x P_{R3} = safety

0.98 x 0.95 x 0.96 = 0.894 = safety (plant shut down in event of gas release)

A check will show that adding the probability of danger to that of safety will give 1. (0.894 + 0.106 = 1).

Figure A3-9: ETA example - with probability figures.   *Source: ACT.*

The initiating event is listed on the left-hand side of the page and the safety functions are listed in a chronological order across the top of the page. The line underneath the initiating event description represents the progression of the accident path from the occurrence of the initiating event up to the first safety function or control (gas detector).

The next step is to evaluate the first safety function. Only two possibilities are considered - success and failure of the safety function. The analyst must decide whether the success or failure of the safety function affects the course of the accident. If the accident is affected, a branch point is inserted in the event tree to distinguish between the success and the failure of the safety function. Usually an upward path denotes the success of the safety function and a downward path denotes the failure of the safety function.

Every branch point developed in the event tree creates additional accident paths that must be evaluated individually for each of the subsequent safety systems. When evaluating a safety function on an accident path, the analyst must assume the conditions dictated by the path of the accident up to the safety function.

General comments on ETA

Event trees are valuable in examining the consequences of failure, because these are greatly influenced by factors such as operator intervention and weather conditions, which can be expressed more readily in event tree form.

ETA is not usually used for the analysis of system failure because of the limited available data, making quantification of failure rates difficult.

Risk control and emergency planning

The intended learning outcomes are that the student will be able to:

A4.1   explain the analysis, assessment and improvement of system failure and system reliability

A4.2   outline the use of cost-benefit analysis in relation to risk control decisions

A4.3   outline the principles of the prevention and control of risk including a description of a general hierarchy of control

A4.4   describe the development, the main features and the operation of safe systems of work and permit to work system

A4.5   outline the principles of prevention, the choice of control measures and their cost benefit

A4.6   explain the need for emergency planning, its benefits and regulatory requirements

Contents

Relevant statutory provisions

Management of Health and Safety at Work Regulations (MHSWR) 1999 - Regulations 4 (and Schedule 1), 5, 7, 8 and 9

Control of Major Accident Hazards Regulations (COMAH) 1999 (as amended 2005)

This page is intentionally blank

ELEMENT A4 - RISK CONTROL AND EMERGENCY PLANNING

A4.1 - Systems failure and reliability

Complex failure analysis

HOLISTIC AND REDUCTIONIST APPROACHES

The *holistic* approach examines the system as a whole. The rationale behind this is the argument that the behaviour of a system cannot be satisfactorily explained merely by the study of its component parts. Thus the philosophy behind this approach is that the system is synergistic - that is, the whole is more than the sum of its parts. An example of the holistic approach is a Hazard and Operability (HAZOP) study which, although it can be used at the sub-system level, most effectively examines the impact of failure on the whole system. Thus the impact of maloperation or malfunction of components is considered in terms of the effect on the system as a whole.

The advantage of holistic analysis is that it draws attention to the relationship between components and the qualitative aspects of the system that may not be appreciated by the reductionist approach.

The *reductionist* approach to examination of any system involves dividing the system into its individual component parts. An individual component is then isolated and the factors that influence it are examined. Thus the reductionist approach to failure analysis begins at the component level by identifying basic modes of failure for each component within the system. Each component failure is then evaluated for its effects on the system. An example of this technique is failure mode and effects analysis (FMEA).

DIFFERENCES BETWEEN SYSTEMIC AND SYSTEMATIC ANALYSIS

Systemic: of the body as a whole.

Systematic: methodical; according to plan, not casually or at random.

This is similar to the differences between the holistic and reductionist approach to complex failure analysis considered above.

A *systemic* analysis considers the whole system whereas a *systematic* analysis considers the component parts of the system in a logical, methodical way that considers each stage of the system in turn. Systemic analysis allows for an intuitive approach that may perceive relationships in an apparently unconnected array of activities.

Explanation of analytical considerations of systems and sub-systems failures

APPLICATION TO ACTUAL EXAMPLES

Systems may be "hard" or "soft". A "hard" system is, for example, a piece of equipment, a vehicle, a plant that processes a chemical, a smoke or heat detector, an automatic fire alarm system, etc. A "soft" system is a management strategy, for example, to manage contractors, recruit new staff, deal with emergencies, etc. Systems are made up of sub-systems; parts that work together to make the system work.

A forklift truck (FLT) may be considered a system that operates within an environment. It can be analysed as to its failure within that environment by consideration of the task it performs and its movements: hitting overhead pipes, overturning, a wheel going down a pothole, etc.

The FLT (the system) can be broken up into a number of sub-systems. The lifting mechanism and the braking mechanism are two of the sub-systems, i.e. parts of the greater whole. Analysis of the lifting mechanism, for example, using an FMEA, will show which parts may fail and how. The failure of component parts in the lifting mechanism, the chain for example, may cause the lifting mechanism to fail while carrying a load or not be able to operate at all. The effect on the system, the FLT, may just be that it cannot perform its duties as a lifting machine and there may be some product damage. Analysis of the braking mechanism could show that failure of the component parts, the brake pads for example, may make the brakes inoperable. The effect on the system (the FLT) could be catastrophic and cause loss by way of personal injury, plant and building damage, loss of product and the inoperability of the FLT.

An analysis of the system and sub-system would have shown the probability of a failure of a weak temporary link (solvent pipeline) between vessels at *Flixborough,* where a major flammable chemical explosion occurred. A HAZOP and/or an FMEA would have shown how the temporary change introduced could have adversely affected the system.

A system to manage contractors will be made up of sub-systems for example, choosing the contractor, site induction, issuing work orders, safe procedures and permits to work, supervising them, etc. On analysis, each of these sub-systems can be further broken down so, for example, issuing permits to work becomes a system that can be broken down into sub-systems such as support documentation, permit authorisers and so on until a further breakdown is no longer possible. Controls can be considered at each stage.

The *Piper Alpha* explosion was due in part to management failure within a permit to work system. The permit to work sub-system had not been analysed to find out what effect its failure in operation could be on the whole system.

If a car and passenger ferry such as the *Herald of Free Enterprise* leaving port is considered as a system, then for the numerous problems that developed, for example, management attitude 'to turn the ship around quickly', failure to follow standard procedures in the sub-systems inevitably led to disaster.

Assessment of system reliability

GENERAL POINTS

Reliability is not confined to single components only; the evaluation of systems, simple or complex, is needed. Evaluation techniques are used for designing reliable systems or for gaining reasonable assurance in advance that a design will meet certain safety and reliability requirements.

System reliability calculations are based on two important operations:

- As precise as possible a measurement of the reliability of the components used in the system environment.
- A calculation of the reliability of some complex combinations of these components.

SERIES SYSTEMS

Generally, the reliability of the series system is computed by multiplying the probability of each component part that it will survive its operating life. Multiplying the probability of survival of A and B in the diagram will give the probability of the system surviving.

Figure A4-1: Series system.   *Source: ACT.*

In general, if there are no components in the series, the system reliability is given by:

$Rs = R1 \times R2 \times R3 \times \ldots \ldots \times Rn$

A series system has drawbacks in that one failed component causes failure to the whole system. Markham Colliery is an example of this, where the one failed component (central pin in the winding mechanism to the lift cage) caused the whole system to fail and hence led to the disaster.

PARALLEL SYSTEMS

If very high system reliabilities are required, for example, on lifts or aircraft, the designer must duplicate components and sometimes whole circuits to fulfil such requirements. Use must be made of parallel reliabilities, called parallel redundancy. In series systems, all components must function for the system to operate. In parallel systems, it is necessary for only one component to operate for the system to operate. The systems can be evaluated in a similar, but more complex way, to the series equation in order to work out the probability of success or failure.

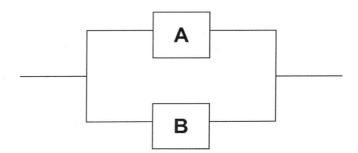

Figure A4-2: Parallel system.   *Source: ACT.*

Three equal components in parallel is represented by:

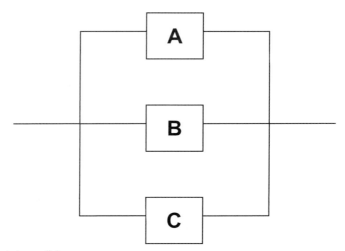

Figure A4-3: Three equal components in parallel.   *Source: ACT.*

The reliability of a parallel system can be calculated as follows:

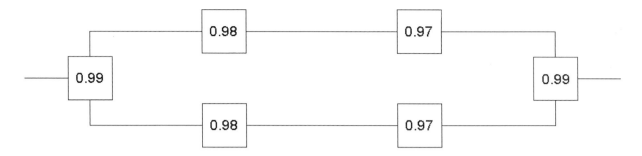

Figure A4-4: The reliability of a parallel system.   *Source: ACT.*

Where there are systems in parallel with a switch in and a switch out, the reliability of the parallel system can be calculated as follows:

Reliability of first system is 0.98 x 0.97 = 0.95

Reliability of two systems in parallel is

        1 - (1 - 0.95) x (1 - 0.95)

=   1 - (0.05) x (0.05)

=   1 - 0.0025

=   0.99 (2 decimal places)

Reliability of the system including the two switches is

=   0.99 x 0.99 x 0.99

=   0.97

Reliability of parallel system = 0.97 which is less reliable with the inclusion of the two switches, but is more reliable than the single system.

Probability of failure = 1 - 0.97 = 0.03

STAND-BY SYSTEMS

A stand-by situation is when a component or unit is operating and one or more units are standing by to take over the operation should the first one fail. The supporting units are normally idle and begin to operate only when the preceding unit fails.

These systems therefore require failure sensing and switchover devices to put the next unit into operation. The reliability of the sensing/switching device must be taken into consideration, as well as the failure rates of the stand-by units.

MIXED SYSTEMS

There are some cases when not all reliability problems can be reduced to the series, parallel and stand-by models. There are combinations of components that are neither series, parallel, nor stand-by. Again, there are formulae available to evaluate the reliability of these systems.

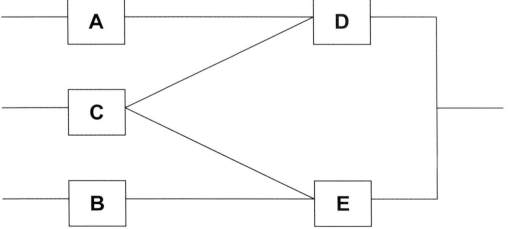

Figure A4-5: Mixed system.   *Source: ACT.*

In the above circuit, the two equal paths, A-D and B-E, operate in parallel so that if at least one of them is good, the output is assured. But because units A and B are not reliable enough, a third equal unit, C, is inserted into the system so that units D and E are supplied with the necessary signal. Therefore the following operations are possible:

    A ⟹ D   or   B ⟹ E   or   C ⟹ D   and   C ⟹ E

COMMON MODE FAILURES

Failure can occur when an external factor affects the systems. For example, in 1980 a leg sheared off an oil platform (rig), the platform tilted and the generator was knocked off. The generator supplied all the electrical power. The rig was plunged into darkness, the resulting fire could not be dealt with and there was no means of escape. The systems for dealing with the various emergency situations should have been so completely apart from each other that their all being affected by the same external factor could have been avoided.

PRINCIPLES OF HUMAN RELIABILITY ANALYSIS

Human reliability analysis (HRA) was developed as a means of quantifying the interaction between human and engineering systems. It aims to improve the understanding of the contribution made by all people to engineering systems. This is significantly greater than the previous man-machine interface analysis. HRA is a systematic evaluation of the factors that influence the performance of humans in the workplace and is used to identify potential human errors, their causes and their subsequent effects.

Human behaviour

Human behaviour is controlled by the requirements of the task, the working environment in which the task is performed and the skills, experience, abilities and training of the human performing the task. Human knowledge can be assigned to one of three categories:

1.   Skill based knowledge and action.

2.   Rule based knowledge and action.

3.   Formal reason based knowledge and action.

Consider the skills required from and exercised by an operator. These are: sensing, perceiving, prediction, familiarity with controls, and decision. The table below summarises some of the errors made be people contributing to the failure of engineering systems over their lifetime.

Examples of errors

Designer	Procurer	Manufacturer	Distributor	End User
Failure to select most appropriate control-display component	Incorrect specification of system type	Incorrect production of design	Incorrect handling and storage	Use of incorrect operating and maintenance
Human is assigned a task which they cannot do or which is best done by machine	Incorrect specification of parameters	Use of wrong machining and fabrication techniques	Incorrect monitoring of environment during transit	Use of incorrect parts in maintenance

Figure A4-6: Examples of errors.   Source: ACT.

Applications of human reliability analysis

For example, in the computer industry, the requirement for reliability safety critical software has led to wide studies for reducing errors by software developers. Based on the findings of HRA, computers are used to check the design decisions of humans and hence improve reliability of software. In the transport industry, analysis of incidents involving the transport of dangerous substances showed that over 40% of these incidents were directly caused by human error rather than by mechanical failure.

Implementation of human reliability analysis

The following steps are taken when implementing HRA.

1.   List the system functions to be performed.

2.   For each function, list all the actions that must be performed by operators to implement that function.

3.   Determine whether any operator tasks have already been specified by a customer procurement document.

4.   Determine sub-tasks that must be performed to implement higher order tasks.

5.   Describe each task and sub-task in terms of a verb that indicates the nature of the action being performed by the task, for example, monitor, check, read, etc.

6.   For each task and sub-task identify error-likely situations.

7.   Rank the errors in the order of severity.

8.   Document the results.

Resources

The analyst should be familiar with the layout of the plant, and in particular the layout of the control room and the alarm systems. The analyst should be assisted by information gathered from discussions with operating personnel and from records of plant procedures.

Type and nature of results

The results of HRA are both qualitative and quantitative. They are qualitative in the respect that they give a listing of the errors and the contributing factors that are likely to be encountered during normal and emergency operation, and they identify systems interfaces that are affected by specific errors. Human Reliability Analysis gives quantitative results in the respect that it provides relative ranking of errors based on probability of occurrence and severity of consequences.

Methods for improving system reliability

GENERAL POINTS

Regular testing is important to identify fail to danger situations before a demand is placed on the system, but is there a danger in testing systems too frequently?

Three risk factors need to be considered if the work is carried out more frequently:

1.   Continuance of plant operation whilst protective devices are removed for testing.

2.   The likelihood of error / damage in removal / replacement of equipment by test engineers.

3.   Potential exists to replace a good component with a component that is defective.

1984 Bhopal, India

A major disaster occurred to the local population following the uncontrolled release of highly toxic vapour when a storage tank containing methyl isocyanate was contaminated with water (major respiratory injury results at exposure to levels at parts per billion) to atmosphere. 2500 people were killed and it is estimated that approaching 500,000 people have been injured from the release. The most significant aspect which contributed to the loss was that the plant was operating whilst the protective trip systems and devices were disconnected for testing and maintenance work. It is essential to include testing / maintenance considerations when conducting HAZOPs at the design stage.

Typically the trip system / devices should be tested to a frequency which gives at least the same reliability as the protective device.

The human element is a very important consideration when calculating the frequency of the test of protective systems and devices, and as a minimum, task analysis should be carried out. For high potential risk considerations other techniques such as psychological profiling will often be required. Formulae are available to calculate these probabilities but these are outside the scope of this discussion.

USE OF RELIABLE COMPONENTS

By considering the data available, the most reliable components can be chosen. The most expensive may not always be the most suitable. For example, the reliability of a system may be lessened because a valve has a probability of failure of 0.05. Using the same level of quality valve, a second valve can be placed in parallel so that if one fails the other will come into use. This means, for a dangerous situation to arise, both valves will have to fail together, the probability of which is 0.05 X 0.05 = 0.0025. The probability has gone from 1 in 20 to 1 in 400.

Another method of improving reliability is derating. This means having a safety margin. For example, a resistor rated for a current of 2 amps is run at 1.4 amps. The derating is 1.4 / 2 = 0.7. This is a typical figure for electronic parts.

Components that are made to specification within a quality assurance system, where rigorous testing is carried out are more likely to be reliable. It is important that reliability is built in from the design stage, through manufacture, through the building of the system, its use, making changes, and maintaining the system and its component parts.

PARALLEL REDUNDANCY

System reliability can be improved by duplication of key components in parallel, so that when one component fails (becomes redundant) the other operates to maintain control e.g. dual breaking to a motorcar. When designing parallel systems consideration must be given to diversity.

STANDBY SYSTEMS

Here we again have duplicity in parallel, however the system is not operating continuously, but is held in reserve. An example of this is a second water supply pump at a water treatment plant provided to be available by valve switching when required following a failure or maintenance of the primary pump. Standby is only appropriate when the system has the capacity to deal with the time for switchover, which may be either manual or automatic.

MINIMISING FAILURES TO DANGER

Minimising failure to danger is a design consideration at the HAZOP stage. Here we need to consider the operation of safety critical equipment and devices at the time of failure of the device, detector communication link or responder.

Consider a remotely operated steam control valve to a reactor. Such valves are usually controlled using compressed air operating the valve against a spring. A typical arrangement would be that the valve closes at zero supply pressure and opens when compressed air at a known pressure is applied.

At the design stage it would need to be determined which is the more critical to the process, failure to open or failure to close. The reliability of the equipment and air supply would be assessed and the design would ensure the correct sequence of events to ensure a failure to a safe condition results.

Certain high risk facilities, for example, the nuclear industry, may need complex duplication of protective devices to meet the societal level of assurance. Such systems are designed to include Majority Voting Systems. Majority Voting Systems use voting logic. For example, consider the temperature of a reactor, we may consider that this needs to be controlled critically. Any message from the thermocouple that shows overheating will set a sequence in play to shut down the reactor. However, some of the messages from the sensor are spurious. The solution is to install three thermocouples to monitor a single process variable. A voting logic analyser will receive readings from each of the sensors, but any response action (e.g. reactor shut down) is only initiated by any two of the three sensors. The logic behind this is that there is a probability that one sensor could send a spurious message, but the probability that two will send spurious messages at the same time is remote. Conversely, there is a probability that one sensor might not pick up a change in temperature, but the probability that two will not at the same time is remote.

DIVERSITY

Diversity is concerned with the identification of common mode failure. Common mode failure may cause a parallel system failure, e.g. if the parallel system requires compressed air and both components are supplied from the same air supply, then failure of the air supply will result in the failure of both components in the parallel system. A single failure of electrical supply may affect many different supply voltages to a plant, including low voltage instrumentation, if not provided with separate back up. Care needs to be taken when considering the need for either redundancy or diversity. The best design systems strive to reduce the need for protective devices as the more protective devices that are included the more likely you are to have spurious trips.

For example, a power press utilises three protective devices to safeguard the operator: electrical, mechanical and pneumatic. If an electrical failure occurred the electric interlock would fail, but in such a diverse system, the mechanical interlock would protect the operator from injury. If both the electrical and mechanical protective devices failed, then the pneumatic interlock would become the protective device. A common fault in the system would be unlikely to affect all three types of safeguarding system. The machine would be guarded by at least one of the systems and the probability of all failing would be very low.

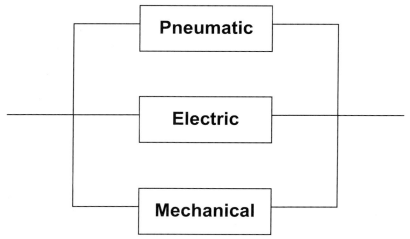

Figure A4-7: Diverse system.

PLANNED PREVENTIVE MAINTENANCE

Plant maintenance systems

The risk management approach to maintenance is to minimise costs (of all types, including accidents) and to maximise productivity and equipment life. There are various strategies that can be adopted including emergency maintenance, breakdown maintenance, shutdown maintenance, planned preventive maintenance including routine condition monitoring. Although there may be some short-term gains in adopting a total breakdown maintenance strategy (no disruption of production, or use of spare parts, no or low maintenance staff costs) this will become increasingly less cost-efficient as time passes. Breakdown maintenance would be appropriate for non-safety or production critical plant where the cost of maintenance outweighs the need for increased reliability.

No matter what maintenance strategy is adopted, some equipment failures will occur. Although the precise timing or location of the failure cannot always be accurately forecast, the fact that a breakdown will occur at some time is mostly predictable - either by examination of historical records or via the risk assessment process. It is important therefore to have a suitable system for emergency maintenance in place. This may be achieved though the use of:

- Contingency plans.
- Model (or generic) risk assessments.
- Safe systems of work (e.g. permit to work system).
- The provision of appropriate skills and training.

Shutdown maintenance, where the renewal work is carried out when the process is stopped, is still common to the chemical and engineering sectors of industry. Traditionally in engineering this occurred during the Easter break. Chemical plants usually have a cycle whereby they shutdown, for example, every two years. The frequency and duration of the maintenance period is dependent on the nature of the plant and processes being operated. This has the advantage of allowing maintenance to take place without the pressures of production. Many organisations combine the shutdown period with a general process employee holiday. Unless adequate management arrangements are in place, this can lead to a lowering of normal safety standards - particularly when third party maintenance staff are involved *(refer to the Associated Octel case law summary)*.

Preventative maintenance seeks to take action which tries to keep the condition of the component at its best by carrying out frequent care of the component e.g. lubrication, adjustment, cleaning. Monitored maintenance seeks to monitor the conditions of components, for example, noise or frequency levels from a gearbox to estimate bearing wear to determining the point just before failure, at which point it would be replaced. The main benefits are:

- Extended useable life of components.
- Assurance of reliability.
- Confirmation of condition of components.
- Reduced risk/loss producing failure events.
- Ability to carry out work at a suitable time.
- Better utilisation of maintenance staff.
- Less peaks and troughs in maintenance activity.
- Less standby facilities required.
- Less expensive (last minute) contracted facility required, e.g. temporary hire of equipment such as fork lift truck.

Routine conditioning monitoring is the comparison of the state parameters of the plant. Traditionally in engineering systems key parameters have been temperature, coolant and vibration. For example, when a local exhaust ventilation system (LEV) is installed the state parameters (e.g. capture velocity and static pressures) will be measured during the commissioning process. These are then used as a benchmark against which the efficiency of the system and thus the need for maintenance is measured. This has the advantages of ensuring that the plant is working efficiently, allows early detection of any deterioration and the carrying out of maintenance tasks at the optimum time. In turn, condition monitoring may be extended to the components that comprise the system. This is particularly relevant to the monitoring of critical components such as the motor/fan within an LEV system. Here the motor and its associated bearings can be monitored to identify any deterioration in performance that might threaten the efficiency of the system as a whole.

The role of statutory examinations of plant and equipment

The role of statutory examinations is to provide a means to identify the condition of critical equipment that, if not maintained to an acceptable standard, would create serious risk. The examinations take the form of a physical examination of the equipment by a competent person to identify patent defects, such as surface corrosion or physical damage, in the condition of equipment and its safety devices.

Statutory examinations have been prescribed for a considerable period. Traditionally the period of 14 months (e.g. LEV under COSHH 2002) was considered an appropriate period. This had the twin advantages of allowing for the movement of Easter, the traditional maintenance period, and gives a variation in the time of year that the examination is carried out. However having fixed intervals between examinations with universal application takes no account of the actual conditions of use. The trend, however, appears to be moving away from prescriptive statutory examinations towards risk based assessment by a competent person (e.g. written systems of examination for pressure systems and lifting equipment). The latter example illustrates the prescribed versus risk bases approach. The Lifting Operations and Lifting Equipment Regulations (LOLER) 1998 provide that operational lifting equipment is to be thoroughly examined:

- At least every 6 months for lifting equipment for lifting persons or lifting accessories.
- At least every 12 months for other lifting equipment.
- In either case, in accordance with an examination scheme.
- On each occurrence of exceptional circumstances liable to jeopardise the safety of the lifting equipment.

Note that the law setting out the requirements for statutory examinations does not precisely define a 'competent person' nor does it stipulate that they should be independent of the employer. Although statutory examinations can be delegated to an outside organisation, this does not absolve the employer from the responsibility to ensure that they are carried out.

MINIMISING HUMAN ERROR

HRA can be used to develop training schemes for skill based behaviour and associated physiological factors, the design of controls, workplace, buildings, environmental conditions, transportation, and communications. A good example is the design of aircraft cockpit control layouts in which human performance at the operator level reaches the highest levels of criticality.

The concept of HRA could be used by management to devise management controls. The recent collapse of Baring's Bank and the huge losses suffered by a Japanese investment bank of the New York bonds market and Black Monday were attributed to human errors in monitoring and controlling the operations of the traders. HRA is increasingly used in the development of expert and machine intelligent systems to improve the performance of humans and equipment.

At the design stage, HRA can be used to identify the features of hardware and job design that are likely to produce a high rate of human error.

Application of HRA requires skilled analysts who understand the plant operation and the tasks performed by operators. The lack of reliable data on operator's behaviour in error-likely situations is a major drawback for the application of the technique.

Analysts must consider that any analysis of operator behaviour is likely to bring about a modification of the behaviour. Operators will modify their behaviour and this can have significant effects on the HRA. One technique to reduce effect on behaviour is to train someone close to the operators in the technique, such as their line manager. The presence of someone known and often in the workplace has less effect on behavioural change, than for example an 'outsider' such as a consultant. Many of the same problems exist in other types of analysis, e.g. Job Safety Analysis, and can be alleviated where the operators have confidence in the approach being taken and the analysts involved.

Failures of components and hardware can be expressed as probabilities. These may be derived from various studies such as in-service or test failures. Predicting the probability of human failure is far more complex. However, if risk assessments are to be done then human reliability needs to be considered and quantified.

When attempting to quantify human behaviour, it is necessary to be clear about what task or step is to be performed, when this task/step is to be performed and how much time there is available to perform it. The next stage is the consideration of how the person can deviate from the step/task. The most common deviations are when the step/task is not carried out correctly, when a step/task is forgotten in a sequence or is performed out of sequence, or when the step/task is not completed in the time required.

Error rates can be affected by a variety of conditions. As previously mentioned, observations of task performance can alter error rates, as can environmental conditions, training and skill levels, and various other stressors. Error rates are likely to be high when the person is under very little stress (bored), or under great stress (emergency situations). Human beings also have the ability to recover from errors, often demonstrating what appears to be an innate ability to control errors of great consequence compared to those of small consequence.

Error rates for a control room situation may typically be as follows:

Error rate	Situation
1 in 1	Impending disaster, rapid action needed, panic
1 in 10	No impending disaster apparent, busy, signals, alarms
1 in 100	Quiet but busy, relaxed
1 in 1000	Familiar, routine tasks

Figure A4-8: Error rates for a control room.   Source: ACT.

For example, we could imagine a situation where studies have been carried out, which may be a number of task analyses, and found out that under no stress conditions there is an error in reading a gauge of 1 in 100 operations (1% of readings). Under pressure, this increases to 1 in 10 operations (10% of readings). If there are 400 readings taken per year, then the probability of an error under no stress and stress conditions within the next 1000 hours is as follows:

*Error rate under **no stress** conditions - based on 400 readings per year and 1 error in 100 readings (1%)*

error rate per year	=	number of readings per year x $\frac{1 \text{ error}}{100 \text{ readings}}$
	=	400 x 1/100 per year = 4 errors per year
	=	4 errors in 24 (hours) x 365 (days) = 4 errors per 8760 hrs
error rate per 1000 hrs	=	$\frac{4 \times 1000}{8760}$ errors per 1000hrs
therefore error rate per 1000 hrs	=	0.46 errors per 1000 hrs
probability of error under **no stress** P_{f1000}	=	$1 - e^{-0.46}$
	=	0.37

*Error rate under **stress** conditions - based on 400 readings and 1 error in 10 readings (10%)*

therefore error rate 1000 hrs	=	4.6 errors per 1000 hrs
probability of error under **stress** P_{f1000}	=	$1 - e^{-4.6}$
	=	0.99

This data can be used in risk assessments to quantify risk once the effect of the error is known. It can help reduce the amount of subjectivity that is usually present when dealing with human error. Once the probability of an accident happening is known, then it is relatively easy to balance the cost of the accident against the cost of controls.

A4.2 - Risk control systems and methods

Concepts within a health and safety management programme

Risk control may be considered in four broad categories. These are avoidance, reduction, retention or the transfer of risk.

AVOIDANCE

Even though it may involve giving up a commercially beneficial activity the organisation decides that the risks outweigh benefits. The risk may involve unacceptable harm to customers, employees or local residents. The risk may be avoided completely by, for example, changing to a radically different and possibly more expensive production method. Another example of an avoidance strategy is to pay employees directly into their bank accounts in order to avoid the possibility of a wages robbery.

It should be appreciated that the avoidance of one risk may introduce others. For example, the decision to avoid siting a factory on a flood plain may mean an increased risk of wind damage due to building on an elevated site. The avoidance strategy is usually considered at the planning stage of the operation in order to avoid potentially substantial costs.

It could be decided to avoid the risks associated with the use of trichloroethylene to de-grease metal by contracting a specialist company to carry it out.

REDUCTION

The risk assessment process is concerned with the consequence and likelihood of potential losses. The reduction strategy is therefore concerned with the reduction of these two variables. This can take a number of forms:

Reduction through organisational planning: here the three key areas of concern, i.e. the organisation, the task and the individual are considered. Specifically, a four-pronged strategy based on education and training, planning, salvaging, and contingency and emergency planning can be adopted.

Redesigning the task can reduce risk, e.g. placing a component on a bench at waist height to be welded instead of the welder stretching up to weld above head height. In some cases, the welding process may be automated, reducing the risk still further, although introducing new, but different risks.

Education and training concentrate on the promotion of a safety culture and the minimisation of the negative consequences of human behaviour. Planning deals with minimising the organisation's exposure to key elements such as suppliers or customers.

Salvaging deals with minimising loss in the same way that a first aider minimises injury. This deals with the provision of trained personnel and equipment, for example to deal with a flood.

The last part of this reduction process deals with contingency and emergency planning.

See also the section - emergency planning - later in this unit.

Reduction through security and safety measures: this can take the form of physical safety devices to prevent loss (locks, alarms, machine guards) or devices to minimise the consequences of loss (sprinklers, fire resistant construction, electrical trip devices). In addition procedural devices such as good housekeeping and storage can reduce hazards.

TRANSFER

Transfer can take two forms:

1.   The transfer to another organisation by, for example, sub-contracting out to a specialist a component which requires a finishing process which involves hazardous substances, such as chromium plating (thus transferring risks to both people and the environment).

2.   The assignment of financial responsibility to another organisation.

The most common form of the latter method is via insurance. Risks may be transferred in full or partially. The options available to a driver buying motor insurance are a good example of this strategy. These range from fully comprehensive cover through to third party cover. Similarly an organisation can opt for something between zero and full insurance cover. The transfer strategy can also be achieved by other means. For example, transferring liability for damage by contract or conditions of sale where this is permitted under civil law (note the Unfair Contract Terms Act 1977).

RETENTION

An alternative name for active risk retention may be 'self-insurance' where potential losses are funded by the organisation. This may arise through a deliberate decision to stand some or all of the potential losses or via the formation of a captive insurance company. Many retail chain outlets do not insure their stores for fire: the cost of insuring all their stores is far greater than the likely cost of losing one store. Another retention strategy is the area of 'claims management'. Here an organisation decides to settle claims up to a certain value directly, for example, to an injured employee. This allows the organisation to control costs and insurance premiums and to get actively involved in the process.

Alternatively risk may be retained by the organisation without their knowledge - either through oversight or inertia. This may not only arise from failing to identify or evaluate risk adequately or at all, but also failure to keep insurance cover in line with current market values. Failure to identify key employees or unique equipment which are not easily to or impossible to replace to the same standard.

SELECTION OF AN OPTIMUM SOLUTION BASED ON RELEVANT RISK DATA

The selection of the best solution (i.e. the avoidance, reduction, transfer or retention of risk) will depend upon the risk analysis and the ability of the organisation to withstand loss. The ability for a multi-national conglomerate to withstand and absorb losses is likely to be vastly greater than a small engineering company. It should be noted that, as with all decisions and policies that managers take, the proposed solutions for handling risks should be consistent with corporate objectives. Thus the risk manager must be attuned to the culture, vision and goals of the organisation. The starting point therefore in the decision making process is the setting of corporate objectives.   These objectives can be ascertained through the identification of hazards, the assessment of risk (i.e. possible consequences, likelihood, numbers of people exposed etc.), and then deciding on appropriate ways of handling them.

The factors to be considered in the selection of the best solution include:

■   Legal and other constraints.
■   The organisation's financial objectives.
■   Cash budgeting and liquidity.
■   Industrial relations and related issues.
■   Ethical considerations.

Legal and other constraints

The selection of controls can be dictated by both civil and criminal law. For example:

■   The need for machine guards dictated by the Provision and Use of Work Equipment Regulations (PUWER) 1998.
■   Contractual conditions and obligations.
■   Strict liability for escape of things brought onto premises under the Rylands v Fletcher rule. *(See also - Relevant decided cases - Element A9).*
■   The need to have compulsory insurance (e.g. employer's liability).

The need for legal compliance should be regarded as the minimum standard which the organisation must achieve in terms of risk control. The selection of controls may also be dictated by external factors such as the agencies upon which the organisation depends, for example, banks (capital loans), customers and the insurance companies.

The organisation's financial objectives

Most private sector organisations would place the need to make a profit high on their list of corporate objectives. This can vary from the wish to make enough money to survive (i.e. cover costs) through to the objective of maximising profits. The selection of remedy will therefore need to be consistent with the organisation's goals.

The risk manager must aim to reduce the potential losses from risks but at the same time balance that need by keeping the cost of controls in proportion. For example, a firm could transfer their risks either by the purchase of insurance or by contracting out a process; however, the costs of doing so are likely to outweigh the expected losses. It should be remembered that insurance companies/specialist companies are also in business to make a profit! It is evident that these risk control overheads reduce profit margins.

Cash budgeting and liquidity

Business financial philosophy dictates that cash is treated as a resource that must be controlled like any other. The aim must be to have enough cash available at the time it is needed. Even in organisations that have large cash reserves, this has a cost.

Money held in reserve could be used for investment outside the business and thus earn interest. The unexpected need to meet the costs of a risky event may disturb this balance. For example, a fire can result in:

- Replacement cost of property and equipment (capital assets).
- Disruption of production and sales - possibly leading to lack of customer confidence and future orders.

This may put an intolerable strain on the business and even threaten the organisation's survival. It has been estimated that some 70% of businesses that have a major fire fail within two years of the event. The transfer of risk to an insurance company (property and consequential loss) with known premium costs therefore allows a greater degree of certainty in the event of the unexpected costs. The balance must therefore lie in the amount of potential loss involved and the cost of transference

Industrial relations and related issues

Although the province of the human resources manager, there are several aspects of industrial relations which concern the risk manager and the selection of the appropriate controls. These are safety and security including:

- The cost of accidents.
- The need for employer's liability insurance premiums.
- Security (e.g. pilfering).

Frequent accidents not only have associated costs but can also lead to a lowering of morale and consequent reduction in efficiency and higher unit costs. Alternatively, the costs of control can include a resistance by employees to use them (e.g. wearing personal protective equipment, using guards). Although not all the costs associated with accidents are necessarily borne by the organisation (e.g. hospital treatment), accident prevention should always dominate these conflicting needs. The need to implement controls to reduce accidents is dictated by legal obligations as well as discharging the organisation's social responsibilities.

Similar considerations apply to security issues. The cost of pilfering can be quite high (in some cases it is thought to exceed 5% of turnover) so the cost of stringent controls can be justified. The imposition of stringent security checks, which affect all employees, to prevent theft by the few who might steal can cause great resentment and antagonise many employees.

Ethical considerations

Finally, the moral argument states that people must matter and that risk control decisions cannot be made purely on financial or legal grounds. The price that an individual pays for lack of adequate control can range from personal injury to death. On the other hand excessive costs can lead to job losses. The manager deciding on the appropriate controls must have a clear idea how far the organisation is prepared to go beyond the bare legal minimum and the need for survival. This stems from the organisation's culture vision and goals.

Risk control systems

MATCHING THE HAZARD PROFILE OF THE BUSINESS

The hazard profile of each organisation will differ according to: what resources they bring into the company, what their work activities are and what they output, products, services, waste and information. The risk control systems (RCS) therefore will vary from company to company in the way hazards are addressed.

Regulation 5 of the Management of Health and Safety at Work Regulations (MHSWR) 1999 requires arrangements to be in place for the preventive and protective measures. HSG65 states that a set of management processes is necessary to organise, plan, control and monitor the design and implementation of the RCSs.

RCSs are the basis for ensuring that adequate workplace precautions are provided and maintained.

CONTROL OF INPUTS

Physical resources

RCSs to deal with the physical resources that are inputs could include a system for purchasing plant, equipment and materials, ensuring suitability for purpose and CE marking. There could also be a RCS for hiring plant, such as a crane or excavator, ensuring thorough examination certificates are available and further procedures are in place for the delivery and use of the plant.

Human resources

The input of people to the organisation will require a RCS for specifying personal profile, selection of personnel: interviewing, assessment and contracts. A RCS will be required for bringing contractors into the organisation: selection, approved list management and induction.

Information

A RCS will be required to ensure the relevant information is brought into the organisation. This will include relevant legal requirements and any changes to the law, new technology such as safeguarding methods and feedback from product issues including proposed changes to work or work activities. Systems to ensure that information is disseminated to the relevant people will be needed as a follow through.

CONTROL OF WORK ACTIVITIES

Premises

RCSs for ensuring the premises are safe, clean and maintained. Clear, defined responsibilities for all work areas and identified individuals to control common or shared facilities such as for fire arrangements.

Plant and substances

Plant will require RCSs to ensure its continued suitability. This will include, where appropriate, guard inspection, planned preventive maintenance schedules, and breakdown maintenance arrangements, particularly when out of hours or continuous processes working is involved. An inventory of all plant and substances should be maintained and updated when new equipment or substances are introduced or replaced. Substances will require RCSs to ensure their safe labelling, storage, and use. Procedures and training for emergencies such as spillage should be in place and updated as necessary.

Procedures

All work activities will have procedures for carrying them out. There should be RCSs to manage their planning, implementation, monitoring and review.

People

There are a number of areas that need to be managed when dealing with people and work activities, e.g. correct selection for the task, training, refresher training, the impact of the work on third parties and disciplinary procedures for non safe working.

CONTROL OF OUTPUTS

Products and services

Whatever the product and service outputs of the organisation, there will need to be RCSs to manage their quality and safety aspects and ensure they are kept up-to-date.

By-products

RCSs are needed to manage waste that may affect the air, land or water. A RCS will ensure correct disposal to minimise impact on the environment; this will include strategies to minimise waste generation and consideration of recycling .

Information

Systems to manage information leaving the organisation are necessary for issues such as: user manuals to accompany equipment, reliability data for equipment (this will include, for those who manufacture for supply the creation of a technical file to comply with CE marking requirements) and individual components and to ensure the information is accurate and up-to-date.

A4.3 - Cost benefit analysis

Cost benefit analysis in relation to risk control cost decisions

Organisational, design, planning, operational

Cost benefit analysis (CBA) is a formal system that is intended to provide a framework which allows the user to identify all the desirable and undesirable consequences of an activity and then quantify them in monetary terms.

The Government published new guidance in 1998 on the form of assessment that must be carried out for all regulatory proposals that lead to new legislation. The Prime Minister's Foreword to this document sets out the key requirements of such Regulatory Impact Assessments (RIAs):

> "The Assessment should include a clear statement of the objectives of the regulatory proposal and its likely effects. It should demonstrate that the proposal is the most effective means of meeting the stated objectives, set out the costs and benefits of the proposal, and identify who will be affected."

Figure A4-9: "The better regulation guide and regulatory impact assessment". *Source: Cabinet Office Regulatory Impact Unit; 1998.*

For new health and safety legislation, the HSC is required to prepare a CBA for all new proposals for legislation (except those with a zero or minimum cost impact). This includes proposed Maximum Exposure Limits (MELs) for hazardous substances under COSHH and draft European Directives in order for a negotiating strategy to be formulated.

This deals with the resources used and saved from society as a whole. For example, the cost to industry of implementing the Control of Asbestos at Work Regulations is offset by the money that industry, the insurance companies and wider society as a whole save through not having to treat asbestosis and related diseases. This technique has three stages:

1. Identify and quantify all positive and negative effects of the proposed action.
2. Apply monetary value to all effects.
3. Compare costs and benefits.

Usually the purpose of CBA is to evaluate in common terms the impact of a particular course of action. It can also be used to consider alternatives such as different levels of MELs for a particular substance. Costs will include items such as managerial time, training, and equipment such as guards or PPE and reduced productivity if safer systems of work slow down production. Examples of benefits would include the reduction in fatalities and injuries which such measures would bring.

EXAMPLE - THE CONSTRUCTION (HEALTH SAFETY AND WELFARE) REGULATIONS 1996

The HSC estimated that the Construction (Health Safety and Welfare) Regulations (CHSWR) 1996 had the following costs and benefits

Negative effects - costs to industry - arising from:
- The requirement to fit an intermediate guard rail to prevent falls from heights.
- The segregation of vehicles from pedestrians on sites.
- The provision of additional welfare facilities.
- Additional inspections of scaffolding and fire and emergency precautions.

Estimated first year cost:	**£45-54 million**
Subsequent additional costs:	**£6 million occasionally rising to £19 million per year**
Total cost over 25 years (present value):	**£113-£130 million (0.2% of the industry's annual turnover (est. £50 billion))**

Positive effects - benefits

About 60% of accidents on construction sites are as a result of falls from height or being struck by vehicles on site. The additional protection measures are expected to achieve a 10% - 15% reduction which, in turn, will mean a 6%-9% overall reduction in construction site accidents.

Estimated annual benefits:	**£18 - £27 million**
Total savings over 25 years (present value):	**£127 - £210 million**

Thus, although the cost of implementing the Regulations will outweigh the benefits in the first year, the overall benefits to society over 25 years (£127 million to £210 million) are expected to outweigh the costs over the same period (£113 million to £130 million).

Although the cost of preventing occupational accidents and diseases is borne by employers, the cost of treating the results of these can rest to a large extent with insurance companies and society as a whole. Thus the employer may use cost benefit analysis having little regard for societal costs. They may also use CBA to determine whether the precautions in place are so far as is reasonably practicable (balance of risk against cost).

Main drawback in using CBA is the difficulty of putting values on emotive or intangible items such as:

- Public relations.
- Customer perceptions.
- The loss of a human life.
- The loss of quality of life.

One way of dealing with the last two issues is the concept of QALY or "Quality Adjusted Life Year". This allows for a scale of disability ranging from zero (dead) through to one (perfect health). QALY's are the number of years (i.e. in terms of age) multiplied by the value determined by a disability scale. A monetary value can then be assigned to a QALY.

In addition the persons who gain the benefits of the risks may not be the same as those who are exposed to them. Thus for those exposed there is no benefit. This drawback could be dealt with by the provision of compensation.

The HSE uses a measure called the value of a statistical life (VOSL). This is an estimate of the monetary benefit that society attaches to reducing the risk of death through injury and ill health. For example, a survey shows that individuals are prepared to pay £10 for a safety device which reduces the risk of a fatality by one in 10,000. If this hazard then affects 10,000 people, then the risk of the number of deaths arising from this use is reduced by one. Thus one 'statistical life' is saved by this measure. The group is prepared to pay £100,000 (£10 x 10,000) for this reduction in risk. The VOSL is therefore £100,000.

The Government/HSC have not endorsed any particular VOSL for the appraisal of health and safety at work legislation. However the HSE uses the VOSL developed for the appraisal of road safety schemes as a benchmark. This figure is adjusted each year in line with anticipated growth output (£850,000 as at June 1996). This figure has been criticised by some external experts as being too low. It had been subject to consultation and endorsed by Ministers when it was developed by the Department of Transport in the late 1980s.

For non fatal injuries and incidence of ill health other costs must be used. The following values were calculated in various reports ranging from the 1994 HSE publication "The costs to the British economy of work accidents and related ill health" to the "Costs and benefits of the Noise at Work Regulations".

Event	*Estimated cost/factors*
Major injury (pre-1995 RIDDOR Definition)	£14,212 (1990 prices). Estimate of typical costs such as business disruption, plant damage, medical treatment plus an allowance for pain, suffering etc.
Over 3 day injury (pre-1995 RIDDOR Definition)	£2,650 (1990 prices). Factors as for a major injury.
Case of Occupational Asthma	£32,300 average case over a ten-year period (1994 prices). Comprises of £26,000 loss of income, £1,300 medical treatment and £5,000 pain and suffering.
Case of hearing loss	Sliding scale (1995 prices): £1,250 for a 10-15 dB loss to £50,000 for a loss of 50 dB or more. An allowance is made for lost quality of life and a corrected take into account that hearing loss will often be experienced many years into the future.

Figure A4-10: Work accident and related ill health values.

Source: ACT.

Risk control cost decisions

The costs of risk control measure can be categorised into direct and indirect costs.

Direct costs relate to the cost of purchasing and maintaining a risk control system or measures such as the provision of first aid points and a training programme. These are usually reasonably easy to identify. In addition to these capital costs the cost of running and maintaining systems must be added. These include the required supervision and maintenance staff.

Indirect costs are often more difficult to quantify as they relate to less tangible issues such as:

- The loss of production incurred by the use of a safety device such as a guard.
- The disruption caused when a risk control system such as security cameras or a sprinkler system is installed.
- Reduced efficiency in the movement of goods and materials due to a fire wall being built.

These indirect costs may be mitigated by, for example, paying extra to have the system installed at the weekend.

The following table summarises some of the organisational, design, planning and operational cost and benefits associated with risk control:

Direct Costs

Capital costs of:

- Higher standards of construction.
- Risk control equipment (e.g. sprinkler system).
- Labour and materials costs.
- Maintenance of plant, building facilities and risk control equipment.
- Additional management and supervision.
- Security systems.
- First aid provision.
- Training.

Indirect Costs

- Interference to production for maintenance/loss prevention purposes.
- Loss of production during staff training (e.g. first aid courses).
- Poor labour relations due to the imposition of controls (e.g. guards slowing down production thereby impacting on piece-work).

Direct Benefits

- Reduction in insurance premiums.
- Tax benefits on Corporation and other business taxes.
- Possible grants available for capital expenditure via incentive schemes such as those intended to stimulate regional development.

Indirect Benefits

Fewer insured and business interruption losses such as:

- Property losses.
- Liability losses (claims).
- Personnel losses.
- Business interruption losses.

Improved relations with:

- The workforce (including productivity).
- Customers.
- The general public.

Figure A4-11: Cost and benefits associated with risk control.   *Source: ACT.*

Break even analysis

Those risks that are retained within a business should be reduced through a programme of loss control. Break-even analysis is simply a technique for estimating the minimum turnover required to cover all costs.

These costs can be divided into fixed costs and variable costs. In business finance terms, the break-even point is calculated using the following formula:

$$\text{Break-even point} = \frac{F}{1 - \dfrac{V}{P}}$$

Where:

F =	fixed costs		those costs which must be paid regardless of production or sales
V =	variable cost per unit	(or total variable costs)	these vary in proportion to turnover.
P =	selling price per unit		(or the total sales value may be substituted by the symbol S)

For example, fixed costs for a year are £40,000, variable costs per unit are £2 and units sell for £10 each. The break-even point is:

$$\frac{40,000}{1 - \dfrac{2}{10}} = £50,000 \text{ break-even point}$$

Thus £50,000 of sales is needed to cover costs (including controls and losses).

A variation on this is the break-even quantity (BEQ).

$$\text{BEQ} = \frac{F}{P - V}$$

Therefore it is in the interest of companies to reduce fixed costs to a minimum. An organisation with high fixed costs is less able to withstand a reduction in turnover.

The break-even point is dependent on profit margin. The organisation has to increase sales in order to finance the loss prevention measure or, alternatively, the associated losses.

Annual Losses	Profit Margin			
£	1%	2%	4%	5%
1,000	100,000	50,000	25,000	20,000
10,000	1,000,000	500,000	250,000	200,000
25,000	2,500,000	1,250,000	625,000	500,000
50,000	2,500,000	2,500,000	1,250,000	1,000,000
100,000	10,000,000	5,000,000	2,500,000	2,000,000
200,000	20,000,000	10,000,000	5,000,000	4,000,000

Figure A4-12: Organisational loss and profit data.   *Source: ACT.*

When considering costs, a quote attributed to a Chief Executive Officer of Du Pont, a company that has a renowned reputation for safety, illustrates the point:

"Had our safety performance been the average for our industry last year we would have had to spend another $90 million to meet the increased costs. To produce another $90 million we would have needed to generate an extra $2 billion of business".

A4.4 - Workplace precautions

THE GENERAL PRINCIPLES OF PREVENTION

Management of Health and Safety at Work Regulations (MHSWR) 1999

In order to control the risks identified by the risk assessment, employers and the self-employed need to introduce preventive and protective measures. Regulation 4 of the MHSWR 1999 requires that, "Where an employer implements any preventive and protective measures he shall do so on the basis of the principles specified in Schedule 1 to these Regulations." The text of the schedule is reproduced below:

Schedule 1   General principles of prevention

(This Schedule specifies the general principles of prevention set out in Article 6(2) of Council Directive 89/391/EEC)[24]

- Avoiding risks.
- Evaluating the risks which cannot be avoided.
- Combating the risks at source.
- Adapting the work to the individual, especially as regards the design of workplaces, the choice of work equipment and the choice of working and production methods, with a view, in particular, to alleviating monotonous work and work at a predetermined work-rate and to reducing their effect on health.
- Adapting to technical progress.
- Replacing the dangerous by the non-dangerous or the less dangerous.
- Developing a coherent overall prevention policy which covers.
- Technology, organisation of work, working conditions, social relationships and the influence of factors relating to the working environment.
- Giving collective protective measures priority over individual protective measures.
- Giving appropriate instructions to employees.

The principles of prevention outlined above are designed to direct the approach of duty holders in identifying and implementing the measures needed. The measures are not intended to be prescriptive; however they should be applied when it is reasonable to do so. The intention is to ensure that risks are adequately controlled to an acceptable level. It should be noted that risks assessments and the application of the general principles of control should not be used as a justification for reducing controls in a situation where high standards already exist. The following table details the general hierarchy of controls and comments on their application.

Measure	Comment
Avoiding risks.	If risks are avoided completely then they do not have to be either controlled or monitored. For example, not using pesticides or not working at height.
Evaluating the risks which cannot be avoided.	Carry out a suitable and sufficient assessment of risks.
Combating the risks at source.	Repairing a hole in the floor is much better than displaying a warning sign.
Adapting the work to the individual, especially as regards the design of workplaces, the choice of work equipment and the choice of working and production methods, with a view, in particular, to alleviating monotonous work and work at a predetermined work-rate and to reducing their effect on health.	This emphasises the importance of human factors in modern control methods. Factors to consider include natural lighting and ventilation, positioning of controls and reducing physical stressors such as manual handling and noise. If the well-being of the person is dealt with, there is less chance of the job causing ill-health and less chance of the person making mistakes which lead to accidents. Alleviating monotony, by rotating staff work can help the individual to remain alert and pay attention to the task.
Adapting to technical progress.	Can lead to improved and safer working conditions, for example, new, non-slip floor surfaces.
Replacing the dangerous by the non-dangerous or the less dangerous.	For example, using a battery operated drill rather than a mains powered tool.
Developing a coherent overall prevention policy which covers technology, organisation of work, working conditions, social relationships and the influence of factors relating to the working environment.	Taking an holistic stance to the control of risk, which includes consideration of the organisation (system), the job (task analysis) and the individual (human factors).
Giving collective protective measures priority over individual protective measures.	Giving priority to creating a safe place of work before (e.g. fire arrangements for a large shopping mall include automatic detection, fire spread, fire suppression, direction and assembly) a safe person strategy.
Giving appropriate instructions to employees.	Ensure all workers, employees and self-employed, understand what they have to do, in normal and non normal conditions.

Figure A4-13: General hierarchy of controls and application.

Source: ACT.

Categories of control measure

The notes below give a more detailed view of the general approach.

Risk control measures:

- Technical   (place)   (job).
- Procedural   (system)   (organisation).
- Behavioural   (person)   (person).

TECHNICAL

Technical strategy includes:

- Equipment - design (e.g. guarding) and maintenance.
- Access/egress - provision of wide aisles, access kept clear of storage items.
- Materials (substances and articles) - choice of packaging to make handling easier.
- Environment (temperature, light, dusts, noise) - local exhaust ventilation (LEV).

PROCEDURAL

Procedural strategy includes:

- Policy and standards.
- Rules and procedures.
- Permit to work.
- Maintenance.
- Authorisation and co-ordination of actions.
- Purchasing controls.
- Accident investigation and analysis.
- Emergency preparedness.

BEHAVIOURAL

Behavioural strategy includes:

- Awareness, knowledge, skill, competence.
- Attitude, perception, motivation, communication.
- Supervision.
- Health surveillance.
- Personal protective equipment.

Reliance on only a safe/healthy person strategy is the weakest of controls. The preferred strategy is the safe/healthy place. By ensuring a safe/healthy place all people that find themselves in it will gain protection. In practice, the most successful organisations use a combination of the three strategies, with the emphasis on making the place safe/healthy and supporting this with procedures and attention to the person. Many organisations that feel they have invested effort in getting the place and procedures right are taking a fresh look at the actions necessary to ensure the person is right also. Studies have shown that this too is a critical aspect of effective management of health and safety.

General hierarchy of control measures

ELIMINATION/SUBSTITUTION

Removal of the hazard in total from the working environment where possible, but this is not always practical. Reducing the hazard to an acceptable level by substituting something less hazardous/or reducing the strength of the hazardous material/or reducing the quantity in use/etc.

CHANGING WORK METHODS/PATTERNS

Utilising mechanical aids: robotics, for repetitive tasks, mechanical aids, for example, lifting equipment or fork lift trucks to assist movement or carrying of loads. Keeping the numbers at risk to a minimum, rotating work to minimise the time of exposure / fatigue, for example, reducing the exposure to radiation or noise.

ISOLATION/SEGREGATION

Enclose the hazard so there is no interface between people and the hazard, for example fitting guards around dangerous parts of a machine.

ENGINEERING CONTROL

Control the numbers at risk by systems of working or by engineering methods, for example, guards or other mechanical or interlocking devices, control fumes released into the atmosphere by local exhaust ventilation, or to limit the noise level emitted by use of sound insulation.

PERSONAL PROTECTIVE EQUIPMENT (REQUIREMENTS, BENEFITS AND LIMITATIONS)

Personal protective equipment (PPE) is a low level control. It is often in the form of a simple barrier between the user and the risk, for example, gloves and acid and as such its effectiveness is subject to correct fit or adjustment. PPE is best used for low risk protection or as additional protection to safeguard against engineering control failure, for example, breathing apparatus to protect against fume extraction failure when dealing with volatile toxic substances. It is important to determine the limitations of particular PPE before use. The main benefits include low cost and portability when considered against engineering strategies.

Factors affecting choice of control measures

LONG-TERM / SHORT-TERM

Short-term measures may be applied until further controls are arranged. For example, if there is a noise problem, hearing protection in the form of ear defenders or plugs may be issued until engineering methods of reducing the noise levels are devised, which could be a long-term project.

Painting yellow lines on the floor may be the short-term control for protecting pedestrians from forklift trucks, while the long-term controls involve re-routing the traffic routes.

The decisions are generally based on ease of implementation, legal requirements and cost. In the first example, the risk of noise-induced hearing loss has to be minimised, but the Control of Noise at Work Regulations say it should be done wherever possible by engineering means. In the second example, the better solution may be very costly, so the company may factor it into its budget over a two-year plan.

APPLICABILITY

It is important not to take a blanket approach to the use of controls. The Safety Signs and Safety Signals Regulation require that only valid signs should be displayed. For example, the requirements to remove the display of an electrical hazard sign to the door of an electrical distribution panel which has been isolated and discontinued in use.

PRACTICABILITY

If the legal requirement is "so far as is practicable", then cost is not an issue when deciding on control measures. The issue is about what is technically feasible. This requires the employer or the competent person on behalf of the employer keeping up to date with modern technology. For example, this will require knowing what the latest and possibly better machinery guarding techniques are.

COST

If the legal requirement is qualified by "so far as is reasonably practicable", then the cost is balanced against the risk. The choice of control measures will then depend on the level of risk. For example, if a floor occasionally got wet and two people had to walk over it, then the risk of slipping might be evaluated as low. The control measures could be a warning sign, a mop or some sawdust to sprinkle on the wet part, with the cost as minimal. However, if the floor had different levels, often got wet and fifty people were milling around the area, the risk might be evaluated as medium or high. The control measures could then be installing a non-slip surface, looking at long-term measures to prevent the floor getting wet, issuing shoes with non-slip soles, etc. The cost would be substantially more then the low risk measures.

Even if there is a medium or high risk that needs to be controlled, there is nothing wrong with looking at cheaper versions of control measures if they do the same job. It may also be cheaper and better if a task is changed rather than putting in expensive control measures. For example, reducing the time an operator spends at a noisy machine will reduce his/her personal d(B)A level exposure to a lower level than the use of expensive engineering techniques.

A4.5 - Safe systems of work and permit-to-work

Safe systems of work

MEANING

The integration of people, equipment and materials in the correct environment to produce the safest possible conditions in a specific work area.

LEGAL AND PRACTICAL REQUIREMENTS

S.2(2)(a) of the HASAWA Act 1974 clearly requires the provision and maintenance of plant and systems of work, that are, so far as is reasonably practicable, safe and without risks to health. The Management of Health and Safety at Work Regulations require employers to establish safe systems of work (SSW) following risk assessments and place a requirement upon employees to follow the systems set up for their protection. Employers also have a general duty of care at common law. A SSW results from a formal consideration of all the hazards and controls involved in a particular task. Where the hazard potential is low and the controls are simple or automatic (e.g. interlocking guard on a photocopy machine) the work instructions may be informal i.e. verbal. Where the hazard potential is high and controls are complex (e.g. entry to a confined space) a SSW must be followed.

COMPONENTS (PEME)

People

Consider: selection, mental and physical, willingness to conform with the systems of work; training, induction, job orientation, change in work practice, adequate knowledge, and skill, safe behaviour; supervision, adequately trained, positive motivation, resistance to pressures to behave in an unsafe manner.

Equipment

Good design and safety through specification of plant, machinery and equipment, including ergonomic factors; planned maintenance.

Materials

Safe in both the raw state and as the finished product; appropriate quality standards; system to manage purchase, receipt, storage and use through to safe disposal of waste products and by-products of manufacture.

Environment

Effective control of heating, lighting and ventilation; safe levels of noise and vibration; effective control of dust, fumes, radiation, chemicals and biological hazards; effective means of access and egress; good standards of welfare amenity provision, sanitation, hand washing, showers, clothing storage, catering, drinking water, and first aid.

DEVELOPMENT AND IMPLEMENTATION

Development of a safe system of work

The development of a safe system of work involves the following steps:

1. Assess the task (task assessment/analysis).

2. Identify the hazards and assess the risks.

3. Define safe methods.

4. Implement the safe system.

5. Monitor and review.

Assess the task

Assessment of the task must consider not only the job to be done, but the environment where it is to be done, to allow a full consideration of the hazards to be made. This may involve a detailed review known as Job or Task Analysis. Job/task safety analysis consists of a formal step by step review of the work to be carried out. All aspects of the task should be considered and recorded in writing to ensure that nothing is overlooked. Typical considerations would be:

- How is the task carried out.
- Where is the task carried out.
- What is used.
- What are the current controls.
- Are the controls adequate.
- Do operators use the controls correctly.
- Factors which may affect behaviour of operators/supervisors (error considerations).

The objective is to establish the hazards and controls at each stage of the procedure to ensure a safe result. How the progress of work, in particular safety arrangements, will be monitored should be considered. Any special requirements for monitoring should be specified during the planning stage, e.g. gas contamination testing, temperature or pressure levels monitoring, measurement of emissions, foreseeable emergencies which may arise.

Hazard identification and risk assessment

The identification of hazards and the assessment of risks are key factors arising from task analysis. The MHSWR 1999, Regulation 3, require a suitable and sufficient risk assessment to be made of all risks to which employees and others who may be affected by them are exposed. Where a significant risk is identified through the general risk assessments a more formal detailed analysis is often required to develop a safe system of work.

Define the safe methods

- Where possible, hazards should be eliminated at source. Residual hazards should be evaluated and controlled.
- Specific responsibilities at various stages and the identity of the person in control of work should be clearly identified.
- The need for protective or special equipment should also be identified as should the need for the provision of temporary protection, guards or barriers.
- Adequate emergency procedures should be in place, or developed, to control likely incidents e.g. fire, spillage.
- If there is a possibility that injury could result during the task, consideration of rescue methods should take place during this stage.
- The system should be checked against three main criteria:

    1. It should adequately control hazards associated with the task.

    2. It should comply with company standards.

    3. It should comply with relevant legal standards.

Implementation

Once the system has been developed and agreed, preparation for implementation can proceed. Provision for the communication of relevant information to all involved or affected should be fundamental to any system of work.

SAFE WORKING PRACTICE	Bench Drilling Machine

Task	**OPERATION AND USE**
Special Equipment	*Swarf (metal shavings produced through machining) rake, clamping bolts and / or work vice; 'Wear Protection' signs; chuck / drill guard and / or trip device.*
Personal Protective Equipment	*Eye protection (BS EN 166)*

Method

GENERAL PRECAUTIONS

1. Do not operate machine unless you have been trained in its use and are authorised to do so. You must know the functions of all controls. In particular how the machine is stopped and isolated.

2. Ensure all pulleys, belts and shafts are fully guarded.

3. The drill bit guard must be used at all times whilst the machine is in motion.

4. If the machine is fitted with a trip device, ensure that it is set correctly (i.e. extended to the correct length and a max. of 75 mm from the bit.)

BEFORE USE

5. Check that the chuck key (used to tighten or loosen the drill bit) has been removed before starting.

6. Ensure all safe guards are in position and all protective clothing is worn.

7. Ensure safe access / egress to machine at all times.

8. Ensure all clothing is tightly fastened. Long hair fastened back or contained in a cap. Jewellery (e.g. necklaces etc.) should be removed.

Figure A4-14: Safe operating procedures example.

Source: ACT.

Importance of training

The Provision and Use of Work Equipment Regulations (PUWER) 1998, require that supervisors be adequately trained to enable them to identify the hazards and control strategies associated with work under their control. Where hazards cannot be eliminated and the risks reduced, procedures to ensure a more formal safe method of work known as a permit to work system must be devised. Job / task analysis is not only necessary to identify the hazards and controls, but is essential for preparing written procedures and specifying, by means of comprehensive training plans, the skill and knowledge content of the work to be carried out. The training plans will not only identify the sequence of work, but often the work rate. Sometimes timeliness is an important consideration, particularly in relation to certain chemical manufacturing processes. The analysis is then incorporated in job training programmes.

■ For certain high risk tasks this will often involve a course to develop knowledge and understanding. This is then followed by practical application either utilising a work simulator (e.g. train driver / air craft pilot) or close one to one supervision (e.g. fork truck driver).

■ Where training requirements have been identified, this should be conducted or confirmed.

The provision and availability of any required equipment or materials should be confirmed.

■ The process of implementation will involve:

  • The person in charge of work must ensure that elements outlined in the Planning and Organisation stages are clearly understood and implemented.

  • If problems arise which necessitate modification to the system, formal approval and documentation should be made.

  • Any permanent record of any monitoring must be kept and regularly checked by a member of the management team.

  • Control. Various methods of control are available. Selection and application should reflect the level of risk in the activity, e.g. permit to work systems and method statements.

PREPARATION OF JOB SAFETY INSTRUCTIONS AND SAFE OPERATING PROCEDURES

All the information arrived at from the identification of the hazards through to the best control measures can be formulated into job safety instructions and/or safe operating procedures. An example is shown above.

Permit-to-work systems

ESSENTIAL FEATURES

Meaning of the term permit

A permit-to-work (PTW) is a document which:

- Specifies the work to be done and the precautions to be taken.
- Predetermines a safe procedure.
- Is a clear record that foreseeable hazards have been considered in advance.
- Defines the appropriate precautions and the sequence in which they are to be carried out.

Before maintenance work is begun, consideration should be given as to whether a permit-to-work is required.

A permit should be only as complicated as the work requires. One permit could not cover all situations without being needlessly complicated for some. A permit is required when the safeguards available in normal working are no longer available and identifies those conditions required to make the operation safe.

GENERAL APPLICATION

A permit-to-work should be used whenever the method by which a job is to be done is likely to be critical to the safety of those involved, other nearby workers, the public or the plant itself.

The type of work may involve:

- Hot work of any type or the use of tools or equipment that may create sparks, in an area where there is the possibility of fire or explosion.
- Entry into a confined space.
- The disconnection or opening of pipelines or vessels which have contained flammable, toxic or harmful substances.
- Work on machinery or electrical equipment.
- Working at height.
- Working in excavations.
- Pressure vessels.

OPERATION

Permit to work systems are used where the work has a high-risk potential. The system is typically formalised through the use of pre-printed forms - used to specify the hazards and controls, which either are in use (e.g. electrical isolation, to prevent electric shock) or the controls which need to be used by the individuals at risk (e.g. safety harness to prevent falls from a height).

The permit will also specify the location and boundaries of the work to be done, the time period during which work may be carried out and any arrangements to deal with foreseeable emergencies. The PTW may only be issued or extended by an appointed competent person(s). To be fully effective those who receive the permit upon whom conditions of work are obligated should be similarly appointed and competent. On completion of the work the persons responsible should formally sign off the job stating that the work has been completed satisfactorily or, alternatively, if the work is incomplete what is necessary to ensure a safe re-instatement of the work process. The appointed issuer of the permit should formally receive the work back and sign to indicate that all isolations etc. have been reinstated. PTW should be formally monitored and records kept of compliance and effectiveness.

A4.6 - Emergency planning

The need for emergency preparedness within an organisation

GENERAL POINTS

It is important to consider emergency planning not only as a response to disaster but also in terms of threat to the commercial survival of the organisation.

There have been many attempts to define the word 'disaster'.

'An adverse or unfortunate event; a great and sudden misfortune; a calamity'.

Figure A4-15: "The term disaster". *Source: Chambers dictionary.*

'Sudden or great misfortune; calamity; ill-luck'.

Figure A4-16: "The term disaster". *Source: Oxford dictionary.*

In industrial terms the names Bhopal, Piper Alpha, Chernobyl and Clapham Junction immediately convey the meaning of the word 'disaster'. They were all events which happened, which needn't have happened or which could have been contained with the minimum effect on life, environment and plant. Yet disasters can be caused by events not directly of our making - earthquakes, floods, landslides etc. and also by events outside our control - air and rail disasters, civil disturbances, terrorist attacks and even war.

Depending on one's own circumstances the definition of an emergency is quite flexible. What could be deemed disastrous to a small retailer would perhaps be a minor setback to a large, international chemical company. Whatever the definition or type of emergency, the principles of emergency planning apply to both small and large companies, with the depth of planning increasing in direct proportion to the magnitude of risk.

The legal requirement for all organisations to plan for emergencies is in the Management of Health and Safety at Work Regulations, regulation 8 "Procedures for serious and imminent danger and for danger areas", and regulation 9 "Contacts with external services". In regulation 8, the employer has an absolute duty to:

- Have appropriate procedures to be followed in the event of serious and imminent danger to persons at work in his undertaking.
- Have sufficient numbers of nominated competent persons to implement those procedures so far as they relate to the evacuation from the premises.
- Ensure only authorised persons have access to certain areas that may be restricted on the grounds of health and safety.

The employer shall also, so far as is reasonably practicable inform those exposed to serious or imminent danger of the hazard and the steps taken or to be taken to protect them. These people must be enabled to take those appropriate steps even if there is no instruction or guidance at the time of danger, and be prevented from returning to work if the danger is still there.

The competent person in this respect must have sufficient training and experience or knowledge and other qualities to enable him to carry out the evacuation procedures properly.

Regulation 9 places an absolute duty on the employer to ensure that any contacts with external services are arranged, particularly for first aid, emergency medical care and rescue work.

Prompt, effective emergency response reduces accidental losses and the consequences of natural and man-made disasters. There is not enough time during an emergency to decide who is in charge, to survey outside agencies to identify sources of help, or to train people for emergency response. These actions must be taken prior to the emergency.

Disaster can strike at any time. It may seriously damage or even destroy a large proportion of our resources, and a disaster could have fatal repercussions on the financial viability of an organisation. Therefore, emergency planning is, in effect, an orderly assimilation of the arrangements and activities necessary for the control and co-ordination of the event, to minimise loss.

Emergency planning may be considered as a form of risk management and asset protection, as the effectiveness of what we do if an emergency should strike will depend on how well we have prepared the plans and trained the people in their role who will have to implement those plans.

The exercises for testing not only the plans but also the people, who will have to implement the plans, are essential if we are to prevent confusion during an emergency and ensure the utmost protection and care of lives and property.

It should be emphasised that when planning to minimise the damaging effects of an emergency the aim is not only to rescue resources, but first and foremost to protect life and the environment. The good plan aims to achieve both.

To summarise, the purpose of emergency planning is:

- To envisage the most probable loss factors.
- To consider which areas of the site/business could probably be the scene of a serious incident and what could be the cause.
- To estimate to what extent any foreseeable incident could escalate.
- To assess what the likely impact on the surrounding area and the environment would be.
- To estimate how long disruption can be expected to continue and what can be done to minimise it.
- To establish resources and systems to control the event.
- To define the degree and timescale for the provision of outside help, e.g. fire, medical and others.

PERSONAL INJURY

All organisations are required to have some emergency plan for dealing with personal injury. The first person to deal with an injury is usually a first aider. The number of first aiders and approved persons will depend on a number of factors: type of hazard, number of employees, geographical distribution and complexity of the facility and buildings, distance from the public hospital emergency services, etc.

EXPLOSIVE DEVICE

Excavation work can sometimes unearth an unexploded bomb that has lain dormant since the 1939-45 war. For organisations that deal with underground services, construction or demolition, this is an emergency that has to be dealt with. Other organisations may have to deal with the threat of a bomb being planted on their premises.

FIRE

All organisations have the threat of fire, some at a higher risk than others, depending on the presence of flammable materials and sources of ignition.

LOSS OF CONTAINMENT

The accidental spillage of chemicals or release of biological agents must be prepared for. The release of chemicals to rivers or the atmosphere or biological agents into the general community will present a major threat to society and adequate arrangements must be in place to deal with all likely scenarios.

Consequence minimisation via emergency procedures

The emergency procedure must deal with the minimisation of consequences both in terms of the commercial survival of the organisation and the minimisation of losses. For example, when dealing with a disaster, those involved in the response should work to the following common objectives:

- To save life.
- To prevent escalation of the disaster.
- To relieve suffering.
- To safeguard the environment.
- To protect property.

- To facilitate criminal investigation and judicial, public, technical, or other inquiries.
- To continue to maintain normal services at an appropriate level.
- To inform the public.
- To promote self help and recovery.
- To restore normality as soon as possible.
- To evaluate the response and identify lessons to be learned.

FIRST AID/ MEDICAL

The consequences of personal injury can be minimised by fast treatment, which is the role of the first aider. The first aider treats minor injuries that do not require further medical treatment and for serious injuries, sustains and preserves life and prevents deterioration until medical help arrives. Liaison with the emergency services is also essential. This is a requirement of regulation 9 of the MHSWR 1999.

FIRE EXTINGUISHMENT

It is said that about 70% of companies that have a major fire go out of business.

If a fire starts, the speed of detection and extinguishment is crucial for consequence minimisation. The objective is to minimise loss to people, the buildings or facility, the product and the environment. Good compartmentalisation will reduce damage from smoke and the installation of interceptor systems will manage the high volume of water used in fire fighting to minimise contaminated runoff water.

Fire marshals have a central role to play and should be organised by a co-ordinator, a role that should be duplicated in case of absence. This will be in part fulfilment of regulation 7 of the MHSWR 1999, which requires the employer to have assistance in order to fulfil his legal obligations.

SPILL CONTAINMENT

Stored chemicals should generally be kept in bunded areas to contain spillage. However, the spillage may occur at the point of use or in transit and will require different emergency plans to deal with it. For example, protection of drains, watercourses and porous ground such as soil is essential to prevent environmental damage. There could also be a plan to remove layers of contaminated soil or to neutralise the contaminant in soil or water. Depending on the substance, it may be important to contain the vapour or gas, e.g. chlorine, or to release it to atmosphere, e.g. propane. The method must be in keeping with the hazard and risk.

Emergency plans

NEED TO REDUCE THE IMPACT ON THE ORGANISATION

A good emergency plan will consider all conceivable emergencies and address any which have a significant probability of occurrence and significant potential for loss. In order to minimise loss, the plan must consider how the business can carry on during, and be restored after, the event.

Prior to drawing up an emergency plan a planning team of key site personnel should be formed. The team's membership should reflect a cross section of the organisation and each member should have total familiarity with their particular operation's procedures and hazards.

Although drawing up an emergency/disaster plan may seem a somewhat daunting prospect, the planning team should realise that they will probably have many of the procedures and resources already available to them but that they may need to be reassessed, regrouped or reorganised.

Team effort is important when drawing up a plan. Each area under consideration should be assessed after discussions with front line staff from the area. The 'what if' from the man doing the job will provide relevant expertise and possibly vital information to the planning team. The planning team's emergency plan will ultimately only be as good as the information received from others.

Each company, industry or organisation is unique. Each employs different people and uses different procedures. Each is located in a different area. Nevertheless, the principles of disaster planning apply to all. Although this element highlights areas for consideration and outlines factors to be included, it is only the skeletal framework from which the emergency planning team can begin to work.

When considering the plan, the following potential causes of emergency should be considered:

Natural
- Flooding.
- Gales and other abnormal weather conditions.
- Earthquake.
- Landslide.

Man-made - accidental
- Uncontrolled release of a hazardous substance.
- Building collapse.
- Human error (possibly the hardest to anticipate).
- Fire.
- Explosion.

Man-made - deliberate
- Arson.
- Explosion.
- Bomb threat/attack.
- Terrorist attack.
- Civil disturbance.
- Acts of war.

The plan should be flexible and capable of expansion, with little change, to meet the 'worst case' situation.

ON-SITE PLANS

There are many matters to be considered when preparing or reviewing the disaster plant. Some of these are:

- The areas of the organisation that are hazardous or vulnerable in the event of a potential major accident being realized.
- What these areas are and what are the safeguards.
- The foreseeable consequences of an incident.
- The present resources and arrangements capable of dealing with the initial incident.
- How the incident will affect the neighbouring population, industries or the environment.
- How the alarm will be raised.
- Ensuring all site personnel understand what the alarm means.
- Where to go and how to get there.
- Arrangements for vital services e.g. communication, gas, water, electricity supplies to be provided when your own are out of action.
- Co-ordination with the emergency services.
- Communication of the risks inherent in the operation.
- How to maintain/resume operations during or after an incident.
- Search-and-rescue procedures.
- Number of first aiders.
- Equipment required: emergency protective clothing, first aid and medical supplies, fire fighting, etc.
- Other equipment that may be needed in the event of a disaster e.g. digging equipment, ladders, transport and other engineering or construction supplies and equipment.
- Where they are located.

OFF-SITE PLANS

Plans must also be in place to deal with off-site incidents, which will include most of the above, but may require some additional procedures:

- Good communication so the incident can be co-ordinated from a distance if need be.
- Trained personnel who will be available to deal with off-site incidents.

ONGOING MONITORING AND MAINTENANCE OF EMERGENCY PLANS

It is crucial that the emergency plans are closely monitored following an event and after each 'dry-run' practice. If something in the plan does not work, then this will have to be reviewed to find a better way. Over time people change jobs and work practices may alter. This can have an impact on the emergency plans that may not be obvious, until an emergency occurs. Constant testing and updating is necessary to ensure that nothing gets missed and even subtle changes are dealt with. For example, following a practice evacuation of the building after activating the fire alarms, it may be identified that visitors did not know what to do or where to go. This would require a further procedure to ensure it is known that visitors are on site, they are given information and a member of staff would supervise their leaving the building and take them to the muster point.

To ensure that monitoring is useful, the plans should be tested by conducting a 'dry-run' practice at awkward times, not just when things are quiet. The maintenance of the emergency plans may be best done following a 'dry-run' practice and consultation in order to get the views of the various people involved.

POST-INCIDENT RECOVERY

After the incident, it is important for the organisation that things get back to normal as soon as possible. If not, the danger is that the organisation's clients will go elsewhere and never return.

Companies may have a standby system for the computer system that manages the organisation's information. As one goes down, the other one kicks in.

Some companies have standby premises to move into so there is minimum disruption to the undertaking.

Post-incident recovery plans may include letting neighbours know when it is safe to leave their buildings or homes, arranging for clean up of external premises and any environmental issues, and issuing a press statement.

Internal clean up may be done in sections in a logical sequence so work can continue in those sections.

Control of Major Accident Hazards Regulations (COMAH) 1999

MAIN POINTS OF COMAH

For certain organisations, the Control of Major Accident Hazards Regulations (COMAH) 1999 (amended 2005) apply. The COMAH Regulations replace the Control of Industrial Major Accident Hazards Regulations 1984 (COMAH) and implement most of the Seveso II Directive. They came into force on 1st April 1999.

The main aim of the COMAH Regulations is to prevent and mitigate the effects of those major accidents involving dangerous substances, such as liquefied petroleum gas (LPG), chlorine, explosives and toxic chemicals such as arsenic pentoxide which can cause serious damage/harm to people and/or the environment. One of the effects of the COMAH Regulations is to treat risks to the environment as seriously as those to people.

They require that sites to which they apply must have emergency plans. Regulation 5 requires lower-tier operators to prepare a document setting out their policy for preventing major accidents (a major accident prevention policy or MAPP). Top-tier operators must produce a Safety Report. This is a document prepared by the site operator and provides information to demonstrate to the Control Authorities (CA) that all measures necessary for the prevention and mitigation of major accidents have been taken. The purposes and contents of a safety report are set out in Schedule 4 to the regulations. The CA is comprised of HSE and the Environment Agency or in Scotland, HSE and SEPA. This ensures that health and safety and the environment are all considered.

The amendments to the regulations broaden its scope and reflect lessons learned from major accidents in Europe since COMAH was introduced. They also take account of the results of EC working groups on carcinogens and substances dangerous for the environment. Some new substances have been added, some qualifying quantities have been revised and some changes made to the aggregation rule.

The employer is now meant to consult contractors on his site, as well as his own employees, regarding the on-site emergency plan. The Local Authority must consult members of the public regarding the review of the off-site plan.

Operators must supply information on safety measures to schools, hospitals and other establishments serving the public, and to make all information supplied available permanently to the public.

The COMAH Regulations 1999 are enforced by a competent authority (CA) consisting of:

- The Health and Safety Executive (HSE) and the Environment Agency in England and Wales.
- The Health and Safety Executive and the Scottish Environment Protection Agency in Scotland.

The CA operate to a Memorandum of Understanding that sets out the arrangements for joint working.

The regulations place duties on the CA to inspect activities subject to COMAH and prohibit the operation of an establishment if there is evidence that measures taken for prevention and mitigation of major accidents are seriously deficient. It also has to examine safety reports and inform operators about the conclusions of its examinations within a reasonable time period.

Charging will apply for work undertaken by the competent authority on COMAH. Charges are made on an actual cost basis (i.e. the recovery of the full costs of the time spent by the CA in carrying out COMAH-related activities for a particular establishment). The Regulations apply mainly to the chemical industry, but also some storage activities, explosives and nuclear sites and other industries, where threshold quantities of dangerous substances identified in the regulations are kept or used.

The COMAH Regulations apply to sites which meet the criteria detailed in Regulation 3 and Schedule 1. These detail which substances and the quantities involved that the Regulations apply to. There are two thresholds (tiers) for application. Operators of sites that hold large quantities of dangerous substances ('top tier' sites) are subject to more onerous requirements than those of 'lower tier' sites.

Sites which have threshold quantities of dangerous substances on site on the day the regulations came into force (1st April 1999) are known as 'existing establishments'.

Examples - dangerous substances thresholds

Substance	Lower Tier Sites	Top Tier Sites
	Tonnes	Tonnes
Liquefied extremely flammable gases (including LPG) and natural gas (whether liquefied or not)	50	200
Automotive petrol or other petroleum spirits	5,000	50,000
Arsenic pentoxide, arsenic (V) and/or salts	1	2
Chlorine	10	25
Lead alkyls	5	50
Oxygen	200	2,000
Toluene diisocyanate	10	100
Sulphur trioxide	15	75

Figure A4-17: Dangerous substances thresholds.   Source: ACT.

LOWER-TIER SITES

Key duties for operators of lower-tier sites are:

1. Notify basic details to the CA.
2. Take all measures necessary to prevent major accidents and limit their consequences to people and the environment.
3. Prepare a major accident prevention policy.

Notify basic details to the CA

Operators who come into scope of the regulations after 1 April 1999 must submit a notification before operation begins (operation begins when the quantity of dangerous substance exceeds one of the thresholds and includes commissioning). The amendment now requires the operator to notify the CA of modifications to the establishment that could have significant repercussions with respect to the prevention of major accidents. Operators must notify certain basic details, which are given in Schedule 3 to the Regulations, to the CA. The amendment to this now allows the notification to be made by e-mail and other means allowed by the recipient. The main points include:

- Name and address of operator.
- Address of establishment.
- Name or position of person in charge.

- Details of dangerous substances on site.
- Site activities.
- Environmental details.

Operators of existing establishments who had previously submitted COMAH safety reports do not need to notify as that report contains all the necessary information.

Take all measures to prevent major accidents and limit their consequences

This is the general duty on all operators that underpins the regulations. It is a high standard that applies to all establishments within scope. By requiring measures both for prevention and mitigation there is recognition that all risks cannot be completely eliminated. This in turn implies that proportionality must remain a key element in the enforcement policy of the HSE and the Agencies. Thus, the phrase "all measures necessary" will be interpreted to include this principle and a judgement will be made about the measures in place. Where hazards are high then high standards will be required to ensure risks are acceptably low, in line with the HSE's and Agencies' policy that enforcement should be proportionate.

Prevention should be based on the principle of reducing risk to a level as low as is reasonably practicable (ALARP) for human risks and using the best available technology not entailing excessive cost (BATNEEC) for environmental risks. The ideal should always be, wherever possible, to avoid a hazard altogether.

Prepare a major accident prevention policy

Regulation 5 requires lower-tier operators to prepare a document setting out their policy for preventing major accidents (a major accident prevention policy or MAPP). The MAPP will usually be a short and simple document setting down what is to be achieved but it should also include a summary and further references to the safety management system that will be used to put the policy into action. The detail will be contained in other documentation relating to the establishment e.g. plant operating procedures, training records, job descriptions, audit reports, to which the MAPP can refer.

The MAPP also has to address issues relating to the safety management system. The details are given in Schedule 2 of the regulations but the key areas are:

- Organisation and personnel.
- Identification and evaluation of major hazards.
- Operational control.
- Planning for emergencies.
- Monitoring, audit and review.

TOP-TIER OPERATORS

Top-tier operators have to comply with the above except that they do not have to prepare a separate major accident prevention policy document - their safety reports have to include the information that lower-tier operators provide in their MAPPs. They also have the following additional duties:

1. The preparation of a safety report.
2. The updating of the safety report.
3. Prepare and test an on-site emergency plan.
4. The supply of information to the local authorities.
5. The provision of information to the public.

Prepare a safety report

A safety report is a document prepared by the site operator and provides information to demonstrate to the CA that all measures necessary for the prevention and mitigation of major accidents have been taken. The purposes and contents of a safety report are set out in Schedule 4 to the regulations.

The safety report must include:

- A policy on how to prevent and mitigate major accidents.
- A management system for implementing that policy.
- An effective method for identifying any major accidents that might occur.
- Measures (such as safe plant and safe operating procedures) to prevent and mitigate major accidents.
- Information on the safety precautions built into the plant and equipment when it was designed and constructed.
- Details of measures (such as fire-fighting, relief systems and filters) to limit the consequences of any major accident that might occur.
- Information about the emergency plan for the site, which is also used by the local authority in drawing up an off-site emergency plan.

Safety reports are available to the public via the competent authority registers, subject to safeguards for national security, commercial and personal confidentiality.

The dates for submission of safety reports are set out in regulation 7. These are:

Operators of completely new establishments (so called green field sites) have to provide some information before construction commences and complete the safety report before operation begins.

Update the safety report

The safety report needs to be kept up to date. If there are any modifications to the plant or the way it is operated or if new facts or information become available, the safety report must be reviewed and, if necessary, revised at the time. It must be reviewed after five years even if there have not been any changes.

Prepare and test an on-site emergency plan

Top-tier operators must prepare an emergency plan to deal with the on-site consequences of a major accident. The details are given in Schedule 5 and further HSE guidance is available. For new establishments this must be done before operation begins.

Supply information to local authorities for off-site emergency planning purposes

Local authorities play a key role by preparing, reviewing, revising and testing off-site emergency plans for dealing with the off-site consequences of major accidents at top-tier sites. In order to fulfil this role they need information from operators. Details can be found in Schedule 5 to the regulations. Operators must hold discussions as necessary with their local authorities to determine their exact needs.

The information for the local authority must be supplied no later than the date the on-site emergency plan for the site has to be completed.

Provide information to the public

People who could be affected by an accident at a COMAH 1999 establishment must be given information without having to request it. The details are given in Schedule 6 of the regulations which includes details of the dangerous substances, the possible major accidents and their consequences and what to do in the event of an accident.

As previously mentioned, safety reports are available to the public via public registers.

The information for people who could be affected by a major accident at the establishment must be supplied 'within a reasonable period of time after the off-site emergency plan has been prepared or revised for the establishment'. Six months would be the normal time.

Safety reports are put on the public register shortly after receipt by the CA, unless there is a request for certain information to be withheld (for national security, commercial and personal confidentiality reasons), as provided for in the regulations.

This page is intentionally blank

ELEMENT A4 - RISK CONTROL AND EMERGENCY PLANNING

This page is intentionally blank

Organisational factors

Learning outcomes

The intended learning outcomes are that the student will be able to:

A5.1 explain the internal and external influences on health and safety within an organisation

A5.2 outline the different types of organisation, their structure, function, and the concept of the organization as a system

A5.3 describe the organisational requirements for the management of health and safety and the encouragement of a good cultural environment

A5.4 identify the various categories of third parties in a workplace, the relevant legislative requirements, responsibilities and controls

A5.5 describe the role, influences on and procedures for formal and informal consultation with employees in the workplace

A5.6 describe the development of a health and safety management information system, the relevant legal requirements, and the data it should contain

A5.7 describe the health and safety culture and climate

A5.8 outline the factors which can both positively and negatively affect health and safety culture and climate

Contents

Relevant statutory provisions

Health and Safety at Work etc Act (HASAWA) 1974 - Sections 2, 3 and 4

Management of Health and Safety at Work Regulations (MHSWR) 1999 - Regulations 7, 10, 11 and 12

Construction (Design and Management) Regulations (CDM) 2007

Occupiers' Liability Acts (OLA) 1957 and 1984 as appropriate

Occupiers' Liability (Scotland) Act (OLSA) 1960 as appropriate

Safety Representatives and Safety Committees Regulations (SRSC) 1977

Health and Safety Information for Employees Regulations (IER) 1989

Health and Safety (Consultation with Employees) Regulations (HSCER) 1996

A5.1 - Internal and external influences

External influences on health and safety within an organisation

OVERVIEW

There are many external influences on an organisation. They will have a varying influence depending on the current status of the management of health and safety in the organisation. The status of health and safety management may be observed to be in one of three broad stages, 'young', 'immature' and 'mature'.

The young organisation will tend to be driven by events that are occurring and the pressures put on it by external organisations such as the enforcing authorities. The young organisation tends to see remedies as technical in nature and can be said to be operating at level 1.

The immature organisation will tend to be driven by unplanned events, but is beginning to establish systems and practices in anticipation of events. The choice of preventive systems tends to be those required to comply with the law, e.g. conducting risk assessments and to be procedural in nature and is therefore seen to be operating at level 2.

The mature organisation has spent considerable resource establishing active systems and practices. Unplanned events that result in actual loss are in-frequent. Enhanced systems and practices are being established as the organisation observes opportunities for improvement. Attention is tending to be focused on preventive systems and practices that are behavioural in nature and is therefore seen to be operating at level 3.

LEGISLATION

In the past, legislation has tended to be seen as a punitive influence. More recently, with the introduction of legislation that encourages preventive action and self development, this perspective has softened. Balancing this is the move from specific prescriptive action for the organisation to comply with to management actions that must be carried out as duties by individuals (and the organisation).

For legislation to influence organisations they must either want to comply or there has to be a real prospect of punishment for non-compliance.

PARLIAMENT/HSC

Parliament and the Health and Safety Commission (HSC) can only be an influence on organisations on a strategic basis. They rely on their operational arm, the enforcing authorities, to influence specifics. They have an influence though from the point of view that they decide what laws are appropriate and when they are to be introduced. As such they can control the quantity of law and the scope/extent of a given law. If organisations successfully lobby these bodies, they may be able to gain modification or delay.

ENFORCEMENT AGENCIES

They have a significant role in influencing an organisation's level of performance with regard to health and safety. If the focus of the enforcement agency is on technical specifics then organisations will tend to follow this lead and deal with these issues. It is therefore important that the enforcing agencies demonstrate the value of and interest in seeing organisations use technical, procedural and behavioural preventive measures. The relative influence of the enforcement agencies is highly dependent on them being sufficiently field active to contact a significant number of organisations. It would not be a balanced influence if the only time they were seen was when there had been an accident; they therefore have to be seen by organisations before accidents occur, and encouraging planned preventive actions.

COURTS/TRIBUNALS

Courts and tribunals have an influence on health and safety after the event, in that they consider health and safety based matters after an issue has arisen, e.g. appeal against a prohibition notice. Because they represent a neutral perspective they provide a source of arbitration and moderation of extreme views/practices concerning health and safety.

CONTRACTS

Contracts establish an opportunity for organisations to set standards for health and safety performance of suppliers/contractors. It represents the equivalent of a contract of service for employees. The system of awarding contracts, of itself, does not have a positive or negative influence on health and safety. Influence rather depends on the standards expected of the person that establishes the contract and then the level of monitoring / enforcement of the contract. In many organisations it has been used successfully to establish good health and safety standards in work activities that the client organisation has had trouble achieving with a history of resistant employees.

CLIENTS/CONTRACTORS

Work undertaken by contractors is normally covered by a civil contract. It is good practice for health and safety requirements to be written into the contract. Because health and safety responsibilities are defined in criminal law, they cannot be passed to another party through a contract. However, clients must satisfy themselves that contractors are competent to carry out work without risks to health and safety. Clients should also ensure that contractors are aware of the health and safety standards that are expected of them.

TRADE UNIONS

Trade unions have had a significant influence on health and safety in previous years. In recent times their influence has subsided nationally as the number of members has reduced though they have remained influential in some industries/organisations. Union activities have, in recent times, tended to be distracted by other employment matters. There is now a renewed union interest in health and safety matters as it is beginning to be seen as a worthwhile way of servicing their members' needs. Unions have always maintained a profile of member support in making claims from employers with regard to injury at work. As claims consciousness increases their role and influence will increase.

Trade Unions, through the Trade Union Congress (TUC), are represented on the Health and Safety Commission (HSC). Through this forum they have an influence on strategic aspects of health and safety, contributing to the development of Regulations and Approved Codes of Practice.

INSURANCE COMPANIES

Insurance companies have become increasingly aware that they may have under-valued the risks related to some companies they are insuring. This has caused them to look again at the risks and the factors that lead to claims. In conjunction with this they influence organisations to minimise the risks in order to control their level of premium. The new look includes a focus on the status of management of health and safety in the organisation insured, which has been found to be a useful predictor of future loss.

PUBLIC OPINION

Public opinion tends to fall into two parts: strategic influence by the general mass of public with regard to its tolerance of specific workplace hazards or situations (e.g. Display Screen Equipment or major disasters). Local influences tend to surround acceptability or unacceptability of the practices of a specific organisation. This is most acute following an accident and has had the effect of causing closure of some smaller organisations.

Internal influences on health and safety within an organisation

OVERVIEW

Internal influences on health and safety will once again depend on the maturity of the organisation with regard to health and safety. This maturity and how it is displayed may be described as the culture of the organisation. The culture may be positive or negative, with many shades of grey in between.

FINANCE

Finance is a primary resource of an organisation and all factors come back to this. Even a small health and safety initiative requires a person's time and time has to be paid for. The provision of adequate finance for the phase of development of the organisation is important. Perhaps more important is to use the resource of finance wisely. It is necessary to take a risk-focused approach to health and safety to ensure priorities are resourced first. The absence of this could be a negative influence on health and safety, in the long run. Finance provision tends to be planned and set on an annual cycle, which means that health and safety needs not planned for may have to wait until the next year's budget allocation. It is therefore essential to plan health and safety measures well in advance.

Finance for the cost of accidents is best allocated against budget holders that were the cause of the accident. It defuses the budget holder's focus on health and safety matters if the cost is absorbed into a central point.

PRODUCTION TARGETS

Production targets are an integral part of running an organisation. The setting of targets (objectives) is a positive way of influencing an organisation, provided they are realistic and achievable. They are only considered realistic and achievable if they can be met in a safe and healthy manner. It is not uncommon for employees (including managers) to relegate health and safety by taking risks to achieve a production target. Analysis of the situation often reveals such things as ill communicated health and safety objectives and well defined production targets. This, together with more senior management attention (monitoring of) to whether production targets are being met, leads to focus on production to the exclusion of health and safety.

Individuals may choose to take risks to meet their personal production targets, e.g. when involved in 'piece' work on a production line.

TRADE UNIONS

Internal influences of trade unions, where they exist in organisations, depends mainly on the views of the individuals that comprise the members, but in particular their representatives. In situations where appointed representatives deal with all union matters their efforts on health and safety may be diluted, particularly at times when pay is being reviewed. If the representative is appointed to deal with health and safety alone they may be able to make more contribution and be of a less reactive nature. Many union representatives have received significant training on health and safety matters and therefore have an opportunity to influence health and safety through knowledge. In some organisations union representatives have received more training than managers, which can lead to misunderstanding and conflict.

A5.2 - Types of organisations

Types of organisation

OVERVIEW

The effective functioning of an organisation is dependent on a number of factors:

- Type of organisation - formal or informal.
- Members of the organisation understand the goals.
- Members of the organisation identify positively with the goals.
- Members know what their role and function is in the organisation.
- Members are competent (and confident) to fulfil their role and function.
- Members communicate effectively.
- Members co-operate to reach the goal.
- The organisation controls the actions of members in order to maintain direction towards the goal.

FORMAL

The most common formal structure is hierarchical with authority being dispersed through the lines of the organisation that separate into different roles and then 'down' through the structure to the members of the organisation that carry out specific tasks.

Formal structure to an organisation does not establish a style of organisational working; this is established by the culture and may be autocratic through to democratic.

INFORMAL

Within a formal structure of an organisation informal organisations are created. Their purpose (goal) is varied and may include personal relationships, habitual work-related contact, influence/lobby groups, getting round the structure to avoid bureaucracy, achieve objectives and goals not identified by the formal organisation.

Health and safety might be a good example of the last purpose, in that it may be achieved despite the formal organisation rather than because of it. Necessary improvements that could not get formal backing and budget might be achieved by an informal organisation that uses subtle means to spread/hide costs and get the task done without the knowledge of the formal organisation. Similarly, the informal organisation may decide not to follow the formal requirement for a particular health and safety measure and cohesively resist, and on some occasions agree to hide this fact.

Informal organisations tend to rely on verbal communications, unless it is unlikely that the written word will be discovered by the formal organisation. They can have positive or negative influences on success. They can undermine established systems and elevate the effective importance of people that have the right informal connections and/or a strong personality, but little authority. This can mask persistent bad practice, such as not planning for health and safety, allowing a person to get something done ahead of someone that plans and then puts the task to the formal organisation to achieve.

THE CONCEPT OF THE ORGANISATION AS A SYSTEM

Consider in conjunction with HSG65

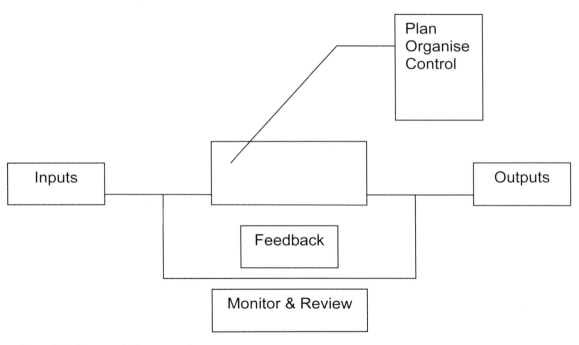

Figure A5-1: The organisation as a system.   *Source: ACT.*

As may be seen by the above diagram an organisation may be represented as a system comprising inputs that are processed to provide outputs, with a feedback loop to adjust the process to ensure the correct output is consistently produced.

If we overlay the health and safety components on this we find the following:

Inputs   Includes resources in the form of raw materials, time, money, people in conjunction with goals (derived from moral, legal and economic sources) and information. Routes into the organisation include design and development of structures, equipment and materials, acquisitions, purchase of products and services, and recruitment.

Process   Includes actions related to planning for health and safety, organising, controlling.

The process part of the system can be broken down further into planning, organising, controlling of the following three main strategies:

- Technical measures.
- Procedural measures.
- Behavioural measures.

Outputs   Includes planned outputs such as provision of products and services, many resultant by-products (e.g. waste) and information for external use. This must be seen in conjunction with the health and safety outputs; negative outputs (if the process is not successful) such as injury accidents, ill-health, fines and positive outputs such as good health, reduced insurance premiums and public respect.

Feedback   Includes monitoring on a short period basis through meetings and inspections, longer term such as accident investigation or audits and review of general / specific actions of the process.

ORGANISATIONAL STRUCTURES AND FUNCTIONS

Organisation charts

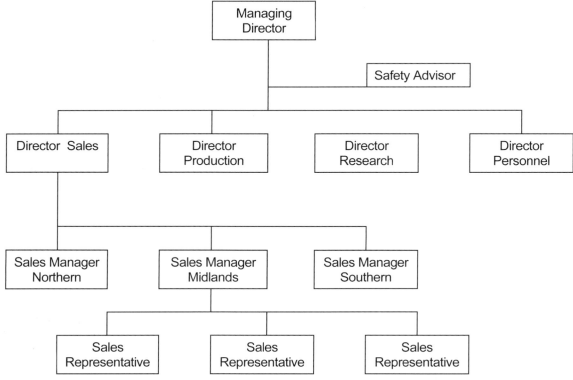

Figure A5-2: Organisational chart - ORG Ltd.   *Source: ACT.*

Role of management

The management's role should be to complement the health and safety policy of the Company. The specific duties should be:

- To recommend to the Board improvements or changes in health and safety practices and to recommend priorities.
- To plan health and safety into their work activities.
- To interpret the policy of the Board to subordinates/employees and ensure that they are understood, action is taken to organise for it and it is implemented effectively.
- To work with technical staff and health and safety professionals in reviewing, inspecting and improving work systems with the object of improving health and safety performance.
- To monitor the work of subordinate/employees and stimulate their interest and involvement in safety.
- To review reports and statistics and investigate adverse results prior to initiating corrective action.
- To take part in particular investigations of hazards and accidents as required.

The relationship of line management to health and safety practitioners should be clearly established. There is much debate on the appropriate position in the organisation for the health and safety professional.

This will depend largely on the existing organisation and set up of the company, but the following factors should be borne in mind:

- The safety specialist should report to an effective senior, who is sufficiently senior to call for action right across the organization.
- They should not report through to a 'Production' Manager as it may produce an intolerable safety versus production conflict. Many companies, therefore, favour administrative or industrial relations biased reporting lines.
- In large companies a number of specialists may be employed and their inter-relationships are important. Each large company has its own culture which will affect the type of structure adopted.   Some are highly centralised, others have complete autonomy.

A5.3 - Organisations and health and safety management

ORGANISATIONAL REQUIREMENTS FOR THE MANAGEMENT OF HEALTH AND SAFETY

Control

Establishing and maintaining control is central to *all* management functions.

Control is achieved by getting the commitment of employees to clear health and safety objectives. It begins with managers taking full responsibility for controlling factors that could lead to ill health, injury or loss.

- Lead by example, demonstrate your commitment and provide clear direction.
- Identify people responsible for particular health and safety activities - especially where special expertise is called for.
- Ensure adequate supervision (control) of activities.
- Set performance standards and objectives.
- Ensure that first line managers (supervisors) understand their responsibilities.
- Ensure all employees know what they must do and how they will be held accountable.
- Establish procedures for compliance and non-compliance.

Co-operation

Participation by employees supports risk control by encouraging their 'ownership' of health and safety policies. It establishes an understanding that the organisation as a whole, and people working in it, benefit from good health and safety performance.

- Consult your employees and their representatives.
- Consult managers.
- Ensure health and safety is co-ordinated (e.g. health and safety professional).
- Involve managers and employees in planning and reviewing performances, writing procedures and solving problems.
- Establish forums for involvement e.g. team meetings, health and safety improvement teams, hazard/improvement reporting.

Communication

Communication challenges organisations generally - not just on health and safety issues. It is often seen as the single most important area requiring improvement. The messages senior management wish to communicate are often not the ones employees receive.

- Communicate (policy) goals and objectives.
- Provide information about hazards, risks and any preventative measures.
- Discuss health & safety regularly.
- Communicate successes and failures.
- Senior managers must take the message to employees, including their positive health and safety behaviour.
- Senior managers should use personal contact with employees.
- Establish systems for cascading information ('down and up').
- Use a variety of communication means.

Competence

If all employees are to make a maximum contribution to health and safety, there must be proper arrangements in place to ensure that they are competent. This means more than simply training them. Experience of applying skills and knowledge is another important ingredient and needs to be gained under adequate supervision.

- Assess the knowledge, skills and experience needed to carry out jobs/tasks safely.
- Assess physical and mental capability requirements for jobs/tasks.
- Establish recruitment and placement arrangements to ensure capability/competence.
- Provide the means to ensure that all employees, including temporary employees, are adequately informed, instructed and trained.
- Establish refresher and transfer programmes.
- Establish arrangements for competent deputies in the absence of key people and managers.
- Ensure that employees on especially hazardous work have the relevant competencies.
- Arrange for access to competent assistance and advice.

POTENTIAL CONFLICT BETWEEN ORGANISATIONAL GOALS AND THOSE OF THE INDIVIDUAL

There can be a wide difference between the goals of the individual and those of the organisation. The differences can result in conflict, for example, where the level of productivity is seen by the individual to be more important to the company than safety issues.

Conflict between the organisations and the individual can also be said to have a positive function. It can result in rules and norms being identified and boundaries established. Each understands the role of the other and can assess the power the other possesses and wields. This 'knowing where you stand' can aid stability which can be beneficial to both parties. However, in general, the aim is to reconcile the differences which cause conflict.

The differences in individual needs and organisational needs may be summed up as follows:

Individual Needs	Organisational Needs
Physical	High productivity
Job satisfaction	Low absenteeism
Personal development	Co-operation
Achievement	Industrial harmony
Respect from work-group	Constructive disagreements
	Low labour turnover
If needs are met, a contented, productive workforce	If needs are met, a successful, efficient organisation

The human relations approach tends to see human needs as relatively fixed; and so it is up to the organisation to create an environment in which both its needs and those of its employees can be met. This can be achieved by analysing the human needs and promoting ways which allow people to achieve them whilst, at the same time, meeting the needs of the organisation.

INTEGRATION OF THE GOALS OF THE ORGANISATION WITH THE NEEDS OF THE INDIVIDUAL

Authority, responsibility, accountability

In order to integrate the goals of the organisation with those of the individual it is important that a sense of involvement or ownership is achieved. This must be part of the wider issue of creating a positive safety culture in which all play a part. Where the individuals and the management form a collective commitment to safety, the organisation develops the positive synergy of a positive safety culture.

In a report published by the **CBI, 'Developing a Safety Culture'**, a number of dominant themes emerged:

■ The crucial importance of leadership and the commitment of the chief executive.
■ The executive safety role of line management.
■ Involvement of all employees.
■ Openness of communication.
■ Demonstration of care and concern for all those affected by the business.

Trade Union Safety Representatives can also make a substantial contribution to the development of a positive safety culture. They are important in the communication between their membership and management. In fact, effective communication is probably the most important safety performance indicator.

Creating the sense of involvement required to bring the goals of the individual and the organisation closer together is no easy task. J. Neumann (1989) found in her research that resistance to participation by the workers is usual where the participation effort by the company is seen as a 'bolt on' adjunct to the basic operation of the organisation. The most important reason for not participating, she found, was when the real decisions of the organisation were made elsewhere and the individual jobs of the workers did not require participative decision making. Early attempts failed because the workers' representatives were insulted by the agenda which consisted of 'lifts and lavatories', and the managers felt despair at the lack of interest. It is important that participation is not restricted to trivial issues if a sense of worth and ownership is to be created and nurtured. Ways should be found of encouraging participation and ownership if the situation of shared goals is to be achieved.

A method of achieving shared goals, which in turn can develop a positive safety culture, is the Japanese approach to individual management known as 'Japanisation'. Whatever its merits and demerits it is worthy of consideration.

Japanisation involves what Friedman calls 'responsible autonomy', which encourages the worker to adapt to changing situations rather than the system of 'direct control' which limits by close supervision and keeps worker responsibility to a minimum.

It is a system of 'paternalism' or 'familyism' where the company is treated as a family: a social organisation that operates in an economic environment. It is also based on lifetime employment from school/college/university to retirement.

Quality is central to the approach and workers are highly trained and have the responsibility of getting it right first time. Workers participate in discussions and problem solving. Management are expected to be team members and there are no outward shows of status differences. The constant aim of all is for an improvement in performance. The objective is that it becomes second nature to behave in a manner that conforms to the shared goal of quality. Safety is incorporated into the system and an accident is seen as a failure in quality assurance. The safety of those using the product is also included in the quest for quality.

There would be several problems if this method were adapted in its entirety, but there is a move in the UK to a flatter management structure and workforce consultation. What is interesting about the Japanese approach is that the employees at all levels are strongly committed to common goals.

A5.4 - Third party control

Identification of third parties

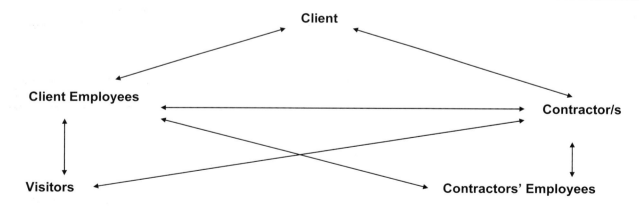

Figure A5-3: Flow chart and summary of third party duties under Health and Safety at Work Etc. Act 1974.   *Source: ACT.*

The act imposes a series of interlocking duties upon Contractors, their employees, client employees and visitors to take reasonable steps to promote health and safety, and to avoid jeopardising the health, safety and welfare of others on site who may be affected by their actions.

CONTRACTORS

Contractors as employers

Have a duty to ensure safety "so far as is reasonably practicable" (sfairp) for their employee (this extends to health and welfare of their employees). The duty includes:

- Provide a safe system of working.
- Provision of information, training and supervision.
- Provision of a safe working environment. *Source: HASAWA 1974 [Section 2].*

Contractors as operators

To conduct business so as to ensure "sfairp" that non-employees are not exposed to risks to health, safety and welfare. This will include providing information about their procedures that might affect health, safety and welfare of non-employees.

Source: HASAWA 1974 [Section 3].

Contractor as controller

Where a contractor has operational control over part of a site, then there is a duty to ensure that ("sfairp"), that area and any access are managed safely and without risk to health. *Source: HASAWA 1974 [Section 4].*

Contractor as designer, installer, manufacturer, supplier

- Duty to ensure "sfairp" that equipment is safe and does not pose risk to health, safety or welfare when manufactured, used or installed on site.
- Duty to provide all necessary instruction and training to ensure that persons using equipment, or affected by the equipment or system, are not endangered or cause danger to others.
- Duty extends to handling, processing, installation and transportation of equipment on site.
- Information is the "key-word" here. *Source: HASAWA 1974 [Section 6].*

Contractors' employees

- Have a duty to take reasonable care for health, safety and welfare of themselves and other persons who may be affected by acts/omissions.
- To co-operate with employer and/or follow instructions re health and safety.
- Not to intentionally or recklessly interfere with health, safety and welfare generally. *Source: HASAWA 1974 [Section 7/8].*

Contractors' directors, managers, controllers

Consenting, conniving or neglect in breach of Statutory Duty under the 1974 Act and Regulations can give rise to personal Criminal Liability along with the Corporate Body. *Source: HASAWA 1974 [Section 37].*

Visitors

General duty to follow reasonable safety instructions and not to interfere with or ignore health, safety and welfare directives whilst on site. *Source: HASAWA 1974 [Section 8].*

VISITORS

Under the ***Occupiers' Liability Act 1957 (OLA 1957)***, an occupier owes a "common duty of care" to all visitors. The duty is to take such care as is reasonable (given the circumstances) to see that visitors are reasonably safe in using the premises for the purposes for which they are invited or permitted to be there.

A visitor is usually extended an 'area of invitation' to which they are expected to stay and to which the duty applies. If a visitor strays outside this area then they become uninvited. A visitor going off to search for toilets, however, is likely to receive special sympathy from the courts.

The OLA 1957 reminds the employer (or occupier) that they must be prepared for children to be less careful than adults. They must also take care that 'allurements' such as attractive poisonous berries or machines are considered. The occupier may be liable even if the child is a trespasser as far as the allurement itself is concerned.

TRESPASSERS

The position towards non-visitors is governed by the ***Occupiers' Liability Act 1984 (OLA 1984)***. Prior to this Act, certain duties were owed under common law by an occupier to those other than lawful visitors - for example, to trespassers. The OLA 1984 superseded the rules of common law ***(See - British Railways Board v Herrington (1972))*** and defines under what circumstances a duty is owed. In particular, occupiers owe a duty if:

- They are aware of a danger.
- They know (or should know) that a person may put themselves at risk.
- The risk is one which the occupier might reasonably be expected to do something about.

The extent of the duty is as follows:

- The occupier must take such care as is reasonable in the circumstances of the case, to see that the other person does not suffer injury.

The Act provides that the duty may be discharged by:

- Giving warning of the danger.
- Discouraging people from putting themselves at risk in the first place (e.g. by making it more difficult for trespassers, etc. to enter the premises).

As with the OLA 1957, the duty is greater towards children. What constitutes a reasonable warning for an adult may not do so for a child. If the occupier, knowing that children trespass onto his land, fails to take action (e.g. by repairing fences) this might be taken as evidence of implied permission and an injured child would therefore be considered a visitor.

MEMBERS OF THE PUBLIC

Members of the public, such as college students, shop customers and the audience in a theatre are protected in statute law by, for example, HASAWA 1974 section 3 and the OLA 1957. The civil law duty of care also extends to cover members of the public.

Differences between lawful/unlawful and invited/uninvited visitors to a workplace

It might be assumed that lawful visitors are invited and that unlawful visitors are uninvited. However, this is not necessarily the case. For example, ramblers following a public footpath would be lawful visitors but not invited by the landowner.

Reasons for ensuring third parties are covered by health and safety management systems

LEGAL

Considerations should include possible consequences of failing to comply with health, safety and environmental legislation, approved codes of practice, guidance notes and accepted standards, plus other relevant legislation concerning fire prevention, pollution, and product liability. Loss may result from the preventative (by enforcement notices), punitive (through criminal sanctions), and compensatory effects of law.

ECONOMIC

Considerations should include the financial impact on the organisation of the costs of accidents, the effect on insurance premiums, possible loss of production / service and the overall effect on the 'profitability' of the organisation. Costs may be direct and indirect.

MORAL

Considerations should include the general well being of employees; the interaction with the general public who either live near the organisation's premises or come into contact with the organisation's operations - e.g. transportation, nuisance noise, effluent discharges etc.; and the consumers of the organisation's products or services, who ultimately keep the organisation in business.

Legal duties

BASIC DUTIES OWED TO THIRD PARTIES

Under the OLA 1957, an occupier owes a "common duty of care" to all visitors, i.e. a duty to take such care as is reasonable (given the circumstances) to see that visitors will be reasonably safe in using the premises for the purposes for which they are invited or permitted to be there. The Act reminds the employer (or occupier) that they must be prepared for children to be less careful than adults.

BASIC DUTIES OWED BY THIRD PARTIES

However, an occupier may expect that persons, in the exercise of their calling, will appreciate and guard against any special risks ordinarily incident to that calling. An employer (or occupier) cannot be prosecuted for a breach of their duties under the 1957 Act, but if a visitor is injured, the occupier may be liable to pay compensation for the injury.

LEGISLATION AND CASE LAW ESTABLISHING THESE DUTIES

The Health and Safety at Work etc. Act 1974

The Health and Safety at Work etc. Act (HASAWA) 1974 covers all employment activities, apart from private domestic workers.

HASAWA 1974 applies to employers, self-employed persons, subcontractors, visitors to places of employment, members of the public affected by the employer's activities, designers, suppliers, importers, employees, directors and managers. It also provides the Health & Safety Executive with various enforcement powers.

A summary of sections 3, 4, 7 and 8 of the HASAWA 1974 is given below.

Section 3 - Duties of employers and self-employed to persons other than employees

Section 3(1)

Employers have a duty to conduct their undertakings in such a way as to ensure, so far as is reasonably practicable, that persons not in his employment who may be affected thereby are not thereby exposed to risks to their health and safety.

Section 3 (2)

Similarly, self-employed persons should conduct their undertakings so that neither themselves, nor others, are affected by their activities and exposed to health and safety hazards. The above are qualified by "reasonably practicable".

Section 4 - Premises

Anyone in control of premises or plant used by persons not in their employment should:

- Ensure safe access and egress to premises and plant.
- Ensure that plant or substances in the premises, or provided for their use, are safe and without risk to health.

Both are tempered by the reasonable practicability of this exercise.

Section 4 (3) - Tenancies

The obligations under Section 4 are transferred to the tenant, or person under contract, if the terms of the agreement are related to maintenance and repair of premises, access or egress therefrom, safety of plant or substances and any health risks arising from these.

Section 7

These sections place general obligations upon all employees, from the Managing Director downwards.

Briefly, the general duties require:-

Employees should:-

- Take reasonable care of their own health and safety and that of others who may be affected by their acts or omissions.
- Co-operate with the employer so as to ensure that the employer can comply with his statutory obligations.

Section 8

No person should intentionally and recklessly misuse or interfere with anything provided under the HASAWA 1974 and other legislation in the interests of health, safety or welfare,

NB. Due to the very general nature of the duties under the HASAWA 1974 it should be noted that failure to comply with sections 2-7 or breach of section 8 confer no right of action in civil proceedings (section 47 of the HASAWA 1974 excludes civil liability). The HASAWA 1974 is therefore primarily criminal law.

The Management of Health and Safety at Work Regulations 1999

The Management of Health and Safety at Work Regulations (MHSWR) 1999 set out some broad general duties which apply to almost all kinds of work. They are aimed mainly at improving health and safety management. The regulations flesh out the general duties contained in the HASAWA 1974.

The principal regulations relating to third parties are detailed as follows:

Regulation 3   Risk assessment

The regulations require employers (self-employed) to assess the risk to the health and safety of their employees and to anyone else who may be affected by their work activity. This is necessary to ensure that the preventive and protective steps can be identified to control hazards in the workplace.

The intention should be to identify the significant risks which arise out of the work activity, trivial risks should be noted, but generally ignored unless the work activity compounds those risks.

The risk assessment should be conducted to determine the measures necessary to be taken to eliminate or control the hazards identified.

Employers with five or more employees are required to keep assessments in writing. (The same threshold is already used in the HASAWA 1974. Employers with five or more employees have to prepare a written safety policy).

Regulation 8   Procedures for serious and imminent danger for danger areas

Employers are required to set up emergency procedures and appoint competent persons to ensure compliance with identified arrangements. To devise control strategies as appropriate to limit access to areas of risk to ensure that only those persons with adequate health and safety knowledge and instruction are admitted.

Regulation 11 Co-operation and co-ordination

Employers who work together in a common workplace have a duty to co-operate to discharge their duties under relevant statutory provisions. They must also take all reasonable steps to inform their respective employees of risks to their health or safety which may arise out of their work.

Regulation 12 Persons working in host employers' or self employed persons' undertakings

Extends the requirements of regulation 9 to include employees working as sole occupiers of a workplace under the control of another employer. Such employees would include those working under a service of contract and employees in temporary employment businesses under the control of the first employer.

Case law

See the following cases - Element A9 - for further details:

- British Railways Board v Herrington (1972).
- Donoghue v Stevenson (1932).
- Ferguson v Dawson and Partners Ltd (1976).
- Mersey Docks and Harbour Board v Coggins & Griffith (Liverpool) Ltd (1946).

Internal rules and procedures

SELECTION AND APPOINTMENT OF CONTRACTORS

Appoint a competent contractor

Acquiring the services of a competent contractor with relevant professional qualifications and a proven safety record is fundamental to any risk control programme. This is also necessary in order to comply with the OLA 1957 and OLA 1984 (or the Occupiers' Liability (Scotland) Act (OSLA) 1960), the general duty of care under section 2 of HASAWA 1974 and the requirement to undertake a risk assessment under regulation 3 of the MHSWR 1999. It is fundamental to the MHSWR 1999 in particular.

This should be a proactive exercise. As far as is possible the types of works and activities that are likely to involve contractors working in the premises should be identified, e.g. electrical, mechanical, gas, maintenance, etc. It will be possible from this to draw up a list of professionally suitably qualified contractors and carry out an investigation into their safety policies and their safety performance at previous locations. Employers should additionally check out their qualification to do the required works. For example, for work involving gas appliances, the contractor should be registered with the Council for the Registration of Gas Installers (CORGI).

The employer should produce a 'check list' to carry out this vetting process. In order to obtain any further information which may be required, the check list should include the following:

- A copy of contractor's health and safety policy document.
- Details of the Contractors' "Competent person(s)" (e.g. Internal Safety Advisor(s) or Consultant(s)).
- Details of assessments which have been carried out and the risk control measures that have been introduced, e.g. MHSWR 1999, COSHH 2002, manual handling, etc.
- References from previous employers of the contractor.
- Details of any accidents or incidents that occurred in any other works contracts (check with the relevant HSE area office if these are reportable under the Reporting of Injuries, Diseases and Dangerous Occurrences Regulations (RIDDOR) 1995).
- Details of the contractor's emergency procedures for their employees, e.g. fire, accident, injury and first aid.
- Information on any Prosecutions, Prohibitions and Improvement Notices issued. (A time limit may be specified, e.g. the last three years).
- Details of Health and Safety training provided.
- Brief details of Safe Systems of Work (e.g. Permit-to-Work).
- Brief details of how the Contractor controls their sub-contractors.
- Copies of the Contractors' Public Liability and Employers' Liability Insurance Certificates.

The Construction (Design and Management) Regulations (CDM) 2007 placed many of these duties upon "clients".

Following the above exercise, a 'short-list' of competent contractors can be produced. This procedure could prove to be invaluable, as often the services of contractors are needed in emergency situations when sufficient time is not available to carry out these vetting procedures.

Consultation prior to commencement of contract

Before any contract work is commenced, a responsible person representing the Principal Contractor must discuss with the occupier the health and safety precautions necessary as far as his own workforce is concerned and any other parties on site.

This requirement was highlighted by the decision in R v Swan Hunter Shipbuilders Ltd. [The Times, July 1981] where both the main contractor and a sub-contractor, Telemeter Installations Ltd., were fined £3000 and £1500 respectively for failing to advise and inform the on-coming sub-contract labour of the dangers produced by oxygen-enriched atmospheres in confined spaces. As a result 8 men were burnt to death whilst working below decks on HMS Glasgow. This incident took place in 1976.

Hence, except on clearly defined "green field" sites, where the Principal Contractor is likely to have primary responsibility for health and safety, both occupier and Principal Contractor should ensure that:

- The site of operations is clearly defined, if necessary on a factory plan, including those areas where contractors' staff are not permitted to enter.
- Agreement is reached as to whether any amenities e.g., catering, washing, sanitation, first aid and clothing storage, are to be made available for contractors' employees.
- Where appropriate, the contractor has full information concerning the occupier's processes or activities which may affect or involve contract work e.g., specific hazards, hygiene requirements, parking restrictions.

Use of owner's equipment

Contractors should generally be expected (by agreement between parties) to provide all their own tools, plant, equipment and materials necessary for the satisfactory performance of work. On no account should use be made of the owner's electricity, gas or air mains without appropriate authority. Where such permission is granted, the method of connection should be approved by the appropriate manager.

Unexpected situations requiring a contractor

It is foreseeable that an unexpected situation can occur where the services of a contractor who is not on the 'approved list' are required. In these circumstances it may be possible to establish a proposed contractor's suitability by contacting organisations that have previously used the contractor.

Whatever arrangements the employer has for appointing a contractor, where reasonably practicable documentary evidence should be produced as proof that appropriate steps were taken to ensure the contractor's competency to carry out the prescribed works. Additionally, information stating that appropriate risk assessments were carried out and risk control measures were introduced should also be able to be reproduced if necessary.

CONTROL OF CONTRACTORS

Liaison

A suitable member of the client's staff must be made responsible for liaising with the contractors on a daily basis. Similarly, a member of the contractor's staff must be responsible for supervising their work.

Concerns about the competence or effectiveness of the supervision must be raised immediately.

Access

Contractor's employees will need to be accounted for in case of fire or other emergency. Several options are available to control access: signing-in systems, pass-card systems, electronic (swipe) systems, etc.

Permits to work

The principal advantage of a permit system is that it forces clients and contractors into contact with each other and ensures that all risks and appropriate control measures are identified before work commences. However, the permit must be properly managed if it is not to become a purely bureaucratic exercise.

The permit to work system may cover any or all of the following aspects.

Contractors' General Work Permit

This will be used for all work which does not involve hot work, electrical equipment, confined space entry or working alone. This permit is suitable for control over access to the occupier's premises, including a booking 'in and out' system, thereby ensuring that the occupier is fully aware of the time when the contractors are at work. The occupier can also use the general work permit to advise contractors of emergency procedures, the requirement to maintain escape routes free from obstruction and accident reporting procedures.

Hot Work Permit

This should be used for work which at some stage will require welding, cutting or use of flame or spark producing tools.

Electrical Work Permit

A dead equipment electrical work permit should be used for work on dead electrical equipment. A live equipment electrical work permit should only be used when it is necessary to work on live electrical equipment, when it has been established that it is reasonable to do so.

Confined Space Entry Work Permit

This permit should be used for work which at some stage requires entry into a vessel or other confined space.

Lone Workers Work Permit

This should be used for work which will be carried out by a person working alone in a remote part of the premises, e.g. in a lift motor room, plant room, or electrical switch room.

Issuing a Work Permit

Work permits may be issued by the occupier and/or the contractor. The contractor's general work permit is most likely to be issued by the occupier to exercise control over access to the premises. However, for works of a specialised nature which the occupier cannot reasonably be expected to understand, e.g. electrical work, the contractor would issue the work permit.

Accepting a Work Permit

It is the responsibility of the person(s) carrying out the work to comply with the conditions laid down on the work permit. Only work stated on the work permit is permitted to be carried out.

Monitoring

The activities of contractors should be included in all routine inspections and audits carried out by the host employer. Conformity with personal protective equipment (PPE) standards, suitability of equipment and compliance with permits and/or method statements are aspects which should be given special consideration. In the case of major failings, repetitive problems or failure by the contractor to take remedial action the host will need to take strong action.

Accident and incident reporting and investigation

The host employer needs to be made aware of any significant accidents or incidents since all such occurrences have the potential to affect his own employees. The responsibility for investigation is a matter to be negotiated by the host and contractor at the earliest opportunity but, if the contractor accepts the responsibility then the host must be sure that the contractor has sufficient skills and/or knowledge to carry out the task. Accidents or incidents that are reportable to the enforcing agency will be of particular interest to the host.

The contractor should be aware of the requirements of the Reporting of Injuries, Diseases and Dangerous Occurrences Regulations 1995, coupled with the company's internal system for reporting, recording and investigating all such incidents. All incidents, including traffic accidents, involving contractors and sub-contractors should be reported to the occupier.

Review meetings

Regular meetings should be held throughout the duration of long contracts. The health and safety performance of contractors is just one of the items that should be on the agenda. During such reviews the host must decide whether or not to continue to use the services of the contractor.

Completion reports

Work completion reports help the client to build up a picture of the quality of the contractor's work with regard to health and safety and other relevant performance. They would take account of such features as: the methods of work, the quality of health and safety management and any significant incidents or problems that occurred.

Plant and machinery

Only in specifically controlled circumstances should a contractor remove the guard, fencing or other safety equipment/devices to machinery and plant, and any guards and/or safety devices should be reinstated and operational before the plant or machinery is handed back for use.

Plant and machinery belonging to a contractor should be adequately guarded before being operated on the premises.

In the case of electrically-operated hand tools, such tools should be of the low-voltage type and connected to a 110 volt mains-isolated circuit where applicable. Alternatively, contractors should provide their own step-down transformer (250/110 volts, 50 cycles) with the mid-point to the secondary winding efficiently earthed. In all cases, the metalwork on portable equipment and any flexible metallic covering of conductors should be efficiently earthed and, in all other respects, constructed and maintained in accordance with the Electricity at Work Regulations (EWR) 1989 and the accompanying Memorandum of Guidance.

Cables supplying portable apparatus should be of correct size and properly connected to approved type plugs and sockets. Makeshift and/or unsafe connections are dangerous and should not be permitted.

In the case of welding equipment, contractors should limit direct current (DC) to 40 volts and ensure the correct use of earth leads for the article being welded.

ELEMENT A5 - ORGANISATIONAL FACTORS

Noise

Where noisy equipment is used in close proximity to a working area on site, operators should be provided with suitable hearing protection (ear muffs) and required to wear same where sound pressure levels are above the second action level (90 dB(A), Lepd) as outlined in the Noise at Work Regulations (NWR) 1989.

Noise from equipment should be minimised in working areas, for example, by the use of bag mufflers on pneumatic drills.

Contractors should also take all reasonably practicable steps to prevent noise nuisance to the inhabitants of the neighbourhood.

Fire protection

Every year fires of varying degrees of severity cause loss of life and devastation on building sites. Reference to the "Fire Triangle" will show the three requisites for fire to take place i.e. an ignition source, fuel and air. Ignition sources on construction sites are many and varied - welding and cutting activities, people smoking whilst on site or in site huts, cooking on open flames in site huts, the use of blow lamps and gas or liquid-fuel fired heating appliances. The fuel can take numerous forms - timber, bitumen impregnated paper, plastics, flammable liquids, such as paraffin, and combustible refuse produced during erection of buildings and in other site work. Oxygen, naturally present in the air, will, on a windy day cause fire to spread at a rapid rate. The need, therefore, for effective fire protection procedures cannot be overemphasised.

Fire protection procedures will vary to some extent according to the type of site e.g. a green field site, where no work has taken place previously, and an existing site, where modification and extension to existing buildings may be taking place.

In the case of green field sites, planning of fire protection procedures should take place well before site work commences.

Here consideration should be given to the following:

- Provision of access for fire brigade appliances.
- The location of buildings and the separation of high risk buildings from other buildings.
- The provision of adequate space between buildings and site huts.
- The actual construction of buildings e.g., site huts, canteens, offices.
- Flammable materials stores, equipment stores, etc.
- The establishment of prohibited areas where smoking and the use of naked lights are forbidden.
- The system for the storage and disposal of combustible and flammable refuse.
- The provision of a separate flammable materials store, suitably constructed and indicated as such.
- The availability of water supply for fire brigade appliances and on-site fire-fighting.
- The provision of adequate fire appliances, located accordingly to the fire risk involved, and an effective fire alarm system.
- Evacuation procedures in the event of fire, including the training of site operators in such procedures.
- The appointment of fire wardens and the operation of fire patrols, particularly at night and weekends.
- The system for liaison with the local fire authority, including inspections by the Fire Protection Officer, not only to ensure compliance with the terms of the fire certificate but to ensure that any new risks which may have arisen are effectively controlled.

Many of the above requirements apply to existing sites. All contractors' employees should understand the fire warning system currently in operation. Instructions on action to be taken in the event of fire should be made available to contractors and work force and be clearly displayed on site. Fire-fighting equipment installed by the occupier should also be made known to contractors or, alternatively, be provided by the contractors.

Where any work involves interference with, or the removal of, fire appliances, alarms or systems, prior notification should be given to the contractor.

The use of petroleum, petroleum mixtures, liquefied petroleum gas (LPG), cellulose and other highly flammable and/or explosive substances should comply with the requirements of the Dangerous Substances and Explosive Atmosphere Regulations (DSEAR) 2002.

Where any form of protective material or covering is used, whether against dust or climatic conditions, it should be fire-resistant or treated with fire-resistant solution.

"Hot work" activities e.g. operations involving the use of oxy-acetylene welding and cutting equipment, electric arc welding, blow lamps and other flame-producing equipment, should not be commenced until authority to do so has been given by the occupier. In certain cases this may require the issue of a permit to work (Hot Work Permit). Gas cylinders, particularly acetylene, should be stored in a manner required by DSEAR 2002.

The contractor should provide and ensure the use of welding screens to give protection to all persons in respect of any arc flash caused by his operators. Combustible materials, such as paper, timber, rags and plastics, should be stored in suitable refuse containers. Non-combustible blankets i.e., fibreglass, should be used to afford protection against "welding spatter".

The burning of refuse on site should be prohibited.

Dangerous substances and wastes

Two aspects must be considered here:-

- The requirements of the Control of Substances Hazardous to Health (COSHH) Regulations 2002 with regard to protecting all persons on site from exposure to hazardous substances.
- Requirements of the Environmental Protection Act (EPA) 1990 covering pollution of air, water and ground, and waste disposal procedures.

A wide range of toxic and other dangerous substances can be encountered in construction activities, including asbestos, lead and many flammable substances. Site management must be aware of the hazards associated with such substances, ensuring correct storage, use and disposal.

Personal protective equipment

Personal protective equipment should be provided and worn wherever hazards to the contractors' workforce exist. This includes safety helmets, eye and face protection, respiratory protection and safety boots. Contractors should be aware of the requirements of the Construction (Head Protection) Regulations (CHPR) 1989 relating to site operators.

Contractors' vehicles

The speed of vehicles within premises on which construction work is taking place should be consistent with safety and drivers should not exceed any speed limits e.g. 10 mph, displayed. Drivers should also comply with any traffic direction systems and signs in use on site. Vehicles used by contractors or their employees should be parked only in specifically designated locations.

All vehicles should be prohibited from moving during times when access roads are crowded with people arriving at or departing from the premises, as the risk of accidents is greater at these times. This prohibition includes cranes, dumpers, concrete vehicles and other lorries.

All vehicles and trailers used on site must be in an efficient state, in sound working order and in a good state of repair, and must not be used in an unsafe manner.

Site clearance

On completion of work, contractors should be required to remove all unused materials and leave the site clean and tidy. This may include reinstatement of perimeter fencing, removal of mud and debris from roads, removal of waste building materials and site refuse, and the levelling of disturbed ground.

On no account should items such as empty gas cylinders, oil drums or paint cans be buried. Excavations and trenches should be filled in and the ground levelled.

Window cleaning and external painting

Cleaning the outer surfaces of windows and painting buildings can present a number of hazards. In order to ensure safe working in either of these situations:-

- The contractor should ensure that any ladder, safety harness or other appliance used, or intended for use, by his employees, is of sound construction, adequate strength, sufficient length and properly maintained.
- Where it is not practicable to clean windows or paint external surfaces from a ladder, and the contractor's employee has to work at a height of more than 2m or otherwise in conditions where any specific danger or risk might be involved, the contractor (or his authorised representative e.g. manager, site foreman) should inspect the place before work is commenced.
- The contractor should satisfy himself that any structural handhold and/or foothold likely to be used by his employees is secure, warning employees, in certain cases, that such a handhold or foothold is not to be used.

Responsibilities for control of risks

CONTRACTORS ON-SITE

Responsibilities for control of risks associated with contractor on site rests principally with the organisation that has primary control of the site this would usually be the client. In some cases the principal contractor will have a key role in providing effective control of contractors on site on behalf of the client. This is emphasised by the Construction (Design and Management) Regulations (CDM) 2007.

Requirements to provide information

HAZARDS AND RISKS TO THIRD PARTIES

A lot of modern legislation requires the provision of information to third parties, notably the HASAWA 1974 (Section 3); the Management of Health and Safety at Work Regulations (MHSWR) 1999 (Regulations 11 and 12); and the CDM Regulations 2007 which require both the designer and the client to make information available to the planning supervisor.

A5.5 - Consultation with employees

The role of consultation within the workplace

The duty of employers to consult all employees via safety representatives was enshrined in sections 2(4) to 2(7) of the HASAWA 1974. However section 2(5) which gave all employees the right to elect safety representatives was repealed by the Employment Protection Act 1975. Thus only those workplaces where workers are represented by officially recognised trades unions are covered by the HASAWA 1974. This requirement was translated into the Safety Representatives and Safety Committees Regulations (SRSC) 1977.

The MHSWR 1992 amended the SRSC Regulations 1977 by stipulating the matters on which the employer must consult; these are:

- Measures introduced into the workplace which may affect employees' health & safety.
- The appointment of competent persons.
- Any health and safety information that the employer is obliged to provide by law.
- The planning and organisation of any health and safety training that the employer is obliged to provide by law.
- The health and safety consequences of the planning and introduction of new technology into the workplace.

The SRSC Regulations 1977 only apply to safety representatives from recognised trades unions leaving many, non-unionised, workers without any consultation rights. This situation was rectified to an extent by the introduction of the Health & Safety (Consultation with Employees) Regulations (HSCER) 1996. It should be noted that the roles and functions of trade union representatives remains unchanged and that the two regulations are designed to sit side-by-side with each other - the application depending on union status.

Both the HSCER 1996 and SRSC Regulations 1977 are outlined below.

THE SAFETY REPRESENTATIVES AND SAFETY COMMITTEES REGULATIONS 1977

The Safety Representatives and Safety Committees Regulations (SRSC) 1977 are concerned with the appointment by recognised trade unions of safety representatives, the functions of the representatives and the establishment of safety committees.

Representatives are appointed when a recognised trade union notifies the employer in writing. Representatives must have been employed throughout the preceding 2 years or, where this is not reasonably practicable, have had at least 2 years experience in similar employment.

Similarly, employees cease to be representatives when:

- The employer has been notified in writing by the trade union.
- The representative ceases to be employed.
- He/she resigns.

FORMAL CONSULTATION

Functions and rights of employee representatives

Trade union appointed representative (Safety Representatives)

Functions

The SRSC Regulations 1977 grant safety representatives (SR) the right to carry out certain functions as outlined below.

Functions are activities that safety representatives are permitted to carry out by legislation, but do not have a 'duty' to perform and therefore are treated as advisory actions. As a consequence the representatives cannot be held accountable for failing to carry out these activities or for the standard of the advice given, when performing their functions. They are, however, still employees and have the same consequent duties as any other employee (for example their duties under HASAWA 1974 Sections 7and 8). Their functions as safety representatives are:

a) To take all reasonably practical steps to keep themselves informed of:

- The legal requirements relating to the health and safety of persons at work, particularly the group or groups of persons they directly represent.
- The particular hazards of the workplace and the measures deemed necessary to eliminate or minimise the risk deriving from these hazards.
- The health and safety policy of their employer and the organisation and arrangements for fulfilling that policy.

b) To encourage co-operation between their employer and his employees in promoting and developing essential measures to ensure the health and safety of employees, and in checking the effectiveness of these measures.

c) To carry out investigations into:

- Hazards and dangerous occurrences (incl. accidents) at the workplace.
- Complaints, by any employee he represents, relating to that employee's health, safety or welfare.

d) To carry out inspections of the workplace.

e) To bring to the employer's notice, normally in writing, any unsafe or unhealthy conditions, or unsafe working practices, or unsatisfactory arrangements for welfare at work, which comes to their attention whether during an inspection/investigation or day to day observation.

   The report does not imply that all other conditions and working practices are safe and healthy or that the welfare arrangements are satisfactory in all other respects. Making a written report, does not preclude the bringing of such matters to the attention of the employer or his representative by a direct oral approach in the first instance. Particularly in situations where speedy remedial action is necessary. It will also be appropriate for minor matters to be the subject of direct discussion, without the need for a formal written approach.

f) To represent the employees they were appointed to represent in consultation at the workplace with inspectors of the Health and Safety Executive and of any other enforcing authority within the Act.

g) To receive information from inspectors in accordance with section 28(8) of the HASAWA 1974.

h) To attend meetings of safety committees during which he/she attends in his capacity as a safety representative in connection with any of the above conditions.

Employers' duties

The Regulations require employers to make any known information available to safety representatives that is necessary to enable them to fulfil their functions. This should include:

- Information about the plans and performances of the undertaking and any changes proposed, in so far as they affect the health and safety at work of their employees.
- Information of a technical nature about hazards to health and safety and precautions deemed necessary to eliminate or minimise them, in respect of machinery, plant, equipment, processes, systems of work and substances in use at work. This should include any relevant information provided by consultants or designers or by the manufacturer, importer or supplier of any article or substance used, or proposed to be used, at work by their employees.
- Information which the employer keeps relating to the occurrence of any accidents, dangerous occurrences or notifiable industrial disease and any statistical records relating to such accidents, dangerous occurrences or cases of notifiable industrial disease.

- Any other information specifically related to matters affecting the Health and Safety at work of his employees, including the result of any measurements taken by persons acting on his behalf in the course of checking the effectiveness of his health and safety arrangements.
- Information on articles or substances which an employer issues to home workers.
- Any other suitable and relevant reasonable facility to enable the representatives to carry out their functions.

Training

The basis of Trades Union Congress (TUC) policy is that the union appointed safety representative will be trained on TUC approved courses. However, there is much to be gained by the employer approaching the trades unions active in his workplace with the objective of holding joint company/industry based courses. In any event it is prudent for the employer to carry out company/industry orientated training to supplement the wide industry based TUC course.

The functions and training of the safety representatives should be carried out during normal working hours. The representative must receive normal earnings, this taking into consideration any bonuses which would have been earned if carrying out their normal work activities.

Elected representatives (representatives of employee safety)

Where there are employees not represented by the SRSC Regulations 1977, the employer shall consult those employees in good time on matters relating to their health & safety at work. In particular they must be consulted on:

- The introduction of any new measures which may affect their safety and health.
- Arrangements made by the employer for appointing or nominating competent persons in accordance with regulations 6(1) and 7(1) of the MHSWR 1999.
- Any safety information the employer is legally obliged to provide to workers.
- The planning and organisation of any health and safety training required under particular health and safety laws.
- The health and safety consequences for employees of the introduction of new technologies into the workplace.

Employers can consult either directly with employees or, in respect of any group of employees, one or more elected representatives of that group. These are referred to as "representatives of employee safety" (RES). If the latter option is chosen, then employers must tell the employees the name of the representative and the group he/she represents. An employer which has been consulting a representative may choose to consult the whole workforce. However, the employer must inform the employees and the representatives of that fact.

If the employer consults employees directly then it must make available such information, within the employers' knowledge, as is necessary to enable them to participate fully and effectively in the consultation. If a representative is consulted, then the employer must make available all necessary information to enable them to carry out their functions, and of any record made under the Reporting of Injuries, Diseases and Dangerous Occurrences Regs (RIDDOR) 1995 which relates to the represented group of employees.

Functions

Representatives of employee safety have the following functions:

- To make representations to the employer on potential hazards and dangerous occurrences at the workplace which affect, or could affect the represented employees.
- Make representations to the employer on general matters of health and safety.
- To represent the employees in workplace consultations with HSE or local authority inspectors.

Training

Representatives of employee safety must be given reasonable training in order to carry out their duties. Employers must meet the costs of the training and any travel and subsistence.

Employers' duties

They must also permit the representatives to take time off with pay during working hours in order for them to carry out their functions. Time off shall also be given, with pay, where this is required for any person standing as a candidate for election as a representative. Employers must also provide suitable facilities for the representatives to carry out their duties.

The Health and Safety (Consultation with Employees) Regulations 1996

As previously stated, the HSCER 1996 extend the rights of consultation on matters relating to health & safety to all workers regardless of trades union status. The regulations place duties on employers whose workers are not represented by a safety representative. Employers have the option to either consult employers directly or through elected representatives. As with the SRSC regulations employers must consult on matters affecting employees' health & safety, the appointment of competent persons, information, training and new technology.

The names of representatives together with the group of workers they represent must be made known to employees as must any changes in their status. If the employer decides to change from consulting representatives to consulting with the workers directly then both representatives and workers must be informed.

Representatives can make representation to the employer on general health & safety matters, matters on which employers are obliged to consult as well as dangerous occurrences and hazards. They may also represent their group of employees when consulting with enforcing authority inspectors.

The regulations also provide for the provision of reasonable paid time off to carry out their functions. Employers must also provide appropriate and reasonable training and facilities. The regulations also amend the Employment Rights Act 1990, to protect employees who participate in consultations from suffering any unfair dismissal or detriment in relation to health and safety cases.

Regulation 1   The HSCER 1996 came into force on 1 October 1996 and are made under the European Communities Act 1972.

Regulation 2   "Employees" do not include persons employed in domestic service in private households. Workplaces are defined as "any place where the employee is likely to work, or which he is likely to frequent in the course of his employment or incidentally to it."

Regulation 3   Where there are employees not represented by the SRSC Regulations 1977, the employer shall consult those employees in good time on matters relating to their health & safety at work. In particular they must be consulted on:

■ The introduction of any new measures which may affect their safety and health.
■ Arrangements made by the employer for appointing or nominating competent persons in accordance with Regulations 7(1) and 8(1) of the MHSWR 1999.
■ Any safety information the employer is legally obliged to provide to workers.
■ The planning and organisation of any health and safety training required under particular health and safety laws.
■ The health and safety consequences for employees of the introduction of new technologies into the workplace.

Regulation 4   Employers can consult either directly with employees or, in respect of any group of employees, one or more elected representatives of that group. These are referred to as "representatives of employee safety" (RES). If the latter option is chosen, then employers must tell the employees the name of the representative and the group he/she represents. An employer which has been consulting a representative may choose to consult the whole workforce. However, the employer must inform the employees and the representatives of that fact.

Regulation 5   If the employer consults employees directly then it must make available such information, within the employers' knowledge, as is necessary to enable them to participate fully and effectively in the consultation. If a representative is consulted, then the employer must make available all necessary information to enable them to carry out their functions, and of any record made under the RIDDOR 1995 which relates to the represented group of employees.

Regulation 6   Representatives of employee safety have the following functions:

■ To make representations to the employer on potential hazards and dangerous occurrences at the workplace which affect, or could affect the represented employees.
■ Make representations to the employer on general matters of health and safety.
■ And to represent the employees in workplace consultations with HSE or local authority inspectors.

Regulation 7   Representatives of employee safety must be given reasonable training in order to carry out their duties. Employers must meet the costs of the training and any travel and subsistence. They must also permit the representatives to take time off with pay during working hours in order for them to carry out their functions. Time off shall also be given, with pay, where this is required for any person standing as a candidate for election as a representative. Employers must also provide suitable facilities for the representatives to carry out their duties.

Regulation 8   The Employment Rights Act 1996 - which gives protection against unfair dismissal or discrimination on grounds of health and safety - is amended to protect representatives of employee safety and candidates for their election.

Regulation 9   Breach of the Regulations does not confer any right of action in any civil proceedings.

Regulation 10   Ensures that certain provisions of health and safety legislation (including enforcement provisions) operate in respect of the HSCER 1996 Regulations. This Regulation enables enforcement by the enforcing authorities appointed under the HASAWA 1974.

Regulation 11   The Regulations will apply in respect of the armed forces. However, the representatives of employee safety will be appointed by the employer, rather than elected. Furthermore, representatives in the armed forces will not be entitled to time off with pay under regulation 7.

Regulation 12   The Regulations do not apply to the master or crew of a seagoing ship.

Regulation 13   The SRSC Regulations 1977 are amended so that they now include employees of coal mines.

Functions of health and safety committees

If two or more appointed safety representatives request in writing the formation of a safety committee, the employer must implement this request within three months. Consultation must take place with the representatives making the request and the appointing trade union.

A basic requirement for a successful safety committee is the desire of both employee and management, to show honest commitment and a positive approach to a programme of accident prevention and the establishment of a safe and healthy environment and systems of work. For any committee to operate effectively, it is necessary to determine its objectives and functions.

Objectives
■ The promotion of safety, health and welfare at work by providing a forum for discussion and perhaps a pressure group.
■ To promote and support normal employee/employer systems for the reporting and control of workplace problems.

Functions
■ To review accident and occupational health trends.
■ To review recurring problems revealed by safety audits.
■ To consider enforcing authority reports and information releases.
■ To consider reports on matters arising from previous safety committee meetings.
■ To assist in the development of safety rules and systems of work and procedures.
■ To review health and safety aspects of future development and changes in procedure.
■ To review health and safety aspects of purchasing specifications of equipment and materials.
■ To review renewal/maintenance programmes.
■ To monitor safety training programmes and standards achieved.
■ To monitor the effectiveness of safety and health communications within the workplace.
■ To monitor the effectiveness of the Safety Policy.

This may be summarised as review and recommend on the overall direction of the health and safety programme, on specific aspects of the programme, on difficulties encountered in its implementation and to monitor the programme in both a specific and overall manner,

Composition

The membership and structure of the safety committee should be settled in consultation between management and the trade union representatives concerned. This should be aimed at keeping the total size as compact as possible, compatible with the adequate representation of the interests of management and employees. Management representatives will naturally be appointed by the management. Employee representatives will either be appointed by a recognised Trade Union (HASAWA 1974 Section 2(4)) or, in a non-union company, elected by their colleagues.

The committee suggested in HASAWA 1974 section 2 (7) will probably be the 'Company Safety Committee.' There is nothing to prevent the formation of smaller committees for parts of an organisation or different sites in order to maintain the company safety committee at a reasonable size.

INFORMAL CONSULTATION

Experience within many organisations has shown that safety representatives can either be very positive or, conversely, seriously undermine the safety effort. The outcome depends on the attitudes of those involved and is a good indication of the culture of the company.

As a minimum, any organisation must comply with the legal obligations outlined above. Implementation should also play an integral part in the drive to improve health and safety performance. This can be achieved by going beyond the legal minimum in order to positively involve staff at all levels. Treating representatives differently depending on his or her trade union status, for example, could promote both confusion and division amongst staff. This would not demonstrate the commitment to employee involvement in all aspects of health and safety required as part of any management system. The advantages and benefits of consulting employees has long been recognised by good organisations who have recognised that employees who have had their thoughts and opinions taken into account will often be better motivated (and therefore more productive) than those who do not.

This, less formal consultation, can be achieved by encouraging communication between individual managers and their staff and by mechanisms such as:

Discussion groups

Meetings between individuals at the same level within the organisation to discuss their mutual safety concerns. This encourages free expression and promotes the efficient use of resources.

Safety circles

Meetings between similar organisations and departments with similar aims to peer groups. Perhaps their biggest advantage is the communication of solutions to common problems thus minimising the need to 're-invent the wheel'.

Departmental meetings

These are additional to the organisation's safety committee which has been formed under, for example, the SRSC Regulations 1977. They can be used to deal with local matters and can be a good way for managers to demonstrate a personal commitment to the health, safety and welfare of their staff.

THE ROLE OF THE HEALTH AND SAFETY PROFESSIONAL IN THE CONSULTATIVE PROCESS

Although the prime responsibility for health and safety at work rests with the management and the other categories of employees, they often need the help and services of specialist and qualified advisers. The safety practitioner is predominantly advisory and is primarily concerned with the detailed implementation of the management action plan.

There is no general requirement for companies to employ safety practitioners. However, the MHSWR 1999 require employers (except the self-employed and partnerships) to appoint one or more competent persons to assist them. Employment of a safety practitioner will depend upon:

- The number employed.
- Degree of risk.
- Complexity of the machinery and processes.
- Type of labour.
- The size of the premises.

The safety practitioner should act as an advisor to both managers and safety representatives alike. Ideally, he or she should act an 'ex-officio' member to any established safety committee providing advice and guidance in accordance with the role and functions set out below.

The safety practitioner's role should be:

- To advise on, promote and co-ordinate all aspects of the Company's safety effort and to be responsible for this to a member of senior management to whom he should have direct access.
- To support line management who carry the direct and ultimate responsibility for all aspects of accident prevention and ill health at work.
- To establish and maintain systems which encourage management and the workforce to treat health and safety as an integral element in the day to day running of the workplace.

A safety practitioner should, therefore, be able to either advise on or, if required implement, the following:

1. Identify the full range of hazards present in a workplace (including ones not previously encountered). Specific functions under this heading include:

- Devising safety inspection systems and hygiene survey programmes.
- Drawing up procedures for vetting the design and commissioning of new plant and machinery, and the introduction of new chemicals into the workplace.

2. Assess the extent of the risks to which employees or people outside the workplace are exposed. Specific functions under this heading include:

- Maintaining and storing adequate sources of information.
- Analysing data on injuries, dangerous occurrences and near misses in the workplace.
- Assessing the risks to third parties caused by products, services and pollutants.
- Arranging for quantitative risk assessment when appropriate.

3. Develop control strategies. Specific functions under this heading include:

- Advising on the steps necessary to meet the standard of "reasonable practicality" where this is allowed when considering the control of risks, thus ensuring legislative compliance.
- Developing a framework of safe systems of work (including permit to work systems).
- Setting priorities for risk reduction in particular problems.
- Setting up strategies for assessing health risks as required by, for example, the COSHH Regulations.
- Contributing to the development of strategies for eliminating or reducing risk in co-operation with other professional staff and with line management.
- Analysing training needs and developing safety training strategies.

BEHAVIOURAL ASPECTS ASSOCIATED WITH CONSULTATION

The consultative process depends on both personal relationships and the culture of the organisation. Conflict will exist if managers view consultation on health and safety matters as a burden which interferes with production. It is management's responsibility to take executive action and to have adequate arrangements for regular and effective checking for health and safety precautions and for ensuring that the declared health and safety policy is being fulfilled. The work of consultative mechanisms such as safety committees should supplement these arrangements; it cannot be a substitute for them. Alternatively, employees can have a negative effect on the process if they view consultation as a way of getting back at managers without having to go through any grievance procedures.

In essence the attitudes towards safety representatives and committees on both sides of the management 'divide' say a great deal about the culture of the organisation. The general attitudes of groups of employees can play either a positive or negative role in the consultative process. The social need of most individuals to both belong to, and be accepted by, a group is a powerful motivating factor. The need to belong to a group provides our need for friendship and affiliation and supports both self esteem and identity. The attitudes of the peer group can play a powerful role in either helping or hindering the consultation and thus the safety effort. Those who manage organisations are well advised to influence both organisational and individual performance by working with and through groups.

Peer group pressures

For example, as previously mentioned, there is a normal process of individual development as a child progresses towards adulthood. This can become skewed due to a lack of "suitable" role models or a breakdown in societal controls. Here the dominant influence during later childhood and early adolescence comes from a peer group which itself is not fully socially developed. This is illustrated by the gang culture which dominates certain areas in the USA. Thus certain attitudes towards risk taking may be shared by members of one adolescent culture, which are markedly different from those of other age groups. Individuals tend to seek out social groups which suit their personality and attitudes, but when there is a mismatch the individual will be changed by the group to a greater or lesser extent depending upon the importance that the individual attaches to acceptance by the group.

In a multi-cultural society it is important for the safety practitioner to understand the influences that are shared by a particular group within the workforce. The individual believes that these culturally-shared values are correct and perhaps the only 'right' way of behaving. Thus these cultural values and needs can often over-ride the 'common' perception of safety needs. For example, the need for a Sikh to wear appropriate head-dress over-rides the need to wear a safety helmet. Another example is the wearing of neck-ties by male workers even though they are working with rotating machinery with a real risk of entanglement. Again, the need to conform to the cultural idea of what is respectable over-rides safety needs.

Potential areas of conflict

In the workplace, the majority of people will conform to the norms of behaviour of that particular occupational group/society. Traditional managers encouraged a norm of behaviour based around the work ethic, which in some cases led to a conflict with safety values. The aim of the safety practitioner, therefore, is to encourage a balance of production versus safety.

Often workplace groups are influenced by internal rather than external factors. These are based on such concepts as 'peer pressure' and 'group leaders'. These can have both a positive and negative influence. The good manager will recognise and use these influences to encourage safe behaviour.

THE DEVELOPMENT OF POSITIVE CONSULTATIVE PROCESSES

An essential condition to effective consultation is good communications between all parties. It should be recognised that there is a genuine desire on the part of management to use the knowledge and experience of its employees and an equally genuine desire on the part of the employees to improve the standards of health and safety at the work place.

Contributions of health and safety representatives / safety committee members

The effectiveness of representatives and safety committee will depend on the pressure and influence they are able to maintain on all concerned. In order to achieve this there should be:

- Regular meetings.
- Effective publicity of the committee's discussions and recommendations.
- Speedy decisions by management on the committee's recommendations, where necessary promptly translated into action and effective publicity.
- Participation by members of the safety committee in periodic joint inspections if required.
- Development of ways of involving more employees.

Written communications are not always readily understood. Employees who have learning or language difficulties may have problems in fully understanding the safety information provided. Safety representatives can help in this respect by drawing the manager's attention to people in this position. It should be recognised, however, that a climate of trust is required in order to encourage open communication about such potentially sensitive matters.

A5.6 - Provision of information and development of information systems

Internally

EMPLOYEES, TEMPORARY WORKERS AND CONTRACTORS

Employees

The fundamental duty to provide employees with information, instruction and training is placed on employers by Section 2(2) (c) of the HASAWA 1974. This requirement is reinforced by Regulation 10 of the MHSWR 1999 which requires employers to ensure that all employees are provided with comprehensible and relevant information about:

- The risks to their health and safety identified by assessments.
- Any preventative or protective control measures.
- Details of any person nominated to discharge specific duties in accordance with the regulations.
- Any risks notified by other employers sharing the same workplace.

This general requirement is made specific by other regulations. For example, the COSHH Regulations 2002 requires that personnel likely to be exposed to a hazardous substance be given information on:

- The risks to health created by exposure to the substance.
- The precautions to be taken.
- The results of any exposure monitoring.
- The collective results of any required health surveillance.

The duty placed on the employer by the MHSWR to provide information is also extended to parties such as temporary workers and contractors.

Temporary workers

MHSWR - Regulation 15   *Temporary workers*

Requires employers to provide any person who has been employed on a fixed-term contract with comprehensible information on any special qualifications and skills in order to work safely and also details of any health surveillance arrangements.

Contractors

MHSWR - Regulation 11   *Co-operation and co-ordination*

Employers who work together in a common workplace have a duty to co-operate to discharge their duties under relevant statutory provisions. They must also take all reasonable steps to inform their respective employees of risks to their health or safety which may arise out of their work.

MHSWR - Regulation 12   *Persons working in host employers' or self employed persons' undertakings*

Extends the requirements of Regulation 11 to include employees working as sole occupiers of a workplace under the control of another employer. Such employees would include those working under a service of contract and employees in temporary employment businesses under the control of the first employer.

The Health and Safety (Information for Employees) Regulations (IER) 1989

Require that information relating to health and safety at work be furnished to all employees by means of posters or leaflets in a form approved by the Health and Safety Executive.

The approved poster "Health and Safety Law - what you should know" should be placed in a prominent position and should contain details of the names and addresses of the enforcing authority and employment medical advisory service (EMAS). Since the modification to these Regulations *(see also - 'Modification to the regulations' - below)* the name(s) of the competent person(s) and the names and locations of trade union or other safety representatives and the groups they represent must also be included. Any change of name or address should be shown within 6 months of the alteration.

The Health and Safety Executive may approve a particular form of poster or leaflet for use in relation to a particular industry or employment and, where any such form has been approved, the HSE shall publish it.

If a poster is used, the information must be legible and up to date; the poster must be prominently located in an area to which all employees have access.

If a leaflet is used, revised leaflets must be issued to employees when any similar changes occur.

Modification to the information for employees regulations

The Health and Safety Information for Employees (Modifications and Repeals) Regulations 1995 amended these regulations, which allows the HSE to approve an alternative poster to the basic 'Health and Safety Law' poster. The basic poster required updating in order to take account of European directives and recent legal developments.

The updated poster includes two new sections which allow employers to personalise information. There is now a box for the names and location of safety representatives, and a similar one for details of competent people appointed by the employer and their health and safety responsibilities.

Externally

CUSTOMERS, SUPPLIERS, ENFORCEMENT AUTHORITIES, MEMBERS OF THE PUBLIC AND OTHERS

Section 6 of the HASAWA 1974 places general duties on designers, manufacturers, importers or suppliers of articles and substances used at work (including fairground equipment). This duty includes the need to provide information about the need to take such steps as are necessary to ensure that those who are supplied with the article or substances are provided with adequate information about the use for which the article is designed or has been tested, and about any conditions necessary to ensure that it will be safe and without risks to health. This includes the need to ensure safe eventual dismantling or disposal. This information should be revised if any additional serious risks to health or safety become known. Similar duties in respect of all supplied articles are contained in the Consumer Protection Act (CPA) 1987.

The need to supply information to the enforcing authorities is primarily contained in Sections 27 and 28 of the HASAWA 1974. Section 27 empowers the HSC (with the Secretary of State's consent) to require the provision of specified information in order for the HSC/Enforcing Authority to carry out its functions. Section 28 of this information, which must only be used for the purposes of the HSC/E, must remain confidential - particularly the disclosure of trade secrets. Information must not be disclosed without the consent of the person who provided it. There are, however, some exceptions including the provision of information to public bodies such as the police to enable them to carry out their statutory functions. This requirement to provide specific information to the enforcing authorities is also contained in other legislation such as:

- The Reporting of Injuries, Diseases and Dangerous Occurrences Regulations 1995.
- The Fire Certificates (Special Premises) Regulations 1976.

Progressive organisations have long recognised the need for good relations with the local community particularly in industries which have suffered from a poor press in the past. Some legislation, such as the Control of Industrial Major Accidents Hazards Regulations 1984, now the Control of Major Accident Hazards (COMAH) 1999 specifically requires specified manufacturers to ensure that the local population likely to be affected by a major accident has access to publicly available information.

EMPLOYMENT AGENCIES

Regulation 12(4) of the MHSWR deals with the provision of information by a first employer to a second employer, whose employees are working on the premises. This includes employees of people who have an employment business. Under regulation 15(3), an employment business has to be informed of any special occupational qualifications or skills required to carry out the work safely and the specific features of the job which might affect health and safety (e.g. work at heights).

The person who has an employment business and the user employer both have duties to provide information to the employee. The person with the employment business has a duty under regulation 10 (as an employer) and a duty under regulation 15(3) to ensure that the information provided by the user employer is given to the employee. The user employer has a duty under regulation 12(4) to check that information provided to an employer (including someone carrying on an employment business) is received by the employee. In addition, regulations 15(1) and (2) require that information on requirements for qualifications, skills and health surveillance is provided to any person employed through an employment business or person employed on a fixed term contract by the user employer.

These duties overlap to make sure the information needs of those working for, but not employed by, user employers are not overlooked. User employers and people carrying on employment businesses should therefore make suitable arrangements to satisfy themselves that information is provided. In most cases, it may be enough for user employers to provide information directly to employees. Those carrying on employment businesses will need to satisfy themselves that arrangements for this are adequate. However, basic information on job demands and risks should be supplied to the employment business at an early stage to help select those most suitable to carry out the work (in accordance with regulation 15(3)).

Health and safety management information system

DEVELOPMENT OF A HEALTH AND SAFETY MANAGEMENT INFORMATION SYSTEM WITHIN THE WORKPLACE

The effective communication of the safety message is an important element of managing safety. How we provide and disseminate information will depend on the target audience and the desired effect. These include:

- Written materials such as reports, bulletins, newsletters, memoranda and minutes of meetings.
- Electronic systems such as e-mail, electronic publishing (the intranet) and databases.
- Safety Propaganda:
  - Posters.
  - Signs.

The method chosen will depend on the type of organisation and the people involved. To be effective information must be:

- Accurate.
- Easily understandable.
- Positive.
- Aimed at the correct audience.
- Believable.
- Achievable.

For example, posters exhorting people to 'be safe' or threatening dire consequences if a particular action is not taken are rarely effective. People are not necessarily rational or logical - particularly in giving priority to safety over even a small cut in take home pay or comfort. Information should emphasise positive safety benefits by letting people know 'what's in it for them'.

Information should therefore be relevant, credible and realistic. Peer pressure, which plays a large part in group behaviour, can be used to advantage if there is a general endorsement of the message

IDENTIFICATION OF TYPES OF DATA

Loss event data

Used properly, accident and ill-health data allow comparisons to be made both between organisations and by monitoring year on year performance. Analysis can be made to identify areas, situations of possible concern or the overall effectiveness of implementations of any control measures that may have been introduced. Data can be collected internally using accident books and report forms (e.g. RIDDOR) or from outside sources such as:

- The World Health Organisation.
- The International Labour Organisation.
- The Department of the Environment (Labour Force Survey).
- The HSE (including Statistical Services Unit and HSC Annual Report Statistical Supplement).

There are several methods of presenting data for analysis and some of the more common ones are listed below. Methods should not be mixed and figures should only be used to compare like with like. *See also - 'Loss causation and analysis' - Element A2.*

- Accident/injury incidence rates.
- Accident/injury frequency rates.
- Accident/injury severity rates.
- Mean duration rate.
- Duration rate.

Cost data

Cost and management performance data is generated by nearly all organisations. This internal information is often relevant to the health and safety management system and should not be overlooked.

Suppliers' data

Information from suppliers in the form of Material Safety Data Sheets, maintenance requirements, etc. will form an essential part of any safety management system.

Results of audits/inspections

The aim of audits and inspections is to give management a detailed picture regarding the standards of health and safety management within the organisation. Thus audits and inspection are, essentially, confirmatory exercises which demonstrate that the health and safety management system is effective. The level and detail of audits/inspections carried out will depend on the type of organisation and its confidence in the existing management system.

Information from audits and inspections enables both symptoms as well as the cause to be identified and appropriate action taken. It is important to take this balanced approach where employees see that although they have a part to play in ensuring a safe and healthy workplace. It is also important that the things the organisation provides, including equipment and systems of work also be right and that action is taken to establish and maintain good standards. Auditors and inspectors can obtain information from three sources:

1. Interviewing individuals both about the operation of the health and safety management system and practices and their knowledge, understanding and perceptions of it.
2. Examining documentation for completeness, accuracy and reliability.
3. Visual observation of physical conditions and working practices to ensure conformity to legal and organisational standards.

A5.7 - Health and safety culture and climate

Definition of health and safety culture and climate

Definition of culture:

> *"A word used to describe typical patterns of social, emotional and intellectual behaviour deriving from a shared set of beliefs and values, which are adaptive to the physical environment."*

Figure A5-4: Definition of culture.   *Source: unknown.*

A safety culture can be said to be the collection of attitudes, values and beliefs that members of an organisation hold in relation to health and safety. When taken together they produce an organisational culture that may be positive, negative or neutral.

The style of management is crucial to the type of safety culture within an organisation. Strong leadership and a commitment to health and safety are essential for a positive safety culture. If senior management is only interested in productivity, then a negative safety culture is sure to follow.

The health and safety climate may be considered to be the social, political, business and other factors that the organisation is influenced by; that lead to a given culture existing within the organisation.

Risk management should be viewed from the moral, legal and economic standpoints and the senior manager who is committed to this will encourage a positive safety culture.

As has been shown in the previous pages, the organisation has the most influence on human behaviour. The individual will fit into the culture, positive or negative, and act accordingly.

A positive safety culture once achieved should be self perpetuating if commitment from the top is continued.

Impact of organisational cultural factors and associated values on individual behaviour

BLAKE & MOUTON

Country club management

Comfortable and friendly work atmosphere. Togetherness is the key word. Likes to be liked.

Production is incidental to lack of conflict and good fellowship. Does not push people for production - you can lead a horse to water, but you cannot make him drink.

Tries to avoid direct disagreements or conflict. Production problems are glossed over. New ideas avoided since they might cause stress.

This style can easily grow up in a quasi-monopolistic situation where profit is not important, or work is done on a cost-plus basis.

Task management

Sees people as a commodity just like machines. The manager's job is to plan, direct and control the work of those subordinate to him. Subordinates do what is required but no more. Any creative energy of subordinates goes into how to defeat the system rather than how to improve it. Disagreements are ruled out and suppressed rather than settled. This win/lose thinking leads to the development of militant trade unionism and union/management conflict.

Swinger

Management by crisis. Staff never know just how he will react. It is possible for such a manager to "get it right", but rare.

Dampened pendulum

Marginal shifts round a happy medium.

Middle of the road style - pushes the staff enough to get acceptable production but yields enough to maintain acceptable morale. To aim fully for both is too idealistic.

A compromiser - always aims for a balanced solution rather than the most appropriate one.

Impoverished management

Sees effective production as unobtainable because people are lazy, apathetic and indifferent. Sound and mature relationships are difficult to achieve because, human nature being what it is, conflict is inevitable.

Little concern for either production or people.

Avoids responsibility or personal commitment.

Often frustrated, having been passed over for promotion after years in a routine job.

Waiting to retire. (Has retired but is waiting to leave).

Team management

High concern for people and the task. Seeks to integrate his staff round the task.

Morale is task related. High sense of job satisfaction.

For most people this is an ideal to aim for.

Influence on culture/climate

ORGANISATIONAL STRUCTURES AND ORGANISATIONAL ROLE CULTURES

ADVANTAGES OF "TALL" STRUCTURES

1. Managers can devote their full attention to their immediate subordinates (narrow span of control).
2. Acknowledges that an individual's capacity to supervise others is limited and so it is preferable to deal with fewer numbers directly than deal with larger numbers on a more casual basis.
3. Fewer people in the "Span of Control" - should be easier to co-ordinate.
4. Assists the creation of logically determined work groups/teams/units.
5. Facilitates specialisation of functions.
6. Duplication of work should be unlikely with a small group.
7. Communication should be improved - fewer numbers in each group; less tendency for communication to be informal; memos and notes passed between levels. *But* messages may not reach the top. A manager may decide not to pass on information to the senior manager. Information may be selected before passing on.
8. Should provide more opportunity for promotion in a "tall" structure (More "levels").

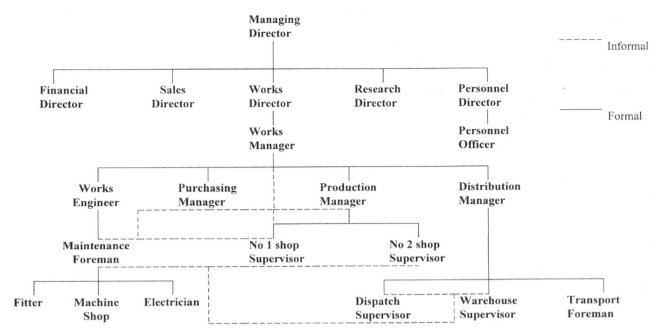

Figure A5-5: Example of a 'tall structure'.   *Source: ACT.*

Advantages of "flat" structures

1. Managers must practice delegation, so staff should be able to obtain some experience of "higher level" work.

2. Could be an improvement in morale because the majority of staff are on the same level.

3. Should be a reduction in Management/supervision costs.

4. Should allow subordinates to use more discretion on how to achieve their objectives.

5. Managers and staff meet more directly, a shorter chain of communication.

6. From 5 (above) - less chance of loss or misinterpretation of information. *But* too much information may become available to the senior manager, who then has the bother of sifting through it in order to prioritise.

7. Managers can more easily keep in touch with the activities of their staff at the base of the structure.

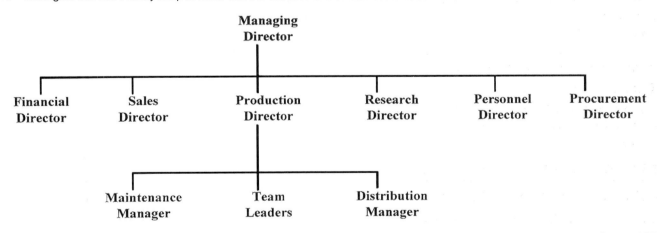

Figure A5-6: Example of 'flat structure'.   *Source: ACT.*

Charles Handy (1985) popularised a method of looking at culture which some scholars have used to link organisational structure to organisational culture. He describes:

■ ***Power Culture*** which concentrates power in a few pairs of hands. Control radiates from the centre like a web. Power Cultures have few rules and little bureaucracy; swift decisions can ensue.

■ In a ***Role Culture***, people have clearly delegated authorities within a highly defined structure. Typically, these organisations form hierarchical bureaucracies. Power derives from a person's position and little scope exists for expert power.

■ By contrast, in a ***Task Culture***, teams form to solve particular problems. Power derives from expertise so long as a team requires expertise. These cultures often feature the multiple reporting lines of a matrix structure.

■ A ***Person Culture*** exists where all individuals believe themselves superior to the organisation. Survival can become difficult for such organisations, since the concept of an organisation suggests that a group of like-minded individuals pursue the organisational goals. Some professional partnerships can operate as person cultures, because each partner brings a peculiar expertise and clientele to the firm.

Indicators of culture

CORRELATION BETWEEN HEALTH AND SAFETY CULTURE AND CLIMATE AND HEALTH AND SAFETY PERFORMANCE

"Organisations with a positive safety culture are characterised by communications founded on mutual trust, by shared perceptions of the importance of safety and by confidence in the efficacy of preventive measures."

There are various indicators of where on the safety culture continuum an organisation is; the continuum ranging from negative, through to neutral and on to positive. Indicators should be of the type that can be measured and compared in order to be meaningful. For example, knowing the number of lost-time accidents a department has in any one year is only meaningful if it is then compared with the number from a previous year, or compared with a similar department in the same organisation or in the same industry. The departments with which the comparison will be made should have the same type of reporting system. In other words, only compare like with like.

The correlation between health and safety culture and health and safety performance can be illustrated by research that has been conducted. There are two categories in this field of research: correlation studies and intervention studies.

Correlation studies may use the method of comparing low accident rate with high accident rate plants or departments in order to identify the factors that could explain the difference. Much work has been done in the mining industry using this method. For example, Peters (1989) carried out a review of the organisational and behavioural factors associated with mining safety. His methods of collecting information were: direct observation of work methods and physical environment, interviewing miners and issuing questionnaires to a wide range of managers and officials who had a good working knowledge of how things were done.

Intervention studies look at the effects of interventions by studying before/after comparisons. For example, after the introduction of a safety programme in the range of forestry and logging organisations in Columbia, it was found by Painter and Smith (1986) that there were dramatic improvements in performance. The accident frequency rate was reduced by 75% and the workers' compensation costs were reduced by 62%. In further research, Lauriski and Guyman (1989) found that after a safety management programme had been introduced at the Utah Power & Light Company, lost time injury rates were reduced by 60% over a period of five years. From 1980 to 1988, the accident frequency rate was reduced from 40 to 8 per annum, while production more than doubled.

Research has shown that improvements in safety management are influential in achieving a positive safety culture. This leads to reduced accident rates, which is seen as a positive step forward, which is a further influence on the safety culture.

SUBJECTIVE AND OBJECTIVE NATURE OF CULTURE AND CLIMATE

An organisation that desires a culture where achievement is paramount would most likely favour a system based on results, which is the most favoured system by many organisations. This can be manifested in what is actually being appraised, that is, personal traits, behaviours, results or methods of appraisal used e.g. objective or subjective methods. The objective measures output of workers while the subjective evaluates their performance; the subjective, however, is more commonly in use by many organisations.

Measurement of the culture and climate

Developing and promoting a positive safety culture is an important aspect of health and safety management. A safety culture is an intangible thing, which has tangible manifestations. It is these manifestations that can be measured.

There must be a clearly defined system for assessing achievement which is both measurable and achievable. Targets should be set and performance measured against them. There are a number of ways of measuring performance:

ATTITUDE SURVEYS

Attitude surveys can show how employees view all aspects of the organisation and their role in it. They may perceive that what controls their lives at work is what has been labelled external or internal loci of control. There are those who believe that what happens is down to luck, chance or fate, which is external control, and those who believe that events are either wholly or partially down to themselves, internal control. Research has shown that those who were 'internal' had a greater sense of responsibility for their own and others' safety.

The extent to which employees believed their safety depended on their own skills and care compared with the conditions and control set by the employer is another factor that can be considered when measuring attitude. A number of different attitudes have been shown to relate to low accident rates. Therefore an attitude survey can measure the safety culture of an organisation.

'PROMPT LISTS'

'Prompt lists' can be used when seeking to establish the adequacy of the steps that the organisation is taking to ensure that everyone in the organisation is genuinely committed to the successful implementation of the safety programme. A prompt list can be designed to probe at a greater depth than other indicators of safety culture. The following table is part of a prompt list devised by the ACSNI Study Group, which is intended to be an in-depth probe into a safety culture.

1. ***Review of organisational culture - licensees***

    Has the organisation evidence to demonstrate that:

    1.1 Communications at all levels are founded on mutual trust?

    1.2 All personnel understand, and agree with, corporate goals and the subordinate goals of their work group?

    1.3 All personnel understand, and agree with, the means adopted to achieve corporate and work group goals?

    1.4 The work practices of the organisation are under continuous review to ensure timely responses to changes in the internal or external environment?

    1.5 Managers and supervisors demonstrate care and concern for everyone affected by the business?

Figure A5-7: A safety culture prompt-list.

Source: ACSNI Human Factors Study Group.

At ground level, lists can be devised of what is expected in the workplace and used in inspections. The degree of compliance can be used to indicate the interest and attitude to safety. Generally, the more safeguards in place and the cleaner the workplace, the more likely there will be a positive safety culture.

FINDINGS OF ACCIDENT INVESTIGATIONS

Findings of accident investigations can be used as a measurement of a safety culture. The root causes of accident investigation can show where things are going wrong: have control measures considered the technical, procedural and behavioural aspects; are they being implemented; do the management controls need to be reviewed; is everyone committed to working safely, etc.?

The procedure for dealing with the findings of the accident investigation, that is, the recommendations for improvement and prevention is another way to measure the safety culture. For example:

- Are people named for action?
- Are time limits set?
- Is there a system to check items have been actioned?
- Are the findings communicated to the employees?

EFFECTIVENESS OF COMMUNICATION

Effective communication is a factor in achieving a positive safety culture; therefore effectiveness of communication can be used as a measurement. Considering a practical example: an organisation's safety policy must be communicated to the employees, therefore asking them about it will give an indication as to how well it has been communicated. Communication can be measured at all levels of the organisation with each person knowing and understanding his area of responsibility. Various means of communicating can be brought into the equation to measure which is the most effective medium for the information to be conveyed.

EVIDENCE OF COMMITMENT BY PERSONNEL AT ALL LEVELS IN THE ORGANISATION

Evidence of commitment by personnel at all levels of the organisation can be measured. The evidence can be shown by the acceptance of responsibility for health and safety from the top, as in the statement of intent in the safety policy; as Du Pont say: the chairman takes the role of Chief Safety Officer. Areas that can be considered are: membership of safety committee and attendance; responsibilities accepted and taken seriously - whatever they should do they do; rules apply to everyone, for example, the wearing of necessary PPE; etc.

Measurement of what the organisation is achieving compared to the standards that have been set in the safety policy can be done by safety audit. Any shortfalls promptly dealt with is another indicator of a positive safety culture.

A5.8 - Factors affecting health and safety culture

Factors that may promote a positive health and safety culture or climate

Organisations need to produce a climate that promotes staff commitment to health and safety and emphasises that deviation from corporate safety goals, at whatever level, is not acceptable.

Producing such a climate requires clear, visible, **management commitment** to safety from the most senior level in the organisation. The commitment should be not just a formal statement but be evident in the day-to-day activities of the company. This commitment must be known and understood by the employee. Individuals may be reluctant to err on the side of caution in matters that have safety implications if their decisions to do so are likely to be subject to unwarranted criticism from their superiors or their peers.

The attitude of a strong personality at a senior level within the organisation may have either a beneficial or an adverse effect on a safety climate. Inevitably, junior employees will be influenced by that person's example.

Health and safety procedures soon fall into disuse if there is no system of ensuring that they are followed. Too often procedures lapse because of management neglect, or operators are discouraged from working to them by peer groups or other pressures, such as production targets. Where managers become aware of deficiencies in safety procedures but do not act to remedy them, the workforce readily perceive that such actions are condoned. It is essential that organizations create a **high business profile for health and safety.**

Individuals may not understand the relevance of procedures or appreciate their significance in controlling risk. **Involvement** and consultation in the making of rules and decisions will **promote ownership** of health and safety.

Sometimes procedures are faulty, irrelevant, or lacking in credibility. When accidents happen managers cannot blame individuals for taking short cuts which seemed safe and were allowed to become routine, if they have not explained the importance of, or **provided sufficient information** on the procedures they originally laid down.

To promote a proper working climate, it is essential to have an effective system for monitoring safety that identifies, investigates and corrects deviations. The introduction and operation of such systems requires considerable effort by managers and only by allocating adequate resources can they be confident that failures will be prevented or controlled. In short, the organisation needs to provide:

- Clear and evident commitment, from the most senior management downwards, which promotes a climate for safety in which management's objectives and the need for appropriate standards are communicated and in which constructive exchange of information at all levels is positively encouraged.
- An analytical and imaginative approach identifying possible routes to human factor failure. This may well require access to specialist advice.
- Procedures and standards for all aspects of critical work and mechanisms for reviewing them.
- Effective monitoring systems to check the implementation of the procedures and standards.
- Incident investigation and the effective use of information drawn from such investigations.
- Adequate and effective supervision with the power to remedy deficiencies when found.

The organisation should *identify and set standards* through key performance indicators (KPI's) for health and safety. The standards should be achievable and designed not to compete with other organisational performance standards such as those set for production / service or quality. The standards must be agreed at the highest level within the organisation and standards for establishing management control must be established. The management controls must be designed to send a clear signal, that health and safety is an equal partner to the other organisational objectives. Management controls may take many forms, but should include system checks, such as random examination of completed permits to work, observations of high risk work activities or periodic tours.

The organisation should identify the safety critical tasks and establish suitable controls. The task analysis should not only take account of engineering controls, such as guard design or fume extraction requirements, but the requirements of the personnel involved in the task. This will include ensuring that the relevant *knowledge, skill and work experience* is established, before an individual is put to work. Any deficiencies must be clearly identified and any necessary *training* must be provided. Factors such as individual aptitude, dexterity and physical ability / endurance may also be important. High-risk tasks may utilise simulation equipment to allow skill to be developed, at no risk to the individual or others, for example, the use of aircraft flight simulators. Similarly, it may be necessary for the trainee to be under close supervision (an instructor flies with a new pilot of an aircraft) until their skill can be demonstrated as appropriate through their displayed actions and ability.

Factors that may promote a negative health and safety culture or climate

Just as a positive safety culture starts with commitment from the top, a negative safety culture will develop from lack of it. There are, however, other factors involved which may lead to a negative health and safety culture.

When a company is going through a period of *organisational change*, it is a time of upheaval, personal as well as corporate. Individuals and groups tend to be resistant to change, especially when they are unsure of the need for it. Lack of proper communication can lead to rumours of closure, redundancy or changes in the company's structure. The resulting fall in morale and period of *uncertainty* may lead to a lack of belief in what the company is committed to.

Reorganisation can also lead to people changing their position in the company structure with more, less or different responsibilities than previously. Without proper communication and necessary training this can lead to a mistrust of the company and its aims and objectives.

The company may state the aims and objectives, but the actions do not seem to be a clear way of achieving them. The aims and objectives may state a commitment to health and safety, yet the changes in work patterns do not allow for safe working. These conflicting messages will lead to a *lack of confidence in the organisation's objectives and methods.* This could be from the point of view that production is seen as all important and safety must be secondary, or an add on only if time allows for it. A practical example would be: if a company decided on a speed limit of five miles an hour for the fork lift trucks as a control to prevent accidents, but then increased the amount of product a driver had to move on a shift, it would be seen as mixed signals. On one hand, the company is showing commitment to safety by restricting the speed of the vehicles, but on the other, no one seems to care that the increased workload means that the drivers must break the speed limit to get their job done. *These management decisions prejudice mutual trust and lead to mixed signals regarding commitment to health and safety.* This promotes a negative safety culture. The management and the employees then have differing aims and objectives and energy is exerted each fighting the other.

Effecting change

Most industries must recognise the importance of a positive safety culture and the need to review and, when necessary, take steps to improve the culture. For progress to be made, careful *planning and communication* is essential. A piecemeal approach is time consuming, can be costly and is usually ineffective. As the ACSNI Study Group said, "While the outcome of well-conceived plans to improve the safety culture of an organisation may be revolutionary, the plans themselves should be evolutionary. *A gradualist (step-by-step)* approach is essential."

The major steps of the plan should be:

- To review the existing safety culture.
- To decide the aspects that have the highest priority for change.
- To decide on actions that may change those aspects, and to launch those actions.
- To repeat the previous three steps indefinitely.

The fourth step implies that the effects of each step are checked and *performance is measured regularly*. The results may mean that new actions or new priorities are chosen. This means that the process is continuous and not just a momentary enthusiasm.

Achieving the long-term goal of developing a positive safety culture can be daunting, but a step-by-step approach can make it more manageable. The most urgent issues are addressed first and this process itself will generate a wider effect. At each of the steps, the methods chosen should be interactive and encourage open communication. A wide range of people must be involved, from different levels of the organisation and having different skills and backgrounds. All members of the organisation must feel a strong sense of ownership of the need and drive to improve safety standards.

This *direct action* to promote change is likely to succeed in developing a positive safety culture, as the continuing process will show management's interest in the activities and their willingness to support them in terms of time, trouble and finance. Each problem that is successfully dealt with will add to the positive development of the safety culture.

As the safety management plan unfolds, there will be increased awareness of hazards and risks, and the methods of controlling risk, which will come from, for example, *risk assessments and training.* This increased awareness, along with the knowledge that the company is carrying out its plans for safety, can reap cultural dividends. If it is also seen that everyone's performance is measured to ensure safety remains a priority at all levels, then it will give credence to the general plan. The spin-off from this is all levels of staff are working for the same aims and objectives, resulting in mutual trust and a visible commitment.

As part of the communication and consultation processes, **feedback is essential**. It should be part of the overall plan and involve everyone. "How are we doing?" and "How am I doing?" are necessary question to ask and feedback is needed to answer them. Development and improvement will only come from the feedback of the findings of inspections, surveys, audits and prompt lists. It must be part of the continuing process in the plan to effect change in the safety culture.

Problems and pitfalls

There are a number of problems and pitfalls to be aware of when trying to change the safety culture.

The two main barriers are:

- **Attempting to change culture too rapidly** by adopting every conceivable measure that might lead to improvement. This becomes too demanding a task and may lead to a loss of interest because not enough seems to be happening. From the employees' point of view, it may be seen as just another short-lived scheme where a lot of things are happening at once, but then it fizzles out. As discussed earlier, producing a positive climate requires clear, visible, management commitment to safety from the most senior level in the organisation. The commitment should be not just a formal statement but be evident in the day-to-day activities of the company. Failure to display long term commitment will lead to an **absence of trust in communications.**

- **Adopting too broad an approach.** The breadth of the concept of changing the safety culture may make the task of managing improvement appear to be both abstract and daunting.

Further barriers include problems with communication and people being **resistant to change.** Absence of trust in communication will only be overcome as the methods of communication improve and when the topic of that communication is seen to be carried out and the results fed back. In simple terms, if what is said is to happen, happens and everyone knows about it, barriers to communication will start to fall.

People are naturally resistant to change and this barrier can be broken down by helping them see that the new ways will be beneficial to them. It requires giving full information, explaining the benefits, including them in making the changes thereby enabling them to take ownership, and take a gradual approach.

As previously mentioned, the step-by-step approach is essential to avoid the barriers which might impede progress.

Regulating the workplace by encouraging companies to develop a safety culture transcends the setting and imposing of external criteria. Instead, it concentrates on the organisation of the system and the internal climate. Rather than feeling that actions for improvement are imposed from the outside, individuals are encouraged to own those actions.

Developing and promoting a positive safety culture is an essential part of safety management. There must be commitment and clear leadership from the top. Aims, objectives and standards must be set, which are measurable and achievable.

This page is intentionally blank

Human factors

Learning outcomes

The intended learning outcomes are that the student will be able to:

A6.1   describe the factors which give rise to specific patterns of safe and unsafe behaviour in the working environment

A6.2   explain the nature of the perception of risk and its relationship to performance in the workplace

A6.3   discuss the impact of human error in a range of major disasters

A6.4   describe the appropriate methods of improving individual human reliability in the workplace

A6.5   describe how organisational factors could contribute to improving human reliability

A6.6   describe how job factors could contribute to improving human reliability

Contents

This page is intentionally blank

A6.1 - Human behaviour

Basic concepts of occupational psychology, sociology and anthropology

Occupational psychology

Psychology is the study of the human mind. The individual receives information through the senses: sight, hearing, touch, smell and taste. The information is processed in the brain/mind and there will be resultant behaviour. Sometimes the behaviour is not what is expected, which suggests that something has gone wrong with either the information received or the processing in the brain/mind.

Reasons why the communication stage has gone wrong are relatively straightforward: sensory impairment, for example, deafness or blindness, or due to wearing hearing protection or goggles or being in a noisy environment.

What is not so straightforward is what has happened at the processing stage. We cannot see into the human mind to know how it works nor see what has caused the behaviour we did not expect. Occupational psychology attempts to explain the processing in order to understand why people behave the way they do and so influence and predict human behaviour in the workplace. Controlling behaviour and human error in the workplace is an important consideration in the management of risk. If we consider the human mind as a "black box" then we can study the inputs and the outputs - but not the processes in the mind that produce them. These processes are governed by personality (the 'nature' versus 'nurture' factors).

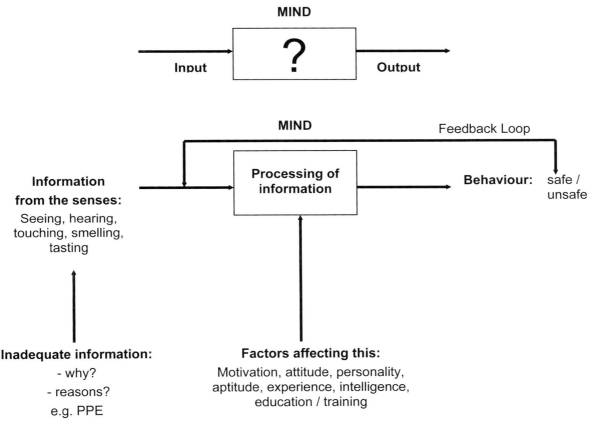

Figure A6-1: The black box.

Source: ACT.

Sociology

Sociology is the study of the development, structure and functioning of society. The question of whether each individual helps to form society or society forms each individual who is born into it, is central to the study of societies. The workplace/organisation can be considered as a society, with each employee as a member. That society will function in a different way from others. It is the task of occupational sociology to describe the differences and the reasons for the differences in various workplaces, how each individual fits in to the society and how groups function. Individuals form into groups which will affect the society more than each individual will, on most occasions. It takes a very strong individual to change society and in the workplace this may have positive or negative effects.

Anthropology

Anthropology is the study of societies and customs. Within each society there are beliefs and customs that are passed on from generation to generation. These are learnt from birth and so are considered to be the norm. They are so ingrained into everyday behaviour that to act any differently is just not considered. This also has a parallel in the workplace/organisation. New starters will fit into the culture of the organisation and learn the ways of it. They will be kept to the ways by everyone else's behaviour and by peer pressure. So, a person will fit into the customs of the workplace whether it is a positive or a negative safety culture. Sometimes the customs of the outside society will overcome those of the inside society (the workplace) and cause conflict. The individual may have to accept being left out of the mainstream culture and any informal groups that form within it.

That person may eventually form an informal group with like-minded people where the members of the group support each other. This overlaps with sociological studies and individual behaviour, all three areas of study being interlinked.

Factors affecting human behaviour

Individual differences

All individuals are different. These differences will influence patterns of work behaviour and may limit the effectiveness with which an individual carries out a job. They will also influence how safely the work tasks are carried out.

These individual differences arise from an interaction between the 'inherited characteristics' (passed on from the parents) and the various 'life experiences' through which the individual passes from the moment of conception.

- Family influences.
- Geographical location.
- Pre School influences.
- Education opportunities, quality, support.
- Occupational factors - training and retraining.
- Hobbies and interests.
- Own family influences marriage, children.
- Ageing.

Any, many or all of the above will help to 'mould' the individual into a unique person different from all other individuals.

The ways in which people differ are many and varied and it is important to bear this in mind from the point of view of work effectiveness and safety. It is vital to know what a particular job entails (the job description) and to specify the characteristics required to enable a person to perform that job effectively (the personnel specification).

Summary

Individual Differences

Physical	**Mental**
Gender	Attitude
e.g. females not exposed to lead	e.g. all PPE is uncomfortable
Build	Motivation
e.g. may restrict movement in a confined space	e.g. risks v reward
Capability/strength	Perception
e.g. manual handling	e.g. not perceiving a risk in using an unguarded machine
Health	Capability
e.g. colour blindness	e.g. ability to understand and follow safety rules

Key theories of human motivation

F.W. Taylor (Economic Man)

> *"What the workmen want from their employers beyond anything else is high wages.*
> *What employers want beyond anything else is low labour costs."*

Figure A6-2: Economic man.   *Source: Shop Management - F W Taylor, 1903.*

The earliest human reliability theory, as set out by F.W. Taylor, was that people worked for money. Financial reward was seen as the only motivator and the more money a worker was paid, the harder he would work.

Taylor divided people into two groups:

1. Potential managers who were competent at and enjoyed planning, organising and monitoring work.

2. The majority of the workforce who did not like those activities but preferred to have simple tasks set out for them.

Taylor considered that, once work had been rationally organised by the former and the latter had been trained to carry it out, money was the main motive force to get more work out of them. His theory of Scientific Management encouraged the development of division of labour and the flow line process, work-study and the concentration on training, selection and study of the optimum conditions for work.

His theory has five main principles:

1. Managers should plan only and workers should do only.

2. The one best way to do any particular job should be discovered by scientific methods, i.e. by systematic observation and recording of the most efficient methods used by the best workers doing the job.

3. The carefully selected best workers should then be individually trained in the best way to do the job.

4. Instrumental (i.e. goal achieving) financial incentives should be given (again on an individual basis) to the workers chosen to do the job in the new way.

5. There should be direct communication between the foreman/manager and the worker. It should be clear instruction and there should be no back talk, discussion or argument.

This philosophy of management has now been widely discarded in favour of other motivating theories. The financial reward that an individual receives is important; however other factors are even more significant.

Mayo (Hawthorne experiments)

Elton Mayo, an Australian Industrial psychologist, conducted a lengthy series of experiments between 1927 and 1932 at the Hawthorne Works of the General Electric Company of America.

They were originally intended to be a short investigation into the "relation of quantity and quality of illumination to efficiency in industry".

During the first experiments an experimental group was moved into a special area where illumination was increased and then decreased. A reference or control group was left where it was and was not subjected to any changes in illumination.

The observers predicted that output would vary with the illumination level. This did not prove to be the case, as output appeared to vary independently of the lighting level. Indeed in some cases, as the observed group's level of activity went up, sometimes so did that of the reference group (despite the fact they had not suffered from or benefited from any obvious physical changes in their environment).

These first observations drove the observers to devising a fresh series of experiments, which would control or eliminate the "various additional factors, which affect production output in either the same or opposing directions to that which can be ascribed to illumination".

The observers started to ask themselves what factors motivated individuals who worked in groups. They then extended the variables to include those factors which might be influencing the level of activity of the group.

For example, in one experiment, an individual was allowed to select the other members of his group; as a result productivity was improved and the group appeared to work more harmoniously. Other variables the experimenters introduced included variations in:

- Rest pauses.
- Working periods.
- Systems of payment.

Eventually, the company called a halt to these investigations as they caused too much disruption. For example, the workers who did not benefit from the changes felt that they should have been involved. Finally, there was a downturn in production due to lack of demand for the product as a result of the Great Depression of the 1930s.

The conclusion drawn from these experiments was that social interaction and a sense of belonging to an important working group contributed a great deal to job satisfaction. This was more important to the workforce than financial reward. Work was seen as a social activity not just as a means of earning wages.

Maslow (Hierarchy of needs)

Each individual has needs to fulfil, from the basic need to eat to the need to attain his true potential. The drive to fulfil these needs is known as motivation.

Maslow defined motivation as a striving to satisfy a need. When we have a need (or a want) we are motivated to act in a way that will lead to a removal or diminishing of that need. We all have needs and strive to satisfy them.

Maslow put forward the idea that needs can be categorised and that these categories can be placed in rank order. Once one need has been satisfied, it ceases to act as a motivator and the individual then strives to satisfy the needs in the next category. Some needs are continuous, such as eating, while others can change at different times of one's life. Money may be of paramount importance to the parents of a young family, while recognition is more important to an older person. The model suggests that it would be difficult to fulfil the higher needs in the hierarchy if the lower needs were not fulfilled. For example, it would be difficult for a person to feel job satisfaction if they were worried about redundancy (security needs not fulfilled).

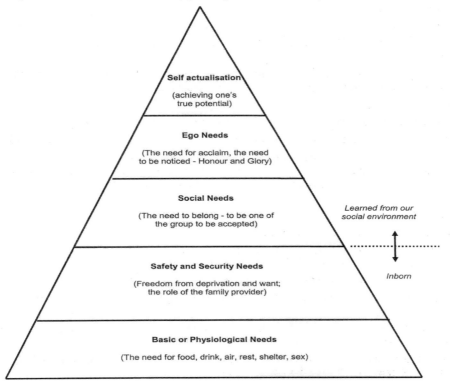

Figure A6-3: Maslow's hierarchy of needs.

Source: Maslow.

Contemporary theory (complex)

Other theorists who have studied achievement motivation are Atkinson and McClelland who studied the motivation of entrepreneurs compared with government employees, showing a clear difference in the importance they accorded to risk taking and to success.

Herzberg carried out an extensive survey in the U.S.A., Canada and the U.K. involving many thousands of workers at all levels in a wide range of organisations. His intention was to identify exactly what factors give rise to a sense of job satisfaction.

He found that there was no one factor that determined the presence or absence of job satisfaction. Instead he found that there were two types of factor. One factor if present would give rise to job satisfaction but if absent would not necessarily cause dissatisfaction. The other if absent would cause dissatisfaction, but if present - no matter in what quantity - would not result in job satisfaction.

He called these factors, respectively, "Motivators", e.g. status recognition, and "Maintenance Factors", e.g. salary and working environment.

These 'maintenance factors' have also been termed 'hygiene factors' or 'satisfiers'.

Description of HSG48 model

HSG 48 "REDUCING ERROR AND INFLUENCING BEHAVIOUR" 1999

This is a model of types of human failure based on the work of Rasmussen and Reason. Human failures are divided into two types: errors and violations. A human error is an action that was not intended. Errors can be separated into two types: skill-based errors and mistakes. Skill-based errors can be further divided into slips of action and lapses of memory, and mistakes can be divided into rule-based mistakes and knowledge-based mistakes.

Violations are deliberate deviations from the rules or procedures and can be separated out into three types: routine, situational and exceptional.

CAUSE OF HUMAN FAILURE

There are different types of human failures: errors and violations.

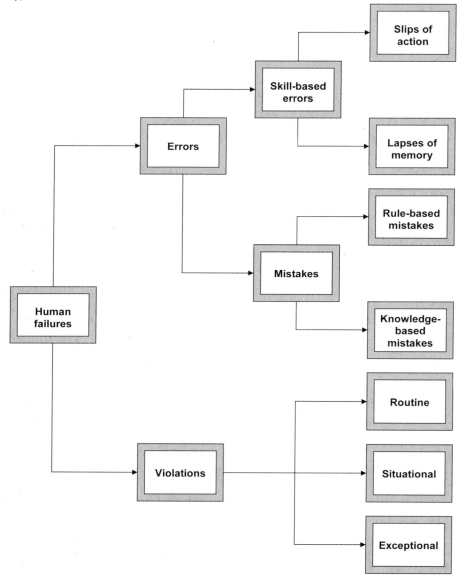

Figure A6-4: Causes of human failure.

Source: HS 48 "Reducing Error and Influencing Behaviour" 1999.

Slips and lapses

Once we have learned a skill, there is little need for much conscious thought about what we are doing. We can carry out a task without having to think too much about the next step. We learn to ride a bike or drive a car in this way. We need to pay attention to the road and the traffic, but we manipulate the pedals and change gear without thinking about it. If our attention is diverted, we may fail to carry out the next action of the task, or we could forget the next action or lose our place resulting in an error.

Mistakes

Mistakes are a little more complex than slips and lapses. We may do the wrong thing believing it to be right. We have a tendency to use familiar rules or procedures, often when they don't apply. The wrong application of a rule to a situation can result in an error.

In unfamiliar situations we may have to apply knowledge-based reasoning. If this is miscalculated or the situation is misdiagnosed, then a mistake may occur.

These errors typically occur with trained, experienced people, but also occur with untrained and inexperienced people. The untrained and inexperienced may base their decisions on misunderstandings and a lack of perception of risk.

Violations or breaking the rules

These violations are rarely acts of vandalism or sabotage, but are often carried out in order to get the job done. Many accidents, injuries and cases of ill health come about because of violations.

Routine violations are where breaking the rules or procedure has become the normal way of working. New workers come in and learn the incorrect ways, not realising they are wrong. The incorrect method may have come about because it is a quicker way to work or because the rules are seen as too restrictive. In one company it was felt that the work could not be finished on time if all of the rules were followed.

Situational violations may occur with pressures from the job: time pressure, extreme weather conditions and/or wrong equipment. Roof work may continue without edge protection because the correct equipment has not been provided. The person concerned may believe that he is doing a good job by making do with the wrong equipment and getting the job done quickly.

Getting the job done without the proper controls may be condoned explicitly or implicitly by the supervisor, if nothing has gone wrong, which reinforces the violation. After a period of time, the situational violation may become a routine violation.

Exceptional violations occur when something has gone wrong. A decision has to be made to solve the problem and that might involve breaking a rule and taking a risk. It is erroneously believed that the benefits outweigh the risk. An employee, who has a meeting with a client and is running late, may decide to speed in his car to get there in time.

The decision making processes

INDIVIDUAL DECISION MAKING PROCESSES

Humans are far more complex than machines and become even more so when they interact in groups and organisations. Their behaviour changes as they learn, when they know they are being watched and because of various experiences relatively unique to each individual.

Decisions made by the individual are influenced by a variety of factors, including: attitude, motivation, perception, personality, intelligence, aptitude, the culture in which they are working, ergonomic issues and physical and mental well being.

The way in which an individual makes a decision is governed by his or her goals and objectives (motivational factors). Thus, in order to understand the individual decision making process, we must start with an attempt to describe the goals and objectives of the human system. As described in Maslow's hierarchy of needs model, individuals have many goals at various levels. Some, such as the acquisition of food and drink, are innate. Others are acquired, sometimes as means of achieving the innate goals, and sometimes as ends in themselves, for example, getting promotion or buying a house. Some goals are short term (food at meal-times). Others goals are much longer term (e.g. pension contributions). In some cases these short and long term goals may conflict; e.g. a driver fails to check a vehicle before starting on a long journey in order to satisfy the short term goal of getting to the destination as quickly as possible, as a result jeopardising the long term goal of preserving his/her own health and safety.

Some goals are unconscious, either because the individual may not want to admit even to themselves that they are pursuing a particular goal, or because it is an inbuilt basic goal that no longer requires any conscious thought.

An individual's goals can be thought of as a conflicting system where there are several competing for overall control of the system from moment to moment. People will therefore show to some extent different and sometimes contradictory short and long-term behaviour depending on which goal is uppermost at the time.

DESCRIPTION OF ON AND OFF LINE PROCESSING

Input to the system or information to the person must be processed to be of use. This may be done on-line or off-line.

On-line processing is the moment-to-moment decision making about what action to take when dealing with the environment the individual finds himself in. It involves the least thought in order to carry out the action, as the action will be a series of pre-learned steps. A human being could not function efficiently if everything he did had to be carefully thought through. Some groups of actions work together to form a habit and through repetition they become a skill. Repetitive tasks become a skill that require little thought. We seldom think about what we are doing when we change gear in a car or walk upstairs. Once set in motion it is difficult to halt the sequence of steps that make up the action until it has run its course. These learnt packages of actions rely on correct learning in the first place because it is difficult to insert new actions into them later.

Off-line processing requires a lot of 'thought energy' as the individual will consider the results of a number of actions before deciding on which course of action to take. Some courses of action will be rejected because the consequences will be predicted as being unpleasant. Many factors need to be manipulated in order to do this and it requires knowledge of a variety of facts. It is, therefore, a great skill that depends on intelligence and the amount of practice in using the skill.

Intelligence is difficult to define, but it is said to be based on the ability to learn, to manipulate concepts and to solve problems. Earlier this century it was common for child psychologists to carry out intelligence testing. This formed the idea of the 11+ exam, the results of which were used in deciding which secondary school a child went to. The child psychologist, Binet, who invented the term IQ (Intelligence Quotient), said that children with a high IQ, i.e. over 100, were able to do tasks quicker than the average child.

Intelligence can be subdivided into special aptitudes: numerical, verbal, musical, mechanical, etc. Tests can be devised for all these aptitudes.

Errors in off-line processing are said to be related to intelligence. There may be limitations on thinking through the courses of action to take and this can lead to unsafe decisions being made.

Individuals may also make decisions based on illogical factors such as 'luck'. They also view things in a subjective way, the personality of the person having a great influence.

The level of arousal in the brain can also affect decision making off-line. Low arousal in the brain is associated with drowsiness resulting in poor performance.

There is a standard framework for classifying error - the skill-rule-knowledge based model, which comes from the work of Rasmussen. The three levels of behaviour show an increase in conscious control.

Skill-based behaviour (Rasmussen)

Skill-based errors involve slips or lapses. This is where highly practised action becomes routine or automatic action and a slip can occur in that routine.

Rule-based behaviour

Rule-based errors can occur where routines are selected from a large number of possible routines and the wrong ones are chosen.

Knowledge-based behaviour

Knowledge-based errors occur where people have to cope with what would happen if they tried particular sets of actions. This is the most complex situation and errors occur where the plan that is formed is mistaken.

A shortcoming of the Rasmussen model is the fact that it does not cover violations. This is where a person deliberately carries out an action that is contrary to company rules.

These types of error that have been proposed by Rasmussen and Reason have been developed in the HSE Publication HSG48, *(See - HSG48 "Reducing error and influencing behaviour" 1999 - earlier in this element).*

Factors contributing to individual differences

PSYCHOLOGICAL

Psychology is the study of the human mind. The individual receives information through the senses: sight, hearing, touch, smell and taste. The information is processed in the brain/mind and there will be resultant behaviour. Sometimes the behaviour is not what is expected, which suggests that something has gone wrong with either the information received or the processing in the brain/mind.

Reasons why the communication stage has gone wrong are relatively straightforward: sensory impairment, for example, deafness or blindness, or due to wearing hearing protection or goggles or being in a noisy environment.

What is not so straightforward is what has happened at the processing stage. We cannot see into the human mind to know how it works nor to see what has caused the behaviour we did not expect.

Occupational psychology attempts to explain the processing in order to understand why people behave the way they do and so influence and predict human behaviour in the workplace. Controlling behaviour and human error in the workplace is an important consideration in the management of risk.

SOCIOLOGICAL

Sociology is the study of the development, structure and functioning of society. The question of whether each individual helps to form society or society forms each individual who is born into it, is central to the study of societies. The workplace/organisation can be considered as a society, with each employee as a member. That society will function in a different way from others. It is the task of occupational sociology to describe the differences and the reasons for the differences in various workplaces, how each individual fits in to the society and how groups function. Individuals form into groups and will affect the society more than each individual will, on most occasions. It takes a very strong individual to change society and in the workplace this may have positive or negative effects.

ANTHROPOLOGICAL

Anthropology is the study of societies and customs. Within each society there are beliefs and customs that are passed on from generation to generation. These are learnt from birth and so are considered to be the norm. They are so ingrained into everyday behaviour that to act any differently is just not considered. This also has a parallel in the workplace/organisation. The new starter will fit into the culture of the organisation and learn the ways of it. They will be kept to the ways by everyone else's behaviour and by peer pressure. So, a person will fit into the customs of the workplace whether it is a positive or a negative safety culture. Sometimes the customs of the outside society will overcome those of the inside society (the workplace) and cause conflict. The individual may have to accept being left out of the mainstream culture and any informal groups that form within it. That person may eventually form an informal group with like-minded people where the members of the group support each other. This overlaps with sociological studies and individual behaviour, all three areas of study being interlinked.

The influence on human behaviour

PERSONALITY

There are as many personalities as there are people. The individual develops with inborn tendencies, nature, and outside influences, nurture. According to Cattell's Trait Theory, there are more unique character personality combinations than the number of human beings that have ever lived. People behave according to their personality traits, which may be inherited as well as learnt. They may be: cheerful, pessimistic, slapdash, perfectionists, and/or the many variables Cattell suggests. Personality is extremely difficult to change, and probably it is unethical to even consider the prospect.

Research has been done on the link between personality and accident proneness, but with no clear-cut conclusions. The link between certain individuals and accidents is more likely to be because of sensory impairment, for example, colour blindness or short-sightedness, or because of the lack of compatibility between the person's build and their particular task.

Using accident proneness as a reason for accidents reinforces a blame culture and does not encourage looking for root causes.

It is part of the management of risk to choose people for a task according to their physical and mental capabilities. This must include a consideration of the person's personality. For example, a person who tends to be a lively, hyperactive type should not be given a job sitting watching a gauge for a crucial rise in temperature. Accidents resulting from the mismatch of individual and task are usually not the fault of the individual.

ATTITUDE

"A pre-set response to conditions that are presented to the person".

Attitudes are a set of factors that constitute ways in which individuals differ one from another. Attitudes are not directly observable and can only be assessed by observing behavioural expression (physical or verbal behaviour).

Clearly, a person's attitudes will govern the way in which an object or situation is viewed and it will dictate the resultant response or pattern of behaviour. This is obviously very important when considering an individual's working patterns and any safety aspects associated with them.

Attitudes, like other aspects of individual differences, are formed (not necessarily consciously) as a result of a lifetime of experiences and although not totally immutable are not easily changed.

A person's attitudes are not simply an aid to coping with the world; they are the means by which that person copes with the world. Any attempts to change such a fundamental part of an individual's personality will be resisted. His very being is under threat.

Attitudes can be changed, although it is a difficult process. They have been changed within our society by pressure groups and government campaigns. Examples of where this has happened are drink driving campaigns, anti-smoking and the wearing of seat belts.

Smoking cigarettes was once considered the norm in our society, but a long campaign against it has changed society's collective mind. This has been achieved through information and education, price rises, the banning of smoking in most workplaces and public places, and peer pressure. It is now acceptable behaviour to complain to someone if they smoke near you. Passive smoking is considered a hazard to health.

In some cases, changes in other attitudes can affect the attitude to cigarette smoking and cause it to increase. It may be used by young women to keep their weight down. One attitude over-rides another.

> *"People's attitudes and opinions that have been formed over decades of life, cannot be changed by holding a few meetings or giving a few lectures."*

Figure A6-5 Observation made by Chairman Mao Tse Tung.   *Source: "Little Red Book".*

Examples of attitudes affecting safe working:

- It will never happen to me.
- We have never had an accident.
- Its only the price of a plaster.
- I know my limits.

Everyone at work should attempt to change their own and their colleague's attitudes to health and safety from - Work safely because -

I have to. →   I should. →   I want to. →   It is automatic.

Remedial action
- Train, and retrain when need for reinforcement is evident.
- Change by experience (involvement), e.g. selection of personal protective equipment (PPE).
- Peer pressure.
- Role model.

APTITUDE

Aptitude is closely linked to personality. Some people are particularly good at certain things, for example, an individual may be good at working with his hands, while another may say they "could not change a light bulb".

Aptitude can be developed over time as a skill, but it is more likely to be part of that person's characteristics. This again can be a factor when placing people in particular jobs. A person with no aptitude for precision work, but superb at felling trees is an accident waiting to happen if given the job of soldering electronic components.

MOTIVATION

"What makes people strive to satisfy their needs"

In the context of the working situation there have been, over the years, many attempts to identify why people work.

The earliest approach (by F.W.Taylor) was that people worked for money and fear of losing their livelihood. Financial reward was seen as the prime motivator. The more they were paid the harder they worked. This led to a new management philosophy:

- Payment by results.
- Incentive schemes.
- Piece work.

From a safety management viewpoint, this theory is unsound since most bonus schemes encourage people to work unsafely by cutting corners, taking short cuts etc. with safe working practices the inevitable victim.

Money IS important but other factors are more important. e.g. social belonging, acceptance by one's peers.

Elton Mayo, as a result of a lengthy series of experiments carried out at the Hawthorne Works of the General Electric Company of America, came to the conclusion that it was social interaction and a sense of belonging to an important working group that provided the job satisfaction. This was more important to the workforce than financial reward. Work was seen as a "social activity" not just as a means of earning wages. He found workers were interested in "a fair day's work for a fair day's pay".

Herzberg said that there was no one factor that determined the presence or absence of job satisfaction. He found what he called: "Motivators", e.g. status recognition, and "Maintenance Factors", e.g. salary and working environment.

BEHAVIOUR PATTERNS

Resulting from ancestry and social background

Nature vs. Nurture

Are human characteristics inborn or are they acquired from the environment in which an individual develops? Which characteristics are inborn and which acquired - and to what extent? This question has exercised the minds of psychologists for many decades in the past and, no doubt, will continue to do so for many more to come. Theories abound, but the problem comes from our inability to experiment. We cannot assess one individual who has grown up in a particular environment and then turn back the clock and allow the same individual to develop in a completely different environment. Likewise we cannot take two identical individuals (if such exist) and deliberately bring them up in separate, controlled environments.

We have to rely on "accidents" that have occurred in real life:

- Twins (identical or non-identical) who have been separated at birth and brought up in different family environments.
- Children of different parents who have been brought up together.

Even then we cannot exercise precise scientific control over those environments. In spite of the above difficulties, detailed studies have been made and evidence is still being collected. Comparisons between individuals have been carried out, using I.Q. (Intelligence Quotient) as a measure; I.Q. has been found to be a useful measure, but not necessarily of "Intelligence". Interesting, if not useful statistics have been published.

If a person's behaviour comes only from their genetic makeup, it will be impossible to change, which is bad news for the risk manager. If it comes from the environment they are in, then it will be capable of being changed. However, it is probably a little of each, which means that some elements of behaviour may be changed, but others will not. A knowledge of occupational psychology, sociology and anthropology will help the risk manager deal with this.

Effects on behaviour at work

EXPERIENCE

The experienced worker will know the hazards in the workplace and can make a decision on the risk he can take based on past experience. The problem with this is that his accident-free past may well be down to luck and that may change at any time. He may no longer see the hazards because of familiarity with them. More than half the fatalities from electrocution involve so-called competent people. The experienced worker will, however, be more aware of what can cause harm, unlike the inexperienced young person. It would be unethical to cause someone to have an accident in order to heighten their awareness of risk or so they could gain experience. Awareness must be heightened in other ways: training and education.

TRAINING

Training is important for the experienced and inexperienced: the experienced should receive refresher training to prevent complacency, and the inexperienced needs training and education to enable them to work safely. Training is provided to show the person the safe method of working and education to show them why.

INTELLIGENCE

Intelligence is that ill-defined concept, which we often take to mean cleverness, the ability to understand and solve problems or the ability to learn. If any of these definitions is used, we can see that people will be different and so behave in a different way. Education and training should therefore be appropriate to the audience: the content of the training, the language used, the degree of practical application and practice, and the amount of repetition.

Intelligence may not necessarily equate to safe behaviour, but it should respond to adequate and appropriate training and education.

EDUCATION

Levels of intelligence, training and education are closely linked. To a certain extent, a person's intelligence may limit his educational capabilities. Also, well educated people are usually more easily trained.

A6.2 - Perception of risk

THE PERCEPTION PROCESS (PERCEPTUAL DISTORTION)

"The process by which people interpret information that they take in through their senses"

- A boring, repetitive job may result in 'day dreaming', which may result in a lowering of the impact of a stimulus.
- Warnings (or threats) may not be strong enough to get through the perceptual set.
- Patterns of behaviour and habits can be carried from one situation to another where they are no longer appropriate or safe. (e.g. we tend to drive too quickly after leaving a motorway).
- Individuals can get 'used to' a stimulus and, if it is not reinforced, it ceases to command the attention and is ignored.
- Intense concentration on one task may make attention to another stimulus difficult or impossible.

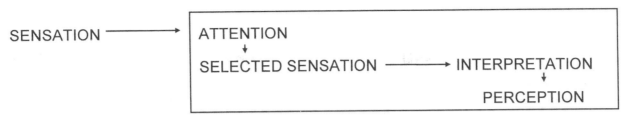

Figure A6-6: A model of perception.

Source: ACT.

PERCEPTUAL SET

Within each individual these processes of attention and interpretation are closely interlinked. The factors which influence these processes and the way in which they operate are often referred to as the "perceptual set" of the individual.

EXTERNAL DETERMINANTS

(The nature of the stimulating conditions)

- Location.
- Senses and Sense combinations.
- Intensity.
- Size.

- Colour.
- Tone.
- Motion.
- Novelty and Change.
- Repetition.

These can, and do, act in combination

INTERNAL DETERMINANTS

- Conscious or Unconscious motives.
- Expectations.
- Capacity.
- Change in attention.
- Fatigue.

- Needs (Deprivation).
- Culture.
- Sensitisation
- Habituation.
- Prejudice.

The **Perceptual set** (which to a greater or lesser extent will govern the impacts of the external determinants and how they are interpreted)

PREJUDICE (PERCEPTUAL DISTORTION)

We cannot treat every sensory stimulus as new and unique. Every experience cannot be reacted upon as a new experience. We would go insane if we tried. In order to overcome the problem of dealing with the vast range of possible experiences, we adopt a system of categorisation. We learn to react to a particular category in a specific way and to make life bearable and workable; we categorise objects, experiences and situations based on our memory of similar things. Sometimes we are forced to categorise a specific item that we have not previously experienced (in order to be able to deal with it) and we have to do this categorisation in the absence of adequate information. We have to pre-judge. Without this process of pre-judging and categorisation we would not be able to cope with the world in which we live. There are two mechanisms that are of specific importance when considering practical applications of perception theory.

PERCEPTUAL SENSITISATION AND DEFENCE

An individual can be or become 'sensitised' to certain stimuli if they are relevant, important or meaningful to that person. Sensitisation can be permanent or temporary and may or may not be accepted consciously by the individual. The stimuli to which the individual is sensitised have a much greater impact than would normally be expected. It could be said that they are seen or 'perceived' as larger, brighter, more attractive or more valuable than other stimuli. (For example - if our next-door neighbour is burgled, then the slightest sound in the middle of the night will cause instant wakefulness for several weeks afterward, sounds through which we would normally have slept.)

No one likes to feel threatened or anxious. The mechanism of 'Perceptual Defence' tends to protect the individual from such unpleasant situations by blotting out these threats and making them difficult to perceive at a conscious level. The individual does not want to register the problem or difficulty so it is pushed into the unconscious. These two mechanisms can have an important influence on the perception of hazards and risks in the workplace. The safety advisor may well be 'sensitised' to observing safety hazards while those actually exposed to the danger are operating their 'perceptual defence' and may not accept that any danger exists.

Remember:

- We do not see what is there.
- We see what we expect to be there.
- We do not see what we do not expect to be there.
- We do not see what we do not want to be there.

Remedial Action

- Information.
- Instruction.
- Training and drills.

ERRORS IN PERCEPTION CAUSED BY STRESSORS

Human error can be defined as an inappropriate response to a signal. In the context of safety, the signal is any message from the environment (including colleagues) relating to an existing or potential danger, which requires a response in order to avoid or remove the danger.

Human error can arise from a variety of causes; examples are indicated in the following table.

Causes of error	Action
Signal Not Received Physical Reasons (usually due to "sender" problems rather than "receiver") Background noise Too great a distance over which to communicate PPE (Dust masks, ear defenders etc.)	Design of work environment
Psychological reasons (internal to the receiver) Non attention: Lack of concentration - boredom - fatigue	Staff Selection
Over-concentration on one task to the exclusion of all other signals Desensitisation Systems overload - too much to attend to, unable to cope and signal missed	Job Design
SIGNAL MISINTERPRETED Not the expected signal Signal perceived incorrectly (incorrect interpretation - sometimes called a "False Perception") Lack of understanding of the signal	Training
INAPPROPRIATE RESPONSE TO SIGNAL Lack of knowledge, understanding or training	Training & Practice
CORRECT RESPONSE - BUT INAPPROPRIATE PRIORITY Lack of training (use of simulated situations as training exercises)	Training & Practice
SIGNAL IGNORED Deliberately ignoring a warning is rare but may arise from: No appreciation of the consequences of inaction False priorities e.g. bonus earnings Attitude to safety (safety is for wimps - taking risks is macho)	Training Attitude Change (Long Term)

Figure A6-7: Causes of error.   *Source: ACT.*

Note: training regarding the appropriate course of action to be taken on receipt of a warning signal must also include the steps to be taken to pass on the warning to fellow workers.

FILTERING AND SELECTIVITY

The system receives inputs through the senses which may be in good working order, defective or defects may be imposed by PPE or clothing. There is always more information in the environment than the senses can deal with. The brain allows certain information through filters on the sense, which is partly conscious and partly unconscious.

We shift our gaze over an area until it rests on an object of interest and we know in advance what characteristics to tune in to. This ability is known as 'perceptual set'. We can tune in to seeking out a defect in a machine or a work piece and blot out all other information. This other information may be important, but we may be unaware of it.

We can also tune out our hearing to certain sounds and be able to hear if a machine is running differently from usual. We can get used to certain sounds. Because they no longer signal anything to us, the filter does not allow them through.

How we perceive the world is built up over years and we have a picture of what the world is like. This is called expectancy. We see what we expect to see which may be different from reality. We do not need to take in a lot of information about a particular scene to understand it because we have stored information about similar scenes. Problems occur where the real word differs from the expectation.

We have population stereotypes, which is expectancy that something will be a certain way. For example, we believe that pulling a lever down will turn something off, or red means danger and stop, or turning something clockwise will turn off a valve or turn the volume up.

Stereotypes change from culture to culture. In Britain we put a light on by putting the switch down, but in the USA the switch is pushed up. If we came across designs that do not match up our stereotypes then we can easily be misled and make mistakes when carrying out a task automatically or making a choice in an emergency we tend to go for the stereotype. If this differs from reality then an error will occur. Standardisation is important to avoid these errors, but it must be total or it will make any expectations more likely to trap someone into an error.

PERCEPTION AND SENSORY INPUTS (HUMAN SENSORY RECEPTORS AND THEIR REACTION TO STIMULI, SENSORY DEFECTS AND BASIC SCREENING TECHNIQUES)

The Hale and Hale model

Hale and Hale devised a model of the human being as a system whereby accidents and ill-health are considered as damage to the system when something in the system fails. The model can be used in the study of accident causation when looking at the human factors element, which can be categorised according to which part of the system failed.

The system or individual has goals and objectives, some of them basic and innate such as acquiring food and drink. Other goals may be longer term, such as earning enough money to save for next year's holiday or saving for retirement. Different goals control the system at different times and often are on conflict with each other. The behaviour associated with a short-term goal may be in conflict with a long-term goal. Attempting to finish a job quickly may mean cutting corners in safe procedures that would be in conflict with the long-term goal of maintaining one's health and safety. The goals and behaviour of an individual as he adapts to his environment may be thought of as that individual's personality.

Apart from the few individuals who wish to harm themselves, e.g. suicides, self-preservation is a basic goal of the human system. Safety may be put at risk if the benefits to the individual are great, but generally the risks are perceived to be small. Failures in self-preservation are often because the individual has failed to perceive the danger and other goals have received priority.

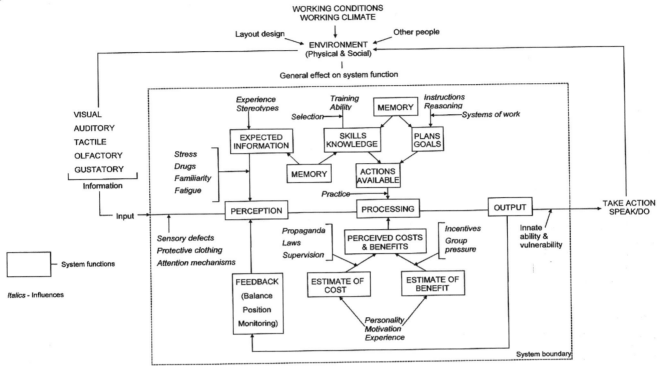

Figure A6-8: Systems model of human behaviour; adapted from Hale and Hale.   *Source: Ridley, J; Safety at Work; Fourth Edition; 1994.*

INDIVIDUAL BEHAVIOUR IN THE FACE OF DANGER (A PERSON'S PERCEPTION OF DANGER AND RISK)

The Hale and Glendon model

Danger is imminent contact with a hazard. The perception of the risk of coming into contact with the danger or even recognising the danger is dependent on many variables, for example: experience, the senses recognising it, i.e. carbon monoxide (which the senses cannot recognise) and believing you can be harmed.

The Hale and Glendon model is a combined accident causation model that has been developed using Rasmussen's error classification and Reason's Generic Error modelling system. It is an input-output model of human behaviour in the face of danger.

The model presumes there is a danger present that has not yet resulted in harm. It is concerned with the way people respond to hazards that threaten them or their fellow workers.

The input is hazard identification, the processing stage is risk assessment and the output is the selection and adoption of measures to reduce risk. The feedback loop shows the steps of the process can be repeated. The behavioural response will cause the danger to increase, decrease or remain the same.

The model states that for people to work safely in a dangerous environment they must have the same skills and the knowledge and know the rules. They must be motivated to identify hazards, assess and prioritise the hazards, accept responsibility for dealing with the hazards, know what should be done, have the skills to carry out preventative actions, monitor and review. In effect, the model embraces the concept of risk assessment as required by the Management of Health and Safety at Work Regulations (MHSWR) 1999 and the Control of Substances Hazardous to Health Regulations (COSHH) 2002.

The model can be applied to people at all levels of the organisation. It embraces latent failures, which are management failures, and active failures, which are operator errors. The management errors will tend to be knowledge based while the operator errors are more likely to be rule or skill based. It can be used to consider designers who need the knowledge and the skills and an understanding of the rules in order to design safety and health products.

The model can be used at all levels of the organisational structure, in risk assessment and personal behaviour in the face of danger.

The model can also be used to aid decisions on warnings of danger. This may be a flashing light, an insistent noise (alarm), fire drills and the training of certain people to be fire marshals and bomb disposal experts.

At the skills stage, a warning of danger could be built into the task to be learnt as part of the skill-developing process. It becomes programmed into the on-line working of the mind.

At the rules stage, a certain danger signal could be introduced as a rule to follow if the danger signal is heard/seen. It will be learnt as a rule alongside the other rules of the task:

Rule: -

If this is heard/seen - then do this.

At the knowledge stage, the extent of the knowledge base should equip the person to act in the correct way or to develop methods of seeking out where danger may be.

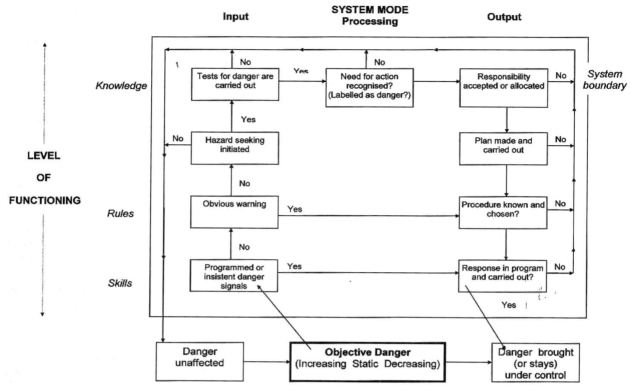

Figure A6-9: Behaviour in the face of danger.

Source: ACSNI Human Factors Study Group; Third Report: Organising for Safety.

A6.3 - Major disasters

Contribution of human error to major disasters

FLIXBOROUGH

1 June 1974

On Saturday 1st June 1974 the Flixborough Works of Nypro (UK) Limited (Nypro) exploded killing 28 people and injuring 36 others on site. The explosion was estimated to be the equivalent of 15-45 tons of TNT. If the disaster had occurred during the normal working week the death toll would have certainly been greater. Outside the site, 53 casualties were recorded together with extensive property damage over a wide area (1,821 houses and 167 shops/factories).

Circumstances

- No 5 reactor (R2525) was discovered to be leaking on the cyclohexane train and was shut down in order to be depressurised and cooled prior to a full inspection. The next morning (28th March '74) a 6 ft crack was found by the Plant Manager.
- The gap between the flanking reactors (No. 4 and No.6) was bridged by a 20-inch dogleg pipe between 2 expansion bellows. The inlet and the outlet of the pipe were at different levels and unsupported.
- The assembly was subjected to temperature and pressure more severe than had been encountered since the dogleg was fitted but still within what should have been normal margins.
- The bridging pipe ruptured which released large quantities of cyclo-hexane, which mixed with air to form an unconfined vapour cloud, which then exploded.

Key factors

- No proper design study had been carried out, nor had the need for support of the bypass pipe been appreciated.
- British Standards were not consulted.
- No safety testing had been carried out.
- The key post of works engineer was vacant and none of the senior personnel, who were chemical engineers, were capable of recognising what should have been a simple engineering problem. A junior engineer was present but his concerns were discounted, as was his sketch for supports.
- There was an inadequate nitrogen supply upon which the hazardous process system depended.
- There was nitrate stress corrosion on the reactor (R2525) thought to have initiated the sequence of events, which led to disaster.
- Many of the stainless steel pipes had suffered from embrittlement due to contact with zinc. The stainless steel pipes had also suffered from creep cavitation fractures that can be produced in a relatively short time under temperature and pressure.

- Note that the events in the control room cannot be determined with certainty as all control room personnel were killed and the instruments destroyed.

Contribution of human error

- Knowledge-based error: decisions were made without having a sufficient knowledge base. The chemical engineers did not recognise the engineering problem.
- The junior engineer's opinions were discounted. More experienced engineers probably did not consider he had enough experience and knowledge to be taken seriously.
- Being keen to get the job done, the engineers could have developed tunnel vision and failed to register (perceive) the problems. Solving the main problem became the only focus.
- With no senior manager to take control and to make a decision, the decision became a group decision. A decision taken by a group is no-one's responsibility (the risk-shift phenomenon) and therefore a decision may be taken by the group that no one individual would have the confidence to take.
- Lack of perception of risk. The engineers were used to their place of work and the processes that took place, which meant they failed to perceive the risks involved in the problem they were dealing with. It was said that they treated the situation as a plumbing job.

KEGWORTH

8 January 1989

A British Midland B737- 400 aircraft operated by British Midland Airways Ltd crashed at Kegworth, Leicestershire on 8th January 1989 at 2025 hrs.

The flight left Heathrow Airport for Belfast at 1952hrs with 8 crew and 118 Passengers (including 1 infant) on board. As the aircraft was climbing through 28,300 feet the outer panel of one blade in the fan of the No 1 (left) engine detached. This gave rise to a series of compressor stalls in the No 1 engine, which resulted in airframe shuddering, ingress of smoke and fumes to the flight deck and fluctuations of the No 1 engine parameters.

Believing that the No 2 engine had suffered damage, the crew throttled the engine back and subsequently shut it down. The shuddering caused by the surging of the No 1 engine ceased as soon as the No 2 engine was throttled back, which persuaded the crew that they had dealt correctly with the emergency. They then shut down the No 2 engine. The No 1 engine operated apparently normally after the initial period of severe vibration and during the subsequent descent.

The crew initiated a diversion to East Midlands Airport and received radar direction from air traffic control to position the aircraft for an instrument approach to land on runway 27. The approach continued normally, although with a high level of vibration from the No 1 engine, until an abrupt reduction of power, followed by a fire warning, occurred on this engine at a point 2.4 nautical miles from the runway. Efforts to restart the No 2 engine were not successful.

The aircraft initially struck a field adjacent to the eastern embankment of the M1 motorway and then suffered a severe impact on the sloping western embankment of the motorway. 39 passengers died in the accident and a further 8 passengers died later from their injuries. Of the other 79 occupants, 74 suffered serious injury.

The cause of the accident was that the operating crew shut down the No 2 engine after a fan blade had fractured in the No 1 engine. This engine subsequently suffered a major thrust loss due to secondary fan damage after power had been increased during the final approach to land. The following factors contributed to the incorrect response of the flight crew:

- The combination of heavy engine vibration, noise, shuddering and an associated smell of fire were outside their training and experience.
- They reacted to the initial engine problem prematurely and in a way that was contrary to their training.
- They did not assimilate the indications on the engine instrument display before they throttled back the No 2 engine.
- As the No 2 engine was throttled back, the noise and shuddering associated with the surging of the No 1 engine ceased, persuading them that they had correctly identified the defective engine.
- They were not informed of the flames which had emanated from the No 1 engine and which had been observed by many on board, including 3 cabin attendants in the aft cabin.

Contribution of human error

- When the captain informed the passengers that they had shut down the right hand engine (No. 2 engine), the passengers that had seen smoke coming out of the left hand engine assumed that the pilots had a different way of seeing left and right. It was as though they described left and right facing towards the cabin. No-one thought to challenge what they said they had done.
- Knowledge based error. The level of training they received to fly the new plane was brought into question. It was said that they were still using trial and error to find out what different instruments did.
- In the emergency situation, they fell back on well-learnt behaviour, which was not suitable for the new design plane. For example, one of the instruments that would have shown a problem was not considered, because in the old design that instrument was so unreliable they used to sometimes shut it down.
- Rule based error. The pilots applied a set of rules to finding the problem engine and it seemed to work. Every time they tried to reapply the rules, they were distracted by questions from the ground control operators.
- Perception of risk. Because that type of plane can fly on one engine, they may not have gone through every procedure available to them. The loss of one engine would not be viewed as a really serious situation.
- The new design control panel had smaller, computerised displays with a cursor instead of a large display with a pointer and a red area to show a dangerous situation, as the old design had. The pilots were not attuned to the new design and there was nothing to draw their eyes to a display showing the danger. The display that showed the problem was the size of a twenty pence piece and was positioned over to the side not in a prominent position.

HERALD OF FREE ENTERPRISE

6 March 1987

Less than half an hour after the ferry Herald of Free Enterprise sailed from Zeebrugge harbour for Dover, it capsized with 459 passengers on board. 188 lives were lost consisting of 150 passengers and 38 crew.

The subsequent inquiry revealed that the Herald left the harbour with both the inner and outer bow doors open. Water flooded into 'G' deck as the ferry increased speed thereby causing it to capsize and settle onto sandbanks with its starboard side above the waterline.

The Chief Officer, who had to be on the bridge 15 minutes prior to departure, was also responsible for ensuring that the bow doors were closed prior to sailing. The Assistant Bosun, Mr Stanley, had a duty to close the doors, but had fallen asleep after relief from maintenance and cleaning duties. The Bosun, Mr Ayling, noticed that the doors were open but did not close them, as it was not his duty. The Captain assumed that the bow doors were closed unless told to the contrary. Previous repeated requests for indicators to be fitted to the bridge had never been actioned - these would have cost about £500.

There was pressure put on ferries to sail early. A company memo issued by the Operations Manager at Zeebrugge summed this up.

"There seems to be satisfaction if sailing is 2-3 minutes early. Where there is a full load every effort must be made to sail 15 minutes early - put pressure on the first officer if you do not think he is moving fast enough."

There was therefore considerable pressure on the crew to meet departure times and the Herald sailed 5 minutes late on the 6 March.

The following factors also contributed to the actual incident:

- The emergency lighting was incapable of operating at large angles of heel and therefore did not work. This severely affected morale as well as hampering the physical rescue work.
- More than 1,000 lifejackets were locked away in order to prevent vandalism. The keys were in a small break-glass container adjacent to the locker door. The locker burst probably due to the buoyancy of the lifejackets. The resulting tangle of jackets and tapes along escape routes impeded people. The cold water also prevented people who had numb fingers from untangling the tapes in order to use the lifejackets.

A further cause of concern was the design of roll on - roll off ferries, which was considered to be inherently unsafe as they are top heavy. The Herald was a double deck ferry, but the berth-loading ramp had been designed for those of the single deck type. This meant that the ship's nose had to be trimmed by filling ballast tanks in order for the upper car decks to be loaded - a further cause of instability. This 'head down' attitude caused increased stresses from bow waves when the vessel was underway which also affected the locking mechanism of the bow doors. It took up to 1½ hours to fill or empty ballast tanks and there was no indication to the bridge about what was going on during the process. A previous request by a Chief Engineer for quicker high capacity ballast pumps to be fitted to this class of ship had been denied on the grounds of cost (~£25,000).

The inquiry heard the following compounding factors:

- Ships routinely sailing with excessive numbers of passengers - sometimes way over the life saving capacity of the vessel.
- The Herald's complement of officers had been reduced by one-third (from 15 to 10) when it was transferred from the Dover-Calais run to the Zebrugge-Dover run on the basis that there was more time to 'relax' on the longer voyage.
- The crew's working schedule was 24 hours on duty and 48 hours off.
- There was no instrumentation to check the draught of the ship.
- There was no monitoring equipment (e.g. CCTV) to observe problems in critical areas such as the car deck, engine room or superstructure doors.

The inquiry report found severe fault with the management system, which allowed the capsizing to happen:

"The Board of Directors did not appreciate their responsibility for the safe management of ships"

"….they did not apply their minds to clear orders for the safe operation of their ships…"

"…they did not have any proper consideration of what their duties were…"

"…there was a lack of thought about how the Dover-Zebrugge run should be organised…"

"… the entire body corporate was infected with sloppiness".

Contribution of human error   *organisational*

- The crew were working for 24-hour shifts, because they were able to rest on the journey. The assistant bosun had fallen asleep after being relieved of his normal duties. Having the responsibility for closing the bow doors seems to have been peripheral to his duties when he got really exhausted.
- *envir* A culture seems to have existed where they stuck to doing their own job. The bosun saw the doors open, but did not close them, as it was not his job.   *individual*
- *org* Perception of risk. Experienced crew get used to their workplace and fail to perceive any risk in it. Human beings cannot function if they are constantly aware of danger. We get round this by failing to see risk in something if it has never hurt us.
- *org* Wrong priorities. Speed of leaving the harbour was given prominence in the company's communication. The priority was perceived as being speed rather than safety. This was further reinforced by the failure to spend money on safety features, e.g. the indicators on the bridge to show the captain that the bow doors were closed.
- Routine violation. Setting sail with the bow doors open was breaking the rules, but became routine. This would be reinforced over time when it seemed to work and it appeared to be or was actually condoned by management.

PIPER ALPHA

6 July 1988

Piper Alpha, owned by Occidental Petroleum, was a key platform in the UK's North Sea oil production. It earned about £3.5 million per day and, at its peak, accounted for 10% of British North Sea oil production. Standing about 100 ft above the surface of the water, it was designed to accommodate over 200 men. A series of explosions ripped through the platform during the night of 6th July 1988 killing 167 people.

A pump had been shut down, using a permit to work, during the day shift in order to remove a safety pressure valve for recertification. A blind flange assembly was put in its place. At the end of the working day the suspended permit was returned to the control room but not displayed. During the night the working pump failed and the night shift started the pump that was fitted with the blind flange. Condensate entered the relief line and gas escaped from the flange assembly, which was not airtight. The gas exploded cutting out the main power supplies.

A public enquiry was held headed by Lord Cullen.

- The containment wall was fire, but not blast resistant.
- Two other rigs feeding into the same oil export line did not shut down until one hour after the initial mayday, which meant oil from the other rigs flowed back towards Piper and fuelled the fire.
- Gas pipelines ended in the area where the oil fire had started. They were eventually ruptured in the heat and the explosion engulfed the rig in thousands of tonnes of burning gas.
- People trapped in the accommodation block waited for helicopters to arrive but the first explosion made landing impossible.
- The routes to the lifeboats were blocked, and there was no message over the public address system telling them what to do.
- Most people stayed where they were until smoke and gas fumes overcame them. The survivors jumped 100 feet into the sea - contrary to the minimal training they had been given.

Permit to work system

- Valve locking off procedure not included in the permit.
- Work on the suspended pump had not been inspected by the designating authority (common occurrence).
- Although the permit system was monitored and frequently audited, failures had not been identified.
- Designating authorities (DAs) were not trained.

Common deviations:

- Multiple jobs on one permit.
- Failure to display permits in working area.
- Inaccurate description of work.

These problems had been highlighted to Occidental 12 months earlier in a report, so they knew about them. Lord Cullen's report concluded that Occidental had "adopted a superficial attitude" to safety.

"The safety policy and procedures were in place: the practice was deficient."

Figure A6-10: Piper Alpha extract.   Source: Extract from Lord Cullen's report into the Piper Alpha disaster.

Contribution of human error

- Knowledge based errors. The policy and procedures were there, but the personnel were not adequately trained. Their decisions were taken from an inadequate knowledge base.
- Misperception. The product was perceived to have priority over safety.
- Routine violations. Breaking the rules regarding the permit to work system had become common practice. This would be reinforced when management appeared to condone it either by overt means or by turning a blind eye.
- Most of the human error resulted from the influence of the organisation's negative health and safety culture. Managers of rigs had not been given authority to make decisions based on safety that could result in loss of revenue.
- Problems had been highlighted, but not remedied.
- In the emergency situation, there was no one person to take control and issue instructions. The personnel followed through their meagre training and went to the living accommodation. This was against the sort of action they would have taken if they had been in a situation where they could have thought it through. They travelled upward to the accommodation block even though heat and smoke rise. The ones who were saved were the ones who travelled downwards and then into the sea. Most of us do not think logically in an emergency situation.

LADBROOK GROVE

5 October 1999

At 0811 hrs on 5 October, two trains collided two miles outside London Paddington station at Ladbroke Grove Junction. One was a Great Western inter-city high speed train (HST) running from Cheltenham Spa to Paddington, the other a Thames Train 3-car diesel unit going from Paddington to Bedwyn, in Wiltshire.

The crash happened when the driver of the Thames Train went through a red light outside Paddington during the rush hour and collided head-on at 130 mph with the Great Western HST.

The crash left 31 people dead, including the driver, and hundreds injured, some critically because of the rapid outbreak of fire in some of the HST carriages.

The driver, Michael Hodder had only been qualified for 13 days when the accident happened. He had received no training from Thames about awareness of "SPADS" (signals passed at danger), and had not been warned that the signal outside Paddington was a black spot. Eight drivers in the previous five years had failed to see the signal. The company had not tested Mr Hodder's knowledge of the labyrinthine route that led into Paddington, nor was he given a map showing accident-prone signals. The layout at the junction is complex. To the west there are four running lines; to the east there are six bi-directional running lines; and at the junction there are connections between the various lines.

An official report into the crash by Lord Cullen said Thames Trains' safety culture in relation to training was "slack and less than adequate". It criticised "significant failures of communication within the organisation".

Lord Cullen concluded in the report that it was likely that Mr Hodder was unable to read the signal accurately because of sunshine glinting on the track.

Contribution of human error

- This disaster shows how human error occurs within the organisational culture and the influences a negative culture will have on the individual.

- Knowledge-based error. The driver did not have the required knowledge base or experience to make an adjustment to his behaviour when approaching the Ladbroke Grove junction signals. Had he known it was a black spot, he would have been more aware that there could be problems and to watch out for them. He may also have slowed down in preparation for the possibility of a problem.
- Behaviour in the face of danger. According to the Hale and Glendon model, working at the rules level, which Mr Hodder must have been working at since he did not have enough time to develop all the skills or the knowledge of the job, would require an obvious signal for him to act on in order to bring the danger under control. If the red light could not be seen then the warning of danger would not be obvious.
- The complexity of the connections between the various lines at the junction could have caused the driver to concentrate on where he was going and not on the signal. This is especially true when the driver is inexperienced, as Mr Hodder was.

A6.4 - Improving human reliability in the workplace

Motivation and reinforcement

Maslow and Herzberg's theories of motivation deal with individual needs that apply to everyone. These are commonly known as content theories of motivation. The process theories of motivation deal with the process of work and consider that people are motivated by expectations that will vary from individual to individual. This involves the identification of what performance is desired and the identification of the key motivating factors needed to achieve the goal. Two such process theories are expectancy theory and equity theory.

WORKPLACE INCENTIVE SCHEMES

Expectancy theory

Many behavioural scientists consider this theory as the most comprehensive and useful approach to understanding motivation in the workplace. Expectancy theory attempts to measure the strength of an individual's motivation to behave in particular ways. Managers should then ascertain what particular outcomes and rewards are most valued by the individual worker. The job should then be designed so that performance is improved through increased motivation. A clear link should then be established between performance and outcomes/rewards.

Thus, in management terms, the key implications of using expectancy theory is that:

- The job, task or role should be designed to allow people the opportunity to meet their own needs.
- The pay/reward system should reward desirable performance (e.g. long service payments should be avoided).
- The organisation should cater for the individual because the needs and values of each individual will be different (e.g. promotion, job enrichment, salary).

Equity theory

This considers that the major input into job performance and satisfaction is the degree of equity (or inequity) that people perceive in their work situation. Inequity occurs when an individual's inputs and outputs are greater than or less than others in the workplace. Where this occurs, the individual will compensate accordingly. For example:

- Overpaid salaried workers will produce more in order to reduce inequity whereas underpaid salaried workers will achieve less in order to restore the balance.
- Overpaid piece-rate workers will produce higher quality and lower quantity than equitably paid piece-rate workers.
- Underpaid piece-rate workers will produce higher volume and lower quality than equitably paid piece-rate workers.

In practical terms, desirable safety performance can be rewarded in a number of ways:

- Bonus schemes based on desirable safety performance.
- Competitions with prizes.
- Award schemes - internal and external.

REWARD SCHEMES

The primary rewards associated with work are pay, status, promotion or intrinsic interest in the job. Perhaps the most fundamental of these is the need to earn enough money in order to live and, after that, other lifestyle benefits including recreation. Unlike other less tangible rewards, money can be counted and used as a measure of worth or appreciation. Earnings can be based on the quantity of goods produced (piece work) or be a guaranteed fixed salary.

Piecework has long been associated with the potential to cut corners in order to increase the reward with the classic example being the removal of a machine guard in order to increase production. This potential drawback in safety performance is balanced by the perceived benefit that the organisation will receive by obtaining the 'maximum' productivity from each worker. The quality of the work however is not necessarily guaranteed by the piecework system that may allow the workers to produce high volume of low quality goods. Although the payment of a fixed salary reduces the pressure on an individual to cut corners in order to increase earnings, it does not follow that this will be the case. The organisational need to ensure that salaried workers produce at the required level may lead to a culture or appraisal system that places undue emphasis on production over safety. Whichever system of reward is in place it should be designed to ensure that safety performance is rewarded just as productivity is.

JOB SATISFACTION

Edwin Locke, in his process theory of motivation, advocates a goal setting approach to motivation. This establishes four main propositions:

- Stretch people by setting challenging goals, not too hard so they will fail, but attaining them will give a sense of achievement.
- Setting specific rather than vague goals. We adjust our behaviour when we know exactly what is expected of us.
- Participation in goal setting increases commitment to those goals. Managerially set goals can also add to job satisfaction, if they are fully explained and justified.

- Having knowledge of the results of what we do, i.e. feedback, is also satisfying, whether it is seeing the finished product we have helped to build or being told we have done a good job.

Modern management theory places an increasing emphasis on the highlighting of employee concerns in order to improve decision-making and to maintain morale. Thus they have a key role in identifying causes of absenteeism, accident and illness incidence, high staff turnover, low productivity and poor industrial relations.

By its nature, the measurement of job satisfaction will involve consultation with individual employees. Many companies consider the use of tools such as attitude and opinion surveys a key component of organisational excellence. The job satisfaction survey is usually more than just a written questionnaire as it involves:

- Open exploratory interviews in order to gain understanding of the major issues involved.
- A closed written questionnaire which has been designed to obtain quantitative data.
- Further open interviews or workshops designed to explore or test issues identified in the written questionnaire.

Properly designed, this will enable the organisation to succeed in gaining valuable data, make better decisions and take more effective action.

APPRAISAL SCHEMES

Staff appraisal has long been a common practice by organisations although the setting of safety performance targets and the measurement of their achievement is a relatively recent innovation except in the most progressive of organisations. The common model is for managers to appraise subordinate staff although there is a trend towards employee appraisal of their managers and towards self-assessment.

An appraisal is a formal systematic method of staff assessment or development. Most appraisal systems are formal and usually involve set procedures, documentation, interview and feedback. In essence the prime purpose of the appraisal process is to establish controls on the behaviour of individuals and to bring about changes to behaviour if necessary. There are six key elements to the achievement of this goal:

1. Auditing to discover the existing and future employment potential of the individual.
2. Manpower planning to ensure staff performance and future organisational management cohesion (e.g. promotion potential for succession plans).
3. Training needs analysis by exposing inadequacies and deficiencies which could be remedied by coaching and training.
4. Staff motivation to achieve organisational goals and standards.
5. Individual development via praise or correction.
6. Fairness so that rewards such as promotion and money are distributed fairly.

Selection and training

IMPORTANCE OF INTERVIEW AND SELECTION

Recruitment and placement procedures should ensure that employees at all levels have the necessary mental and physical abilities to carry out their jobs. If the individual does not have the necessary skills, then he or she must have the ability to acquire them via on and off the job training (including experience).

The procedure may require assessment of individual fitness by medical examination, physical fitness or aptitudes and abilities tests. The selection process should also include an assessment of training needs such as the extent and depth of induction training required. The most common personality assessment method used in the selection of staff is the interview. This is simply defined as a conversation that takes place under controlled conditions with the purpose of selecting a person for the job. The purpose of the interview is to select the most suitable person for the job and, in doing so, the interviewer has three main functions:

- To obtain information from the candidate.
- Observe the interviewee's behaviour and reactions.
- Provide the candidate with information about the job.

The selection process involves:

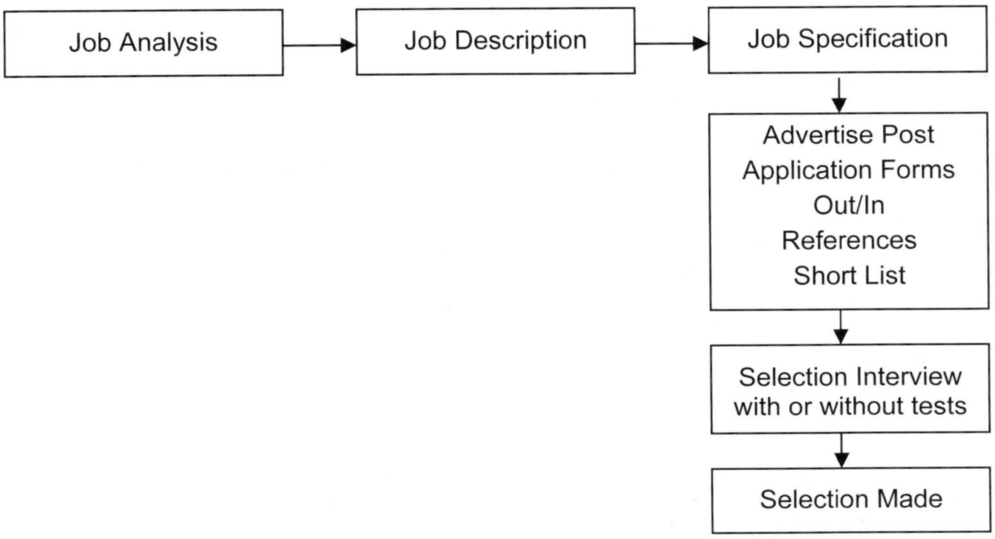

Figure A6-11: Job analysis flowchart.

Source: ACT.

The flow of the interview itself can take many forms. One common format is:

1. **Physical Characteristics** key physical abilities and state of health (e.g. eyesight, hearing).

2. **Attainments** education, training, experience and achievements.

3. **General Ability** general intelligence and knowledge.

4. **Special Aptitudes** occupationally relevant talents (e.g. scientific or mechanical).

5. **Interests** may be of relevance as an indicator of intelligence or skills.

6. **Personality** self-perception, social relationships etc.

7. **Circumstances** family background, financial and current problems.

ON AND OFF THE JOB TRAINING

Training is an essential element of ensuring that people have the skills, knowledge and attitudes to make them competent in the health and safety aspects of their work.

■ Assess the skills needed to carry out tasks safely.

■ Provide the means to ensure that all employees, including temporary employees, are adequately instructed and trained.

■ Ensure that employees on especially dangerous work have the necessary training and experience to carry out the work safely.

Many employees are keen to undergo training as it demonstrates an investment by the organisation in them as an individual. In addition to a natural desire by some, but not all, people to achieve new levels of skills or knowledge, employees may be motivated by the following factors:

■ Pride in the job.
■ Reward.
■ Praise.
■ Curiosity.

■ Job satisfaction.
■ Promotion prospects.
■ Qualifications.

A6.5 - Organisational factors

Effect of organisational factors on the probability of human error

INADEQUACIES IN POLICY

A policy statement which does not make a commitment to health and safety and seems to focus on the responsibilities of the employees can affect the attitude of the workforce and lead to a poor health and safety culture. Human error occurs more readily in a negative culture.

There could be inadequacies in the other sections of the policy following on from the statement. For example, failure to allocate responsibilities and failure to have proper arrangements can lead to human error.

INADEQUACIES IN INFORMATION

Inadequate information may mean that operatives make uninformed decisions which can lead to error. For example, not having enough information on what would happen if two chemicals were mixed together caused an explosion that blinded Ken Woodward of Coca Cola Schweppes.

INADEQUACIES IN DESIGN

Poor design can cause mistakes to be made. This is discussed in ergonomics. For example, a badly laid out control panel with unmarked switches may cause the operator to make an error when choosing the appropriate switch. Furthermore, an operator who intends to close a valve by turning it clockwise may find himself opening it even more if it has been designed (unusually) to close anti-clockwise.

INADEQUACIES IN IMPLEMENTATION

There may be systems of work devised, but they may not be implemented and the operators not properly supervised. This can lead to routine violations creeping in and errors more likely.

THE INFLUENCE OF FORMAL AND INFORMAL GROUPS WITHIN AN ORGANISATION

Wherever people interact or communicate, their behaviour is governed by **norms** (standards or expectations) and they strive for a common purpose. If they ignore a norm they are classified as **deviants** and pressure is put on them to conform. Such pressure can take the form of verbal abuse, physical assault, silence, blacklisting and physical exclusion.

A group must have a minimum of two members and enjoy shared communication. They must have a collective sense of identity as well as shared goals that can only be achieved by the members working together. Groups can be classified as informal or formal. In formal groups the aims of the group are decided by the organisation whereas informal groups set their own agenda.

Formal groups are created in order to achieve specific organisational objectives and are concerned with the co-ordination of work based activities.

People are brought together (by management) on the basis of defined roles within the structure of the organisation. The nature of the tasks to be undertaken and the skills involved are the main feature of formal groups. Goals are defined by management, and certain rules, relationships and norms of behaviour established.

Certain tasks can only be performed through the combined efforts of a number of individuals working together. The variety of experience and expertise among members of the group provides a synergetic effect, which can be applied to the increasingly complex problems of modern organisations.

Moreno - perspective formal groups into

Team Groups - these are fairly autonomous, terms of reference are usually broad and supervision is limited (e.g. problem solving groups, maintenance crews, research teams).

Task Groups - Jobs are clearly defined and individuals assigned to specific positions. The group does have some limited discretion over methods or sequence of work as long as targets are met (e.g. administrative or clerical workers).

Technological Groups - members have very limited autonomy to determine or change operational activities. Content and methods of work are specified as well as the pace of work. Individuals will be assigned to specific jobs. There is little opportunity for individual discretion (e g. people working on an assembly line).

(**Decision-Making Groups** and **Managerial Groups** are other possible categories).

Formal groups, such as the safety committee have an influence on the behaviour of individuals, which may be positive or negative, dependent on the status of the safety committee. A safety committee that is seen to get things done will have a positive effect on the safety culture.

The **informal group**, a group of like-minded individuals who get together for support, may also have a positive or negative influence. The behaviour of the individuals will depend on the others in the group and what the group norms are. If the group are negative about the company, they influence each other to break rules and to act contrary to what they perceive management to want. This can create situations where violations cause errors to be made.

Within the formal structure of the organisation there will always be an informal structure. This informal organisation arises from the interaction of people working in the organisation, their psychological and social needs and the development of groups with their own relationships and norms of behaviour, irrespective of those defined within the formal structure.

Some functions of the informal group system

- It provides satisfaction of members' social needs and a sense of personal identity and belonging.
- It provides for additional channels of communication; for example, information of importance to particular members is communicated through the "grapevine" more quickly than through the formal system.
- It provides a system of motivation, for example, through status, social interaction, variety in routine or tedious jobs, and informal methods of working.
- It provides a means of highlighting deficiencies or weaknesses in the formal organisation, for example, areas of duties or responsibilities not covered in job descriptions or outdated procedures.
- Groups provide companionship and a source of mutual understanding and support from colleagues. This can help in solving work problems and also in mitigating stressful or demanding working conditions.
- Membership of the group provides the individual with a sense of belonging. The group provides a feeling of identity and a chance to acquire role recognition and status within the group.
- The group provides guidelines on generally acceptable behaviour. It helps to clarify ambiguous situations such as, for example the extent to which official rules and regulations are expected to be adhered to in practice, the rules of the game, and what is seen as the correct acceptable behaviour. It establishes its own set of norms, rules and values.
- The group may put pressures on members to resist demands from management on such matters as work output or changes in working methods.
- Group allegiance can serve as a means of control over individual behaviour. The group may discipline individuals who contravene the norms of the group.
- The group may provide protection for its membership. Group members collaborate to protect their interests from outside pressures or threats.

Some positive and negative aspects of groups

- The goals of the group may be at variance with those of the organisation.
- The group can work as well against the organisation as for it.
- Once a group has become fully developed and created cohesiveness, it may be difficult for management to successfully change attitudes and behaviour patterns of the group. It is important that the manager should attempt to influence the group in the early stages of its formation when members are establishing guidelines and standards and their own norms of acceptable behaviour.
- A strong, cohesive group may become critical or even hostile to outsiders or other groups. Lack of co-operation and inter-group conflict may arise to the detriment of the organisation as a whole.
- Group decision making can be more costly and time consuming than if taken by an individual, but :
  - Groups can provide a pooling of resources and can bring together a range of complementary knowledge and expertise.
  - Interaction among members can have a "snowball" effect and provide future thoughts and ideas in the minds of others.
  - Group discussion leads to the evaluation and correction of possible decisions.
  - If full participation has taken place, decisions will have the acceptance of most members and they are more likely to be committed to decisions made and their subsequent implementation.

One might expect therefore, that "better" decisions will result from group discussion. However there are two possible dangers: "Groupthink" and "Risky Shift".

Groupthink

Described by Janis as:

> "A deterioration of mental efficiency, reality testing, and moral judgement that results from in-group pressures. Groupthink results in the propensity of the group to just drift along".

Janis identifies a number of specific symptoms of groupthink:

- A sense of invulnerability with excessive optimism and risk taking. There is an unquestioning belief in the morality of the group.

- Pressures on individual members to conform and reach consensus means that minority or unpopular ideas may be suppressed. Members who oppose the group are stereotyped as evil, weak or stupid.
- The search for group consensus can result in rationalisation by members to discount warnings and there is an illusion of unanimity. There is self-censorship of any deviation from group norms or apparent group consensus.

(Groupthink is prevalent in large bureaucratic organisations, parliamentary departments, the civil service etc.)

The risky-shift phenomenon

There is a tendency for groups to make more risky decisions than would individual members of the group if acting alone. Presumably this is because individuals do not feel the same sense of personal responsibility for group decisions or their outcomes:

"A decision which is everyone's is the responsibility of no-one".

Possible explanations for the risky-shift phenomenon might include:

- People who are inclined to take risks might be more influential in group discussions than more reserved people.
- Risk taking is regarded as a desirable cultural characteristic that is more likely to be expressed in a social situation such as group working.

In spite of these possible problems, groups do seem to be more effective in problem solving than individuals when the problem requires a range of knowledge and expertise.

INFORMAL GROUPS	FORMAL GROUPS
1. Qualifications for Membership	
Personality, Characteristics, Temperament, Attitudes, Common (Shared) Interests, Likes/Dislikes Qualitative: Immeasurable: Subjective Complementary in Social Psychological Terms Individuals "Earn" Membership - Cannot be "Placed" into Group	Skills, Experience, Education, Training Capacity/Capability Quantitative: Measurable: Objective Complementary in Task Requirement Terms Individuals placed into groups to meet Task Needs
2. Leadership	
Leadership "Adopted" by Group Leader must be "Accepted" by each individual in the group "Un-named" leader "Status" awarded internally - by group Not readily identifiable ("Loudspeaker" may not be Leader!) Flexible to meet varying situations Temporary - may change at any time Concerned for aspirations (needs) of the group	Leadership "Appointed" by External Authority Leader need not be "Acceptable" to Individuals Named leader Title - given by External Authority Identifiable - Badge, Uniform, Office, Status Symbols Inflexible - leader in all situations Permanent - May not change at any time Concerned for the Needs (Objectives) of the Organisation
3. Communication	
2-way. From any member to all others Requests, Consultation, Advice, Discussion Always Verbal - Face to Face Slow - Complicated network Understanding ensured Communication through each member Conviction of communicated message Decisions by consensus	1-way. Always from the leader Directives, Orders, Rules, Schedules Can be Verbal - usually Written Fast - Straight from "Boss" to member Understanding expected and assumed Communication to the group Support expected from Higher Authority Decisions imposed from above
4. Size of Group	
Depends on Communication Network	Depends on size and nature of task to be performed
5. Loyalty	
Always to group	Expected to be to the Organisation
6. Identity	
Status, Personal Name, Personal Role, Sense of belonging and being accepted	Title, Job Description, "Clock Number"
7. Compliance by Individual	
Unwritten Rules, Norms, Values Pressure to comply imposed by Group Invisible Variable Sanctions	Written Rules, Standards, Procedures Pressure to comply by Organisation Prescribed Sanctions Visible Organisation Charts

8. Summary	
"Us"	"Them"
"Feelings"	"Facts"
"Social"	"Scientific"
"Democratic"	"Autocratic"

Figure A6-12: Summary of informal and formal groups.   *Source: ACT.*

Stages in group formation

Tuckman has developed a model that represents the changes that take place in both the social and task aspects of group behaviour in the course of its formation and development. There are four stages: Forming; Storming; Norming and Performing. Other writers have added their own interpretations of the processes that can be observed in these four stages. (Their contributions depend upon their individual standpoints and psychological perspectives.)

Stage 1: Forming

On the task dimension this is a period of orientation. Group members try to establish just what the parameters of the task are, how they should go about accomplishing it, what information they will need and so on.

On the social dimension this is a period of testing and dependence. Members try to discover what kinds of interpersonal behaviour are appropriate. There is a tendency to look to the leader or some powerful (outspoken!) member of the group for guidance in this new situation.

Stage 2: Storming

Storming's characterised on the social dimension by internal conflict. There is often polarisation around key interpersonal issues. Members seem to be expressing their own individuality and attempting to resist group influence.

With regard to the task, this stage is typified by emotional responses to the demands it seems to be making on the individual, particularly where the individual experiences a discrepancy between these demands and his own orientation.

Stage 3: Norming

The group begins to share ideas and develop cohesion. Members perceive themselves as part of a genuine "group" which they wish to maintain and perpetuate. New standards and new roles emerge and are accepted. The emphasis is on harmony at all costs. Aspects of the task that are potentially conflict producing are avoided.

The task activities are typified by an open exchange of ideas and opinions. There is a willingness to listen and to accept the views of others.

Stage 4: Performing

The group has established a flexible and functioning structure of inter-related roles. The inter-personal aspects of the group's activity have been sorted out and now group energy can be channelled into the task.

The task dimension sees the emergence of solutions to problems and constructive attempts at successful task completion. The task and social dimensions seem effectively to have come together at this stage.

At the performing stage any future development may not be easy. The group may need to splinter up and reform to meet the change.

The established group may not readily accommodate new members (It may also not accept new Managers with new ideas).

Roles

Social roles are slots in a social system which are occupied by individual persons.

The most widely recognised roles are those that derive directly from the social structure:

- Kinship roles.
- Gender roles.
- Occupational roles.

A social role exists independently of the person who occupies it. It involves a recognised position or slot in the social structure and, additionally, a set of expectations about the behaviour of the person occupying it.

Role positions do not exist in isolation from one another; they interlock and constitute social systems. (For example, we could not have the role of "mother" without the associated role of "child".)

The expectations associated with a role vary:

- They differ in the degree to which there is general consensus of expectations covering all aspects of the role. For example, we may all agree that a mother should look after her child, but we do not agree whether she should teach her child to read and write or just play with him.
- Role expectations vary in their degree of permeation. Some roles pervade all areas of the occupant's behaviour, while others only affect the occupant's behaviour at particular times or in particular places (e.g. we expect a nun to be pious and a paragon of virtue at all times. On the other hand, a bus driver can do what he likes in his spare time, as long as he performs his duties efficiently and safely during his hours of employment).
- Some role expectations may be backed by sanctions (e.g. a mother can be sent to prison for neglecting her child).

Many aspects of role expectations are not backed up by sanctions but people still conform to them.

Some role expectations may be formally laid down and a contract may have to be signed before the occupant takes up his position. The contract may specify precisely what the role expectations are (e.g. a marriage ceremony). Some roles are covered by a code of conduct e.g. the medical profession. These codes do not specify particular expectations about behaviour but lay down certain guiding principles for covering a variety of contingencies.

Role expectations carry with them "norms" of behaviour:

■ What the majority of people do in this role.
■ What would be ideal for people to do in this role.
■ What all people must do in this role.

A norm can acquire a kind of super-human quality so that it appears more as a natural law than as a social contract (e.g. gender roles).A person then in the position of a Bank Manager will:

■ Usually be punctual and efficient.
■ Ideally punctual and efficient.
■ If not neat and efficient he will be sacked!

These customs, ideals and rules will affect an individual strongly while he occupies his role position because they will be expressed in many obvious and many subtle ways by the behaviours of his role partners. He will feel compelled to behave in a way that other people, with whom he has contact, expect him to behave.

Use of sociograms

A sociogram is a device that can be used to provide additional information regarding an employee and how he reacts with his peers. It can show how an employee is viewed by his workmates. It is a tool to assess social interaction and social perceptions. Questions, such as "Write down the name of the person with whom you would like to work on a project" are asked of each member of the group. The results are tabulated to show how many times each group member was chosen. This information is graphically plotted to identify popular employees, social isolates and employees who are disliked. They can also show interaction patterns over time.

The diagram can be drawn as a series of concentric rings like an archery target. Have one more ring than the greatest number of times any student was chosen. Number the spaces starting from outside the last ring. Start with zero and work inwards. Write each group member's name inside the ring corresponding to the number of times he was chosen. Draw arrows from each person's name to the person selected by them. Studying the diagram can show popularity and interaction preferences.

This information can help to show natural leaders of groups who can be enlisted to help change the norms of a group who act negatively towards health and safety issues. It can also show which employees work better together, which is a good motivator. Unpopular employees can be helped with social skills and maybe, with the influence of the popular ones, become accepted in the group. The employee lacking social skills could be helped by placing him in a job with some interaction needed, such as team leader.

PEER GROUP PRESSURES AND NORMS

Most people want to be accepted by the group, especially their peer group, and will act according to the group norms. These peer group norms are extremely influential and can work for or against safety. For example, if a young person's peer group norm is that wearing hearing protection is not cool, then that young person will not wear it. Peer pressure is so influential that even enforcing the wearing of hearing protection will probably mean that the person will wear it only when he is closely supervised and remove it as soon as he dare.

TYPES OF ORGANISATIONAL COMMUNICATION

Organisational communication will be comprised of communication that will take place internally down from the top, horizontally amongst equals and from the bottom up; and with externals, from the organisation out and from the externals in.

Types of communication may be:

■ Verbal: formal and informal meetings such as safety committee meetings or toolbox talks.
■ Written: memos, work instructions, safe working procedures, rulebooks, safety committee minutes, the safety policy and the annual report.
■ Electronic: Intranet, e-mail.
■ Posters: warnings, instructions, information.

PROCEDURES FOR RESOLVING CONFLICT AND INTRODUCING CHANGE

Conflict within the organisation can have a harmful or adverse effect although a certain amount of conflict is inevitable. The harmful effects of conflict can be resolved via a number of strategies including:

The clarification of goals and objectives. Goals and objectives should be clearly defined. Everyone should understand their roles and what they are expected to achieve in order to avoid misunderstanding and conflict.

The distribution of resources. A fair distribution of resources should be encouraged through, for example, the ability to make a case for extra materials and finance based on need. Although it is difficult to achieve a totally equitable system, organisations should strive to reduce possible causes of resentment amongst managers and staff.

Personnel policies and procedures. A just and equitable system should be in place. Rewards and promotion should be made on merit. Disciplinary/grievance procedures should be fair and even-handed. An arbitration system to resolve employer/employee disputes should be carefully considered.

Non-monetary rewards. Non-monetary rewards can be introduced where financial resources are limited, for example, flexible working hours and the use of 'perks' to recognise and reward good performance.

Leadership and management. A combative management style is more likely to lead to conflict than one which is supportive of subordinate's efforts. Managers who participate and encourage co-operation are likely to win the respect, trust and commitment of employees.

Group - team building activities. Encouraging the positive benefits of group behaviour can increase cohesiveness and reduce conflict.

Development of interpersonal/group process skills. Training on individual and group processes can lead to a better understanding of an individual's own behaviour and that of others. This can lead to improved communication and encourage a constructive approach to resolving conflicts.

Attention to **organisational processes** and the **socio-technical organisation** can also bring benefits in terms of conflict resolution. In the former the nature and structure of the organisation is moulded to encourage communication, the sharing of information and discourage unnecessary bureaucracy. The latter encourages the development of psychological and social factors, which are in keeping with the structural and technical requirements, in order to reduce negative sources of dysfunctional conflict.

The management of change and the need to be flexible are integral to an organisation's ability to adapt to its environment and the needs of its customers. Thus change is both inescapable and inevitable if the organisation is to survive. There are two main objectives to planned organisational change that need to be addressed by managers. These are:

- The improvement of the organisation's ability to cope with change.
- The need to modify individual behaviour in order to adapt to change.

The human factors aspect of introducing change is often underestimated. Senior managers who may be filled with great expectations find it hard to understand the fear and uncertainty of others. Loss and grief are just as normal reactions to change as are excitement and anticipation. In order to introduce a programme of improved performance in the introduction of planned change, a systematic, three stage process can be used to modify human behaviour:

Unfreezing. Encouraging the reduction of those forces that maintain human behaviour and encouraging the recognition of the need for change. Potential problems are identified at this stage.

Movement. Developing new attitudes or behaviour. This can be achieved by problem diagnosis, action planning and implementation.

Refreezing. Stabilising and reinforcing the new changes. The consequences of change are analysed and any necessary follow-up and stabilisation work carried out through supporting mechanisms such as policy, structure or norms.

The organisation should recognise that people are not detached from their work but have a sense of emotional involvement. People are resistant to change for many reasons including security, habit, fear of the unknown, mistrust of management intentions and even sheer inconvenience. Unfreezing involves removing these barriers by identifying them and providing the appropriate stimuli in order to reduce resistance. This can be achieved by the creation of an environment of shared trust and commitment with, for example, new contracts or agreements and the development of the consultative processes

WORKPLACE REPRESENTATION ON SAFETY COMMITTEES

General points

The duty of employers to consult all employees via safety representatives was enshrined in sections 2(4) to 2(7) of the Health and Safety at Work Act, etc (HASAWA) 1974. However section 2(5) which gave all employees the right to elect safety representatives was repealed by the Employment Protection Act 1975. Thus only those workplaces where workers are represented by officially recognised trades unions are covered by this section of the HASAWA 1974. This requirement was translated into the Safety Representatives and Safety Committees Regulations (SRSC) 1977.

The MHSWR 1992 amended the SRSC Regulations 1977 by stipulating the matters on which the employer must consult. (Note: it was the 1992 version of the MHSWR that made these amendments to the SRSC Regulations 1977; since then MHSWR 1992 has been formally updated in the 1999 version of the Regulations).

The matters on which an employer must consult are:

- Measures introduced into the workplace which may affect employees' health & safety.
- The appointment of competent persons.
- Any health and safety information that the employer is obliged to provide by law.
- The planning and organisation of any health and safety training that the employer is obliged to provide by law.
- The health and safety consequences of the planning and introduction of new technology into the workplace.

The SRSC Regulations only apply to safety representatives from recognised trades unions leaving many non-unionised workers without any consultation rights. This situation was rectified to an extent by the introduction of the Health & Safety (Consultation with Employees) Regulations (HSCER) 1996. It should be noted that the roles and functions of trade union representatives remains unchanged and that the two regulations are designed to sit side-by-side with each other - the application depending on union status.

While the HSCER 1996 make reference to elected Representatives of Employee Safety (RoESs) where the employer chooses not to consult the workforce directly, no right to form or for employees to attend a committee is conferred. The only legal requirement to form a safety committee is under the SRSC Regulations 1977. The Health and Safety Commission (HSC) has not introduced into its approved Code of Practice (ACOP) relating to these regulations advice on safety committees, but it has published guidance notes.

Basic objectives of safety committees

- The promotion of co-operation between employers and employees in investigating, developing and carrying out measures to ensure the health and safety at work of employees.
- To act as a focus for employee participation in the prevention of accidents and avoidance of industrial diseases.

Functions of safety committees

To consider the circumstances of individual accidents and cases of notifiable diseases, and to study accident statistics and trends, so that reports can be made to management on unsafe and unhealthy conditions and practices, together with recommendations for corrective action;

- To examine safety audit reports on a similar basis.
- To consider reports and information supplied by factory inspectors.
- To assist in the development of works safety rules and safe systems of work.
- To conduct periodic inspections of the workplace, its plant, equipment and amenities.
- To monitor the effectiveness of safety training, communications and publicity.
- To provide a link with the Inspectorate.

Membership

Whilst one of the functions of a safety representative is to attend the safety committee, the SRSC Regulations 1977 do not give every Safety Representative the right to attend safety committee meetings. The SRSC Regulations 1977 do not specify the quorum for committee membership. The guidance given with the Code of Practice attached to the Regulations is that membership of the committee is a matter for joint consultation. The HSCER 1996 does not establish specific rights to set up or attend safety committees.

The committee should be reasonably compact, subject to allowing for the adequate representation of the interests of management and all the employees.

There should be a close but flexible relationship between safety representatives and the safety committee, but it should be fully understood that a safety representative is not appointed by the safety committee or vice versa. Neither is responsible to or for the other.

Management representation should include line managers, supervisors, works engineers and personnel officers as well as specialist medical and safety advisers. The management representatives should have the authority to take action on committee recommendations and should have the knowledge and expertise to cover all aspects of health and safety management.

Meetings

Meetings should be held as often as necessary and should be programmed well in advance. Minutes should be taken and distributed or displayed for everyone concerned.

Arrangements of individual Workplaces

Certain matters will need to be decided at workplace level, namely:

1.   The division of the conduct of activities in which both employee representatives and safety committees might become involved.

2.   The objectives or terms of reference of the safety committee.

3.   The membership and structure of the safety committee.

4.   Whether the safety committee should be made responsible for publicising matters notified by safety representatives and any remedial action which has been jointly approved.

A6.6 - Job factors

The effect of job factors on the probability of human error

TASK COMPLEXITY

There is probably a normal distribution of task complexity associated with the probability of human error. Highly complex tasks have many opportunities for error; and error can sneak into simple tasks because of boredom and distractions.

EFFECTS OF PATTERNS OF EMPLOYMENT

Most people would agree that there is a clear link between the hours of work and degradation in human performance. The Working Time Regulations, with many exceptions and exclusions, place a general limit to the working week of 48 hours. Night workers should not exceed an average of 8 hours for each 24-hour period. Both of these 'limits' are averaged over a 17-week period. This would, therefore, seem to be the starting point for examining the effects that patterns of employment and shift work have on the individual.

Research has demonstrated a clear relationship between the length of the working day and performance, in terms of productivity, and accidents. There is, however, a great deal of individual variation interrelated with individual strength, health and nutrition. This makes a clear link difficult to establish but there appears to be a clear general deterioration if the working day exceeds 10 hours.

For the traditional day-worker accident rates tend to increase at the start of the working period through to mid-morning. The rate then decreases as the morning progresses. There is a slight increase just after lunchtime towards mid-afternoon. The rate then levels off or slightly declines towards the end of the working day.

Rest pauses perform both a physical and social function. Rest pauses should be of sufficient duration to allow the oxygen debt incurred by heavy work to be paid off. However, in light work frequent short breaks appear to improve performance and reduce human errors. The social function can often outweigh the physical benefits of rest pauses.

The choice of working patterns and rest pauses made by the organisation is a balance between the needs of production and optimising human performance.

PAYMENT SYSTEMS

The most important factor for many individuals however is the payment considerations that can often over-ride those such as the disruption of family life produced by nightshifts. Thus many people who work 'anti-social' hours are compensated financially for doing so. This decreases in areas of high unemployment where competition for jobs is greater.

The bonus system of payment can create problems when employees are rushing to get the work done. Shortcuts will be taken and errors can occur.

SHIFT WORK

For night workers the accident rate tends to be high at the start of the working period and then drops towards the break periods. Again they tend to decline towards the end of the shift.

Shift working disturbs the individual's diurnal rhythm which produces impaired sleeping patterns. The most physically disruptive shift pattern appears to be a rapid three-way system. Ironically many workers prefer this to other systems because it disrupts their social life the least. The social effects of disruption to factors such as family life, however, appear to outweigh the physical effects.

APPLICATION OF TASK ANALYSIS

Task analysis can be used in the development of a safe system of work. A type of task analysis known as job safety analysis (SREDIM) can be used. This involves the following steps:

1. Select the task.
2. Reduce the task to steps.
3. Evaluate the risk at each step and put in appropriate controls.
4. Develop the safe system.
5. Implement the safe system.
6. Monitor and review.

Analysis of the task must consider not only the job to be done, but also the environment where it is to be done, to allow a full consideration of the hazards to be made. Job/task safety analysis consists of a formal step by step review of the work to be carried out. All aspects of the task should be considered and recorded in writing to ensure that nothing is overlooked. Typical considerations would be:

- How is the task carried out?
- Where is the task carried out?
- What is used?
- What are the current controls?
- Are the controls adequate?
- Do operators use the controls correctly?
- Behavioural factors operators/supervisors (error considerations).

The objective is to establish the hazards and controls at each stage of the procedure to ensure a safe result. How the progress of work, in particular safety arrangements, will be monitored should be considered. Any special requirements for monitoring should be specified during the planning stage, e.g. gas testing, temperature or pressure levels, measurement of emissions.

All of the cars taken in task analysis will help ensure that there is no or very little margin for error.

Define the safe methods

- Where possible, hazards should be eliminated at source. Residual hazards should be evaluated and controlled.
- Specific responsibilities at various stages and the identity of the person in control of work should be clearly identified.
- The need for protective or special equipment should also be identified as should the need for the provision of temporary protection, guards or barriers.
- Adequate emergency procedures should be in place, or developed, to control likely incidents e.g. fire, spillage.
- If there is a possibility that injury could result during the task, consideration of rescue methods should take place during this stage.
- The system should be checked against three main criteria:
  1. It should adequately control hazards associated with the task.
  2. It should comply with company standards.
  3. It should comply with relevant legal standards.

Implementation

Once the system has been developed and agreed, preparation for implementation can proceed. Provision for the communication of relevant information to all involved or affected should be fundamental to any system of work.

Importance of training

The Provision and Use of Work Equipment Regulations (PUWER) 1998, require that supervisors be adequately trained to enable them to identify the hazards and control strategies associated with work under their control. Where hazards cannot be eliminated and the risks reduced, procedures to ensure a more formal safe method of work known as a permit to work system must be devised. Job / task analysis is not only necessary to identify the hazards and controls, but is essential for preparing written procedures and specifying (comprehensive training plans) the skill and knowledge content of the work to be carried out. The training plans will not only identify the sequence of work, but often the work rate, as sometimes timeliness is an important consideration, particularly in relation to certain chemical manufacturing processes. The analysis is then incorporated in job training programmes.

- For certain high risk tasks this will often involve a course to develop knowledge and understanding. This is then followed by practical application either utilising a work simulator (e.g. train driver / aircraft pilot) or close one to one supervision (e.g. fork lift truck driver).
- Where training requirements have been identified, this should be conducted or confirmed.
- The provision and availability of any required equipment or materials should be confirmed.
- The process of implementation will involve:
  - The person in charge of work must ensure that elements outlined in the Planning and Organisation stages are clearly understood and implemented.
  - If problems arise which necessitate modification to the system, formal approval and documentation should be made.
  - Any permanent record of any monitoring must be kept and regularly checked by a member of the management team.

Control

Various methods of control are available. Selection and application should reflect the level of risk in the activity, i.e. permit to work systems and method statements.

Monitoring

SSW should not be simply imposed upon the people responsible for their operation. A formal system of monitoring and feedback should be implemented and records kept of compliance and effectiveness.

Ergonomically designed control systems in relation to human reliability

THE EMPLOYEE AND THE WORKSTATION AS A SYSTEM

General points - definition

Ergonomics can be defined as:

"the study of the relationship between the person, the equipment with which they work and the physical environment in which this person-machine system operates."

It is a broad area of study, which includes the disciplines of psychology, physiology, anatomy and design engineering.

Ergonomics has a person at the centre of the study where their capabilities and fallibilities are considered in order to, ultimately, eliminate the potential for human error. It is also the study of ways to prevent the so-called 'ergonomic illnesses': work-related musculoskeletal disorders. These areas of ill health are usually insidious and may lead to disability. They stem from poorly designed machines, tools, task and workplace. Research has shown that there are about one million cases of work-related musculoskeletal disorders annually in England and Wales.

DEGRADATION OF HUMAN PERFORMANCE RESULTING FROM POORLY DESIGNED WORKSTATIONS

Man works within certain boundaries, which must be recognised for all situations. However, even when human beings work within their limitations, there will still be degradation in performance. Why, when and how degradation occurs needs to be understood in order to make allowances for or to remedy the situation.

The aims of ergonomics, therefore, are to design the equipment and the working environment to fit the needs and capabilities of the individual, i.e. fitting the task to the individual, and to ensure that the physical and mental well being of the individual are being met. This involves a consideration of psychological and physical factors, including the work system, training, body dimensions, intelligence, noise, temperature and lighting.

The ergonomic concept of the design of a working system involving both man and machine with a view to, say, preventing possible accidents, is to observe both man and machine together as a combined working unit, observing the areas where correlation is important and the extent of the effectiveness of that relationship. Thus at the design stage it is necessary to concentrate on what is required from the equipment and what from the human, when the machine and its user are working together.

PROCESS AND EQUIPMENT DESIGN

The layout of controls and displays can influence the safety of the system. Typical problems are:

- Switches which can be inadvertently knocked on.
- Control panel layouts which are difficult to understand.
- Displays which force the user to bend or stretch to read them properly.
- Badly identified controls which the operator could select by mistake.
- Emergency stop buttons which are difficult to reach.

Systematic analysis of how people actually use equipment can highlight problems that should be designed out, underlining the importance of manufacturers, designers and installers applying ergonomic principles. When designing control systems it is important to consider what people expect (their stereotypical expectations).

At the person-machine interface the operator will have to manipulate parts of the machine to pass a message to it; the machine will act according to the message received and pass a message back to the operator. The operator must be trained to communicate in a way the machine understands and the machine must be manufactured to be able to act according to instructions and communicate in an understandable way with the operator. It would be impossible to carry out a task if every time you pressed the red button you got a different response. We all know the frustration when using a computer and you cannot get it to do what you want simply because you do not know the right key to press or the right icon to click on. There has been an attempt in recent years to make computer software 'user friendly', which means the operator and the computer can understand each other.

The *Man-Machine Interface*, emphasising the performance of the human information processing system. Note that the broken lines underline that displays and controls are links between the operator and the machine.

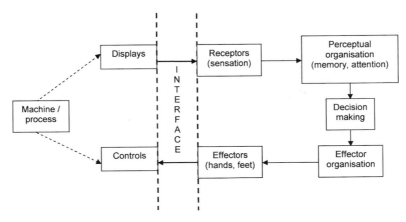

Figure A6-13: Man-machine interface.

Source: Ridley, J; Safety at Work; Fourth Edition; 1994.

The figure above shows the system with the imaginary plane between the human and the machine, known as the interface. The message passed by the machine must be of a type compatible with the human senses. The human must process that information, make a decision and then give a response.

If too much information is given the short-term memory will not be able to handle it and error may occur. It is vital that the design of the machine takes into consideration the limitations of the human information processing system.

Displays and controls must be designed with human expectations in mind.

Which way do we expect to turn a tap or valve to close it, clockwise or anti-clockwise?

Figure A6-14: Tap. *Source: ACT.*

In an emergency situation in a chemical plant this is crucial. Emergency situations do not allow for lengthy thinking time and humans act instinctively, their actions based on past experiences and expectations. The designer must consider questions such as:

- What colour do we expect the start button to be?
- Where do we expect the emergency stop to be?
- Do we expect the hot tap to be on the left and the cold on the right or vice-versa?

The decisions someone takes based on what they expect can have consequences ranging from a 'near miss situation' to a catastrophe.

The design of control boards should take into account the expectations of human beings, their information processing limitations and their physical capabilities. Operators have taken decisions based on misplaced expectations with tragic results.

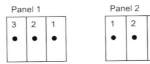

Figure A6-15: Panel/s diagram. *Source: ACT.*

Control buttons on a panel, which were a mirror image of each other, were the cause of an operator choosing the wrong one in an emergency situation. They were set up this way to make the wiring easier.

In the UK switches are pressed down for on, while in the USA they are pressed up for on.

Figure A6-16: Switch diagram. *Source: ACT.*

If we consider 'fail safe' devices, it would be more logical to have the USA systems for switches. Gravity would cause a switch to drop if it was faulty, and with the UK system this would be a 'fail to danger' situation, that is, the switch would fall causing the power to be present when it may not be desired or safe.

In most accidents people have been found to be the instigators or have not adequately intervened in the situation. For almost all cases this has not been due to wilfulness, but for a variety of reasons a wrong decision was made. On the other hand were it not for the quick thinking and skilful intervention of people, there would be many more accidents. Many very poor procedures are held together by skilful operatives.

A further consideration in the design of control systems is the science of anthropometry. This is the science of the measurement of human bodily dimensions applied to the space in which the operator works.

The human body is flexible and can adapt to operating in uncomfortable positions. Over time damage will result because of the poor posture caused by badly designed workspaces.

ELEMENTARY PHYSIOLOGY AND ANTHROPOMETRY

The general design of machines and workspace has not always taken account of the human bodily dimensions. This was demonstrated by researchers at the Cranfield Institute of Technology who created 'Cranfield Man'. They examined the positions of controls on a horizontal lathe and compared them to the bodily dimensions of an average human being. The large discrepancies between the two sets of measurements led the researchers to create the man who could use the lathe with comfort.

'Cranfield Man' - 1.35m Tall With A 2.44m Arm Span:

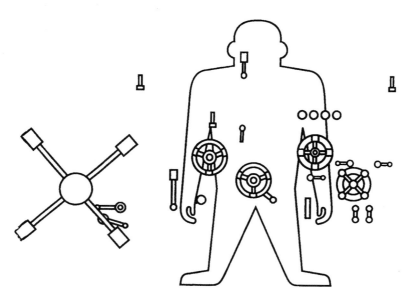

Figure A6-17: Cranfield man.

Source: Stranks, J; Human Factors and Safety; 1994.

The physical dimensions of the average operator compared with those of 'Cranfield man'

Average Operator	Dimensions	Operator who would suit these controls ('Cranfield Man')
1.75m	Height	1.35m
0.48m	Shoulder width	0.61m
1.83m	Arm span	2.44m
1.07m	Elbow height	0.76

Figure A6-18: Physical dimensions comparison.

Source: Stranks, J; Human Factors and Safety; 1994.

Anthropometry can also find useful application when considering the need to prevent access to dangerous parts of machinery. Here, the measurements of bodily dimensions can be used in the safe placing of barriers from danger points and from necessary, permissible openings in fixed guards. Placed beyond a certain distance, a person should not be able to reach into the danger zone.

CLASSICAL, ERROR AND SYSTEM ERGONOMICS - EXAMPLES OF APPLICATIONS

Some tasks are better performed by people than machines, and vice versa. For example, a computer can make mathematical calculations far quicker than a human being. A human, in cases of unplanned events, can assess a situation and make an informed judgement as to how to proceed. A computer, however, would continue with the program until it could go no further and then grind to a halt or crash. The consideration of what is best done by what or whom is known as the allocation of function. The decision to use people, to automate a process or any combination in between these extremes does not rest solely on health and safety factors. The reasons may also rest on social and political issues. Human beings are creative creatures and may feel under-utilised when just tending machines. A comparison between people and machines is shown below:

Advantages / People	Disadvantages / Machines
Adaptable and flexible	Relatively inflexible
Can detect minute stimuli and assess small changes	Can detect if programmed, but not assess
Can interpolate and use judgement	Can do neither
Can synthesise and learn from experience	Can do neither

Advantages / Machines	Disadvantages / People
Can operate in hostile environments	Lower capability
Fast response to emergency signals	Slow response
Can apply large forces smoothly	Can apply large forces coarsely
Information storage: large short-term memory	Easily distracted: limited short-term memory
Perform routine repetitive task reliably	Not reliable for this
Compute fast and accurately	Compute slowly and inaccurately
Can operate for long periods without maintenance	Suffer relatively soon from fatigue and monotony

Figure A6-19: Comparison between people and machines.   *Source: Stranks, J; Human Factors and Safety; 1994.*

A schematic representation of the shift in the man-machine interface and change in allocation of function in different types of vehicle production.

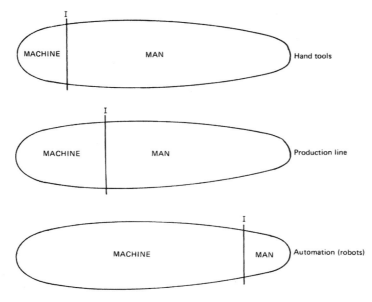

Figure A6-20: Man/machine interface.   *Source: Ridley, J; Safety at Work; Fourth Edition; 1994.*

This represents three types of manufacturing process in the production of motor vehicles. The first represents the manufacture of a car mostly by hand machining. The worker is skilled and creative and satisfaction is derived from the high quality finished product. The second is where the worker assembles pre-formed car body parts using power tools. This is repetitive and does not allow for creativity. The third represents the automation of the car building process where the person has a monitoring and maintenance role. Each process requires a different input from the person and has different problems.

Often the part played by the person is just doing what is left over after the machine has done its bit. This results in a fragmented and piecemeal job for the person, who is often left to hold together a badly designed system. This allocation of function is susceptible to safety problems.

Whatever the allocation of function, ergonomics can be used to find solutions to the problems.

The allocation of function can be decided in a number of ways. Fitts drew up a list of the relative advantages of men and machines. The "Fitts List" below has been modified by Singleton.

Property	Machine performance	Human performance
Speed	Much superior Consistent at any level Large constant standard forces and power available	Lag one second 2 horse-power for about ten seconds 0.5 horse-power for a few minutes 0.2 horse-power for continuous work over a day
Consistency	Ideal for - routine, repetition and precision	Not reliable - should be monitored Subject to learning and fatigue
Complex activities	Multi-channel	Single-channel Low information throughput
Memory	Best for literal reproduction and short-term storage	Large store multiple access Better for principles and strategies
Reasoning	Good deductive Tedious to reprogramme	Good inductive Easy to reprogramme
Computation	Fast, accurate Poor at error correction	Slow Subject to error Good at error correction

Input	Can detect features outside range of human capabilities Insensitive to extraneous stimuli Poor pattern detection	Wide range (1012) and variety of small stimuli dealt with by one unit, e.g. eye deals with relative location, movement and colour Affected by heat, cold, noise and vibration Good pattern detection Can detect very low signals Can detect signal in high noise levels
Overload reliability	Sudden breakdown	Gradual breakdown
Intelligence	None Incapable of goal switching or strategy switching without direction	Can deal with unpredicted and unpredictable Can anticipate Can adapt
Manipulative abilities	Specific	Great versatility and mobility

Figure A6-21: An updated version of the Fitts list (from Singleton).

Source: Ridley, J; Safety at Work; Fourth Edition; 1994.

Examples of applications

Aircraft cockpit

An example of the need for good ergonomic design was highlighted in the training of pilots during the Second World War. Poor design of controls and instruments in aircraft cockpits meant that pilots often made fatal mistakes such as operating the flaps instead of the undercarriage and misreading altimeters. Even today, the aviation industry is the focus of much ergonomics research because of the ever-increasing mental demands on the flight crew. To give some perspective, a 1940s aeroplane typically had 20 instruments, a 1950s jet about 50, a 1960s airliner about 180, and current airliners have around 450!

In less hazardous activities, the need for good ergonomic design has permeated every aspect of modern life. Drivers of modern motor vehicles reap the benefit of detailed research and development by vehicle manufacturers. It is a relatively easy to design a formula one racing car cockpit for a particular driver; however, designing a car for the mass market is far more difficult. People differ from each other in many ways such as height, weight and strength. Less obvious, is the mental or cognitive aspects such as the ability to perceive and interpret information. Sometimes, it can be very difficult to achieve acceptable solutions.

In some occupations the ability to tolerate human error is drastically reduced because of the potentially catastrophic consequences. For example, the chemical and nuclear industries, and in aviation - including air traffic control.

Production process control panels

The need for good ergonomics is safety critical as can be illustrated by the incident at Three Mile Island nuclear accident. One of the factors leading to the reactor core damage and radioactive water loss at Three Mile Island was a poorly designed control panel that featured:

- Controls that went off scale.
- Key indicators that were sited out of view.
- Hundreds of alarms that were illogically arranged with no means of isolating the unimportant ones were provided.

This information overload did not allow control staff to react as the situation demanded. In a control room design, for example, the designer must consider the room layout in order to ensure:

- That all operators can see each other and all relevant instrumentation.
- That audible warnings are clearly understood and cannot be masked by other sounds.
- That workstations are designed to ensure that displays are clear and that controls are easily identified and operated.
- That lighting is provided which allows clear definition and does not compromise visual displays through reflections or glare.

Routemaster drivers' cabs

London Transport were alive to the ergonomic principles in the design of the driver's cab for the Routemaster Bus. The fact that drivers themselves were asked to take part in tests leading to the eventual design accepted as successful was in itself a good thing from the angle of psychological strategy. The driver's cab and the layout of the controls received most thought and the opinions of physiologists and other medical authorities were sought in order to evolve the best relative positioning of controls, so that the driver could sit in the most suitable position for obtaining the best field of vision and enabling quick responses for movement of the various controls. A mock-up of the cab was made in which various adjustments could take place, such as the angle between the seat and the squab, the position and angle of the footplate, the pedal travel and the steering column angle. A sufficient amount of adjustment was allowed to cover the sizes of most men of between 5'6" (1.68 metres) and 6'1" (1.83 metres). A number of men, including drivers' representatives, were asked to adjust the various components to what seemed to them the most suitable positions, and such positions were recorded. From such information, various points of detail were decided and incorporated in the final design of the Routemaster.

Crane cabs

Similarly, the British Iron and Steel Association carried out work along ergonomic principles on the design and layout of crane cabs. In the traditional type of cabin, even though the driver stood, it was often difficult for him to obtain a satisfactory view of operations; the control handles moved in awkward semi-circles and he was unprotected from the dust, fumes and heat of the shop in a foundry (he is likely to be standing over the controls for a proportion of his working time). In the redesigned cab, the driver sits on a seat which is adjustable to 90% accuracy of all possible sizes, a full view of the working area is possible, the controls are within easy reach and move in straight lines to permit ease and delicacy of control, and the provision of filtered and refrigerated air, where necessary, ensures cool and comfortable working conditions.

Display screen equipment (DSE)

The DSE is the main means of communication between person and computer and is usually comprised of a display screen and keyboard. Most VDU work deals with data enquiries, dialogue or data entry. However, unless ergonomic considerations, such as position, lighting, seating arrangements, etc., are taken into account, those working for long periods with VDUs can suffer from eyestrain, backache, stress and related disorders. New display screen equipment legislation has introduced ergonomic factors into the design of workstations.

Eyestrain can be caused by excessive concentration, reflections on the screen, glare, flickering, poor posture and blurred characters on the screen. Posture is also a cause of backache and tired muscles. Therefore, it is obvious that it is not enough merely to place a VDU in an office; the whole office design needs to be considered. Job design and environmental design must go hand in hand, along with consideration of rest breaks for those who work on VDUs for long prolonged periods.

Environmental hazards, such as static electricity build-up, noise, heat and radiation, also need careful consideration.

The Display Screen Equipment Regulations (DSE) 1992 contains a schedule of minimum standards to be met by display screen equipment first used after 1992.

The schedule covers:

- Character definition.
- Character spacing.
- Stability of image.
- Brightness and contrast.
- Swivel and tilt of screen.
- Maximum glare.
- Tiltable and separate keyboard.
- Space in front of the keyboard.
- Matt keyboard surface.
- Legible keyboard symbols.
- Size of desk.
- Non-reflective surface of desk.
- Adjustable chair.
- Footrest on request.

- Sufficient space around workstation.
- Adjustable chair.
- Footrest on request.
- Adequate environmental factors including:
  - Lighting.
  - Noise levels.
  - Heat.
  - Radiation.
  - Humidity.
- Suitable software for the user.
- Application of the principles of software ergonomics.
- No qualitative or quantitative checking without the user's knowledge.

Where equipment and workstations comply to the ergonomic requirements contained in British Standard BS 7179 they will also comply with the minimum requirements contained in the Schedule to the DSE Regulations 1992.

Other examples

Many other examples of 'ergonomically designed' products can be given. There is the cordless switchboard of the Post Office in which the traditional vertical board has been eliminated, the keys are easily accessible to the operator, the dial is superseded by push buttons and the lights are always visible even in bright sunlight but produce no glare.

The fitting bench designed by the Boot, Shoe and Allied Trades Research Association enables the operator to work in the most suitable position with everything he uses readily to hand. Such things as instrument dials, together with their calibration and figuring, and the shape and layout of control knobs on panels have received a great deal of attention, in close collaboration with the eventual user.

A further example of an ergonomically designed workplace is the dentist's surgery with its easily adjustable couch chair for patients and noiseless, high-speed instruments that help to put patients at their ease, at least in comparison with the old hand-pedalled variety.

Fortunately for engineers and designers alike, the human being is not rigidly constructed but possesses great adaptability or, in technical parlance, a wide tolerance. It is this adaptability that has forced man into work situations to which he/she is not really adapted, to the detriment of his psychological well-being and his physical performance as well as his/her use of his mental powers.

Effect of stressors on human reliability

PHYSICAL STRESSORS

The performance of the human system is only at an optimum within certain environmental limits. Physical conditions such as noise, glare and lighting level, dust and fumes etc. will influence the individual. For example, noise can affect concentration at levels well below the levels dictated by the Noise at Work Regulations (NWR) 1989. A noise source at 5dB above ambient is sufficient to be a 'nuisance' and affect concentration. These, and other physical stressors such as lighting (too much, too little) and high and low temperatures, can affect on the accuracy of detection of information and the speed of processing information.

It is evident that human beings, unlike machines, rarely breakdown completely. They are more likely to show a slight degradation of performance over a wide range of environmental conditions that can be difficult to detect. This results in the maintenance of individual's function as they can maintain some sort of functioning long after they have passed the peak of their performance, but it also blurs the point at which they should stop in order to avoid errors. Regulations and good practice on working hours for coach drivers, hospital doctors and others must wrestle with the problem of matching specific limits with the multitude of factors that can affect performance.

Performance is degraded under the following types of situations:

- Working for too lengthy a period which produces fatigue.
- Working at times of day when body mechanisms are not functioning efficiently, i.e. the diurnal rhythm is disturbed.
- Loss of motivation to perform.
- Lack of stimulation resulting in low arousal.
- Working under conditions of conflict, threat, both physical and psychological, or conditions that threaten the body's homeostatic or coping mechanism and cause stress.

The relationship between the length of the working day and performance is not clear. Studies have suggested that there is a highly significant reduction in output and an increased risk of accidents if a working day of about ten hours is exceeded. Obviously this will vary with workload, intensity of work and any outside activities undertaken by the individual. It should be appreciated that this dip in performance applies to mental work as well as physical activities.

FATIGUE AND STRESS

Repetitive or awkward movement or having to stay in the same position for long periods at a time can result in muscular fatigue. Poorly designed tasks and workstations may mean that the operative has to sit awkwardly for long periods or stretch constantly to reach operating buttons or levers. If the task is machine-paced then there is little or no scope for rest and this can result in high levels of stress as well as muscular fatigue.

Medical opinion states that possibly 70% of patients being treated have conditions that have their origins in stress. Physical manifestations of mental stress can be very serious: coronary heart disease, bronchial asthma, etc. Change in the workplace has meant for most people that the pace has speeded up and increasing numbers are unable to cope with it.

Causes of stress can be divided into two groups: environmental and psychological. The environmental stressors are things such as bodily injury, noise, extremes of temperature, etc. The psychological stressors include periods of intense mental activity, being unable to achieve what is required, physical or social isolation, etc.

The body's response to stress is to increase the secretion of the hormone adrenaline. This increases muscle tension and heart rate to prepare the body for fight or flight, a primitive response not really appropriate for modern industrial society. If this state is maintained for long periods it can result in such conditions as high blood pressure, gastric ulcers, etc. In this state of agitation, the individual is prone to make errors. Ergonomic considerations can go a long way to relieving or even preventing stress. Task design, machine design, operator-controlled pace and appropriate rest periods can all help reduce fatigue and stress, thereby reducing error and accidents.

Principles of health & safety law

Contents

This page is intentionally blank

ELEMENT A7 - PRINCIPLES OF HEALTH AND SAFETY LAW

This page is intentionally blank

A7.1 - Sources and types of law

Sources of law

STATUTE LAW

Statute law is a source of both criminal and civil law. Some statutes such as the Health and Safety at Work etc. Act (HASAWA) 1974 are entirely criminal law. Similarly some statutes are actionable only under civil law (e.g. the Occupiers' Liability Act 1957).

It must be understood, however, that many health and safety related statutes may be used both as a basis for prosecution and as a platform for civil actions relating to personal injury suffered in the workplace.

Statute law consists of primary legislation (Acts of Parliament) and delegated legislation such as regulations (e.g. the Management of Health and Safety at Work Regulations (MHSWR) 1999) and Orders.

UK acts of Parliament and regulations

Parliament may make law as it sees fit, subject to the rules of continued membership of the European Union, and may, for example, repeal both earlier statutes or overrule common law (case law developed by the courts). Statute law often starts life as a consultative document (i.e. a green paper) and then proceeds as a bill. The bill is debated in stages, namely:

- First Reading (permission for printing).
- Second Reading (policy debate).
- Committee Stage (clauses considered in detail).
- Report (report of amendments made at Committee Stage).
- Third Reading (finalised bill).

This procedure has to be followed in both the Commons and House of Lords before the Bill can receive Royal Assent. This is a lengthy procedure which explains why some Bills never become law (particularly Private Members' Bills).

Where the House of Commons and the House of Lords disagree over the same bill, the House of Lords may delay the bill by up to one year. After this the Act becomes law on the day on which the Royal Assent is given or on a date which the Act provides.

Some Acts allow delegated legislation such as regulations to be made by Ministers of the Crown. In some cases, these statutory instruments can be laid before Parliament for 40 days before they can come into force rather than being positively voted upon. During this period a member may propose a negative affirmation to veto the statutory instrument. Delegated legislation is, therefore, particularly important especially in the changing field of safety in the workplace.

European Directives and regulations

The European Union (EU) influences health and safety legislation in the UK, for example, the Working Time Directive.

Since the Single European Act 1986 the EU has had an interest in harmonising working conditions. In 1986 Article 118A was introduced to enable Directives to be made on this subject. (Note: this Article has been renumbered under the Treaty of Amsterdam to Article 95.) They are made by a system known as qualified majority voting. In this system, each member state casts a number of votes allocated according to their population size and no single state has the power of veto. Directives set out the requirements of the EU to control agreed health and safety matters. Each member state is required by the Directive to enact these requirements in their state law. This requirement to do so is enforceable by the EU.

In the case of the UK, EU Directives are implemented by the creation of appropriate statutes. For example, In the case of Health and Safety EU requirements are implemented using the delegated facility of the HASAWA. An example of this process was the six sets of regulations which became law in 1993 (the so called 'six pack'). The EU Directives through this process are now an integral part of UK law.

COMMON LAW

Nature and development

Common law, rather than being laid down by Parliament, has traditionally grown up over the centuries.

Judicial precedent

Common Law is often referred to as Judge made law. The judgements made create binding precedents on subsequent similar cases on all lower courts. Decisions made by courts of equal status create persuasive precedent only. A decision made by the House of Lords would be binding on all lower courts. The Court of Appeal binds all lower courts (i.e. High Court, County Court, Employment Appeals Tribunals and Tribunals).

There is scope for the courts to interpret such precedents in the light of changing circumstances. This does allow some deviation from an established precedent, but the decision making has to be justified.

An example of this arose in the late 70's before the Road Traffic Act made it compulsory to wear front seat belts. A number of cases went to the High Court involving claimants who had not been wearing a seat belt. The High Court judges reduced their compensation by differing amounts. Finally the Court of Appeal decided the matter. In Froom v Butcher (CA) (1975) (Not listed in the syllabus). It was held that compensation should be reduced by up to 25% if a person who was involved in a car accident was not wearing a seat belt.

Since 1966 the House of Lords is no longer bound to follow its own decisions but it would be rare for the House of Lords to overrule a previous precedent.

Whereas common law is reliant on precedent for its existence and application, this does not apply to statute law. This does not mean that precedent and case law do not exist for statute law. Statute law attempts to establish clear obligations to be followed. However the application of the law can reveal some variance of perspective. It is sometimes only when a case is brought to court that the correct perspective can be confirmed. This decision in a particular case sets a precedent. A decision in a civil case, for example, involving personal injury, may be referred to in respect of the standard applicable to safety related statutes.

Types of law

CRIMINAL LAW

Purpose

Society (the state) decides the standards which should be adhered to maintain a safe and secure existence for all in the community. Offences against the state are actionable through the criminal court system and guilt or innocence is decided in relation to the perceived offence. Cases are decided 'beyond reasonable doubt', because the sanctions available to the courts may be severe and include financial punishment and or imprisonment. Those accused are presumed innocent until proven guilty for all offences, except offences brought under HASAWA 1974, where the burden of proof is reversed and the accused must prove their innocence.

Sanctions

A number of sanctions may be imposed on a person or organisation found guilty of a criminal offence. These are prescribed by the relevant legislation. They may include restriction on activities or punishment. These sanctions are usually brought about by the State, though there is some scope to bring private prosecutions. In a case involving contravention of health and safety legislation such as HASAWA 1974 the prosecution is brought by the Health & Safety Executive or Local Authority - (Environmental Health Officer).

In a criminal case the person charged is known as the accused. The outcome of a trial is a verdict of "guilty" or "not guilty" or, in Scotland, "not proven". Penalties are intended as a punishment, although compensation may be ordered separately by the court.

Manslaughter

When employees are killed at work their employer may be successfully prosecuted for manslaughter.

For example, in 1997 the Managing Director of a transport firm was imprisoned for 12 months. An employee, who was not wearing personal protective equipment, died after being sprayed in the face with a chemical used in the manufacture of pesticides.

A corporation may also be found guilty of manslaughter; for example, OLL Ltd was found guilty after 4 teenagers drowned on an activity holiday in Lyme Bay, Dorset. Proof of corporate manslaughter currently requires establishing gross negligence on the part of the company's controlling mind. However, the Corporate Manslaughter and Corporate Homicide Act 2007, which received Royal Assent on 26 July 2007 and comes into force on 6 April 2008, is not reliant on finding a controlling mind individual. It allows for an organisation to be prosecuted for Corporate Manslaughter by looking at the wider corporate picture.

Persons in authority can be called to account, particularly where an accident has occurred that could have been avoided if the person had taken such action as lay within the normal routine of his job.

Delegation of a job does not in itself absolve that person from responsibility, since they must satisfy themself (ensure) that such delegation is effective.

Sanctions available at criminal law include the restriction or improvement of a situation or activity (i.e. a prohibition or improvement notice) or the imposition of penalty (i.e. fine or imprisonment). Restrictions do not usually need the confirmation of a court as they are depicted in legislation, and authority to impose them is given in the same legislation. They will tend to be applied prior to or instead of going to court to receive a penalty. An example of this is the serving of a prohibition notice by the Health and Safety Executive (HSE).

There are three categories of conviction:

Summary conviction	Case taken in a Magistrates court (No Jury) - less serious offences.
Triable either way	Defendant and prosecution can make representation for trial by jury and higher sentencing powers of the Crown Court or in Magistrates' Court.
	The defendant can choose the Court, but the Magistrates can refer the case to a higher court for sentencing.
Conviction on indictment	Case is tried by a judge and jury in the Crown Court. This is for serious crimes and penalties are higher than those available to magistrates.
	The maximum fine a magistrate can impose for most health and safety infringements is £5000, for example, breaches of Section 7 of the HASAWA 1974 (relating to the employee); also Sections 8 and 9, subordinate regulations and other relevant legislation.
	The maximum penalty that a magistrate can impose for breaches of Sections 2-6 of the HASAWA 1974 and other sections of HASAWA 1974 relating to breaches of improvement/prohibition notices and court remedy orders is £20,000 for each offence.
	In addition to this, magistrates may impose a prison sentence of up to six months for an offence which required a licence to be held, such as the removal of asbestos, or for failing to comply with an improvement/prohibition notice.
	On indictment (i.e. a case heard in the Crown Court) the penalties are increased to an unlimited fine, two years in prison, or both. For a conviction relating to manslaughter, the court can impose a sentence of up to 25 years' imprisonment.

CIVIL LAW

Purpose

Civil law exists in order to regulate disputes between individuals over the rights and obligations people have when dealing with each other. There are many branches of civil law including contract law and the law of tort. Contract law deals with the legally binding relationships which individuals enter into, whereas tort law is aimed at redressing the wrongs committed by one person against another. Examples of torts include defamation and negligence.

The branches of civil law applicable to heath & safety at work are "contract law", "employment law" and the law of "tort". A tort is a civil wrong committed by one party against another. The tort most relevant to health & safety is that of "negligence". Negligence together with action for breach of statutory duty is the most common cause of action for injury caused at work.

Types of remedy

Once liability has been established, civil law provides compensation for an injured party known as the claimant. This compensation may be in the form of damages, other financial penalties or an injunction (a court order prohibiting or demanding certain actions).

Damages can take into consideration:

- Recovery of lost earnings.
- Recovery of resulting expenses.
- Compensation for pain, suffering, and other quantifiable loss.
- In the case of nuisance, an abatement of the nuisance (i.e. bringing it to an end).

Proof of negligence includes establishing some form of damage.

Burden of proof

CIVIL LAW

At criminal law the prosecution must prove that the accused is guilty "beyond reasonable doubt". This contrasts with the burden of proof in most civil cases in which the case must be proved on the "balance of probability". Here the claimant sues the defendant and, whilst the burden normally rests with the claimant to establish the facts of the matter a presumption of liability is not made before the case is heard. The burden may therefore shift between the two parties as the case proceeds. It is generally accepted that the "balance of probability" is less onerous on either party to prove than that of "beyond reasonable doubt".

Civil cases are dealt with in the:

- Small Claims Court for claims up to £5,000.
- County Court for claims up to £50,000.
- High Court for claims over £50,000.

These amounts are general guidelines only. Appeals are heard in the:

- Court of Appeal (Civil Division).
- House of Lords.

CRIMINAL LAW

The prosecutor in most criminal proceedings has to prove that the conduct of the accused led to an event forbidden by criminal law, and that the conduct of the accused was accompanied by the prescribed state of mind i.e. guilty mind, his attitude being one of:-

Intention   The person intended the act or knew that there was a very high degree of probability of the consequences.

Recklessness   Whilst not desiring the consequences of his act, either he can foresee the probability of it occurring, or a reasonable man would have foreseen the consequences.

It must be shown that the event not only occurred, but that the accused either intended it or should have perceived it occurring.

In the case of health and safety matters, such as a breach of Section 2 of the HASAWA 1974 by an employer, it is not necessary to show any of the above. The Act caries an absolute duty to comply and as such the state of mind of the person found to be in non-compliance does not enter into the matter. There are sections, such as section 37, related to offences committed by senior officers of the body corporate. This refers to a breach occurring with the consent, connivance or neglect of the accused. Clearly in such cases the above comments are appropriate in determining if the accused's recklessness amounted to gross (criminal) negligence.

The prosecution (Crown) must prove guilt to the standard of "beyond reasonable doubt". In the case of the HASAWA 1974 this requirement is modified by a duty placed on the accused to show that they were in compliance with the requirement that they were accused of breaching (Section 40). This differs from the traditional criminal stance where the accused has no need to prove compliance and the emphasis is on the prosecution bringing sufficient evidence to convince the court of the non-compliance. This does not take away the over-all burden of proof for the prosecution to establish the case beyond reasonable doubt, in relation to the facts of the case, but this will clearly depend on the employer's ability to illustrate that compliance existed.

Law of contract

DEFINITION OF CONTRACT

A contract may be defined as:

> *"An agreement between two or more parties, which is intended to have legal consequences."*

A contract is more than the mere exchange of promises - there must be an intention to create a legal relationship. Both parties giving something, or have promised to give something, of value in consideration for any benefit accrued from the agreement.

The agreement requires a 'meeting of minds' whereby all parties concerned are in agreement about the subject of contract. They must therefore have common understanding of that subject.

PRINCIPLES OF THE LAW OF CONTRACT

Civil law exists in order to regulate disputes between individuals over the rights and obligations people have when dealing with each other. There are many branches of civil law including contract law and the law of tort. Contract law deals with the legally binding relationships which individuals enter into whereas tort law is aimed at redressing the wrongs committed by one person against another.

APPLICATION

Components of a contract

The following elements are essential items of a valid (and legally enforceable) contract:

- An offer and an acceptance.
- An intention to create a legal relationship.
- Appropriate capacities. All parties must have the appropriate (legal) capacity to undertake the contract.
- A consideration must be present (unless the agreement is by deed).
- The object of the contract must be legally acceptable.
- Consent must be genuine (implying full knowledge).
- It must be possible to fulfil the contract.
- The contract must not be contrary to public policy.

There are three classes of contract:

Contracts of Record:	These are usually judgements of courts, which merge with the original contract which was the subject of court action.
	They may also be recognisance, where one party agrees to be bound by the terms offered by the Court.
Speciality Contracts:	These are for specific transactions where the law requires deeds to be 'signed, sealed and delivered'. Examples are: conveyancing, property leases over 3 years, and legal articles of partnership.
Simple Contracts:	The majority of contracts, and the ones to which occupational health and liabilities generally apply. They may be made orally, or in writing, or may be implied by conduct.
	Express Contracts are those whose terms are stated. They may be verbal or written down.
	Implied Contracts are those whose terms are not specifically expressed, but are implied by the actions of the parties concerned.
	Executed Contracts are those which have been wholly performed by the parties concerned.
	Executory Contracts are those which are either wholly or partly unperformed.

THE CONTRACT PROCESS

The offer

A contract must begin with an offer, made by the offeror, to the offeree(s).

The offer must be made clearly to the offeree, and may be made orally, in writing or by conduct.

The offer must be communicated to the offeree. A person cannot be said to have accepted an offer of which they are unaware.

An offer of contract is not the same as an invitation to treat. An offer, or invitation to treat, means that an invitation to make an offer of contract has been made. If an auctioneer requests bids, he is making an invitation to treat, which is accepted by those who bid. The bids are offers of contract, and the auctioneer accepts one of the offers by the fall of his hammer.

Similarly, goods displayed in a shop are construed as invitations to treat, not as offers of contract being made by the shop. When a customer acts on that offer to treat, the customer's actions are taken as an offer to purchase (i.e. an offer of contract).

The acceptance

Acceptance of an offer may be made orally, in writing, or by conduct **but only by the offeree.** To be valid, an acceptance must be unqualified and must conform entirely to the terms of that offer.

In commercial terms, when a contract is 'put out to tender', that is an invitation to treat. The tenders are offers of contract, one of which will be accepted by the client, to form a contract. Whilst this simple form of contract applies to specific 'one off' services etc., tenders to supply on-going quantities of goods or services receive a separate acceptance each time an order is placed.

Intention

The agreement made between the offeror and the offeree, whether orally, in writing, or by action, must have the intention of forming a legally enforceable relationship. Whilst some contracts - notably those between private individuals for private purposes, may well be enforceable by the court without evidence, the courts will require written or oral evidence in all commercial or business agreements.

Consideration

The 'consideration' is a fundamental part of any simple contract. It has been defined as 'same right interest, profit or benefit accruing to one party, or some forbearance, detriment or loss suffered or undertaken by the other, as part of the contract'. Consideration may be regarded albeit simplistically, as 'the price' involved in the contract. It need not be monetary. It must be real (i.e. definite rather than vague) and genuine; must be legal; must move from the promise; need not be adequate; must be possible; and must not be past.

Appropriate capacities

In general, any person may enter into a binding contract. However, there are special rules governing some 'persons' (e.g. corporations). There are specific restrictions aimed particularly at the protection of minors (i.e. those under 18) and those considered to be particularly vulnerable as a result of mental capacity, insanity or drunkenness.

Consent

Genuine consent, based on a full and accurate knowledge of the matters of the contract are essential to the validity of the contract. That validity may be vitiated (harmed) by a number of factors, and where any one of them exists, there can be no true consent and so the contract may be voided, or may be void. Vitiating factors include:

- Mistakes.
- Misrepresentation.
- Duress.
- Undue influence.
- Illegality.

Voiding of contracts

Grounds for a contract being declared void include:

Mistakes. In general, at common law, mistakes do not invalidate a contract. However, some classes of mistake - 'operative' mistakes of fact undermine a contract to such an extent that they invalidate it. An example is where one party to a contract has one item in mind, as the subject of the contract, and the other has something entirely different.

Misrepresentation. Misrepresentation is a false statement of fact which induces a party to enter a contract and thereby results in that party suffering a loss. Misrepresentation may be fraudulent, negligent, or innocent, and the term applies only to statements of fact, not to opinions.

Duress and undue Influence. In general rule of law, a valid agreement can only be made where both parties exercise their own free will without constraint or pressure.

Duress at common law means violence (or the threat of violence) to a party to a contract, or to members of their family, or the threat of unlawful imprisonment.

Undue influence is a parallel but more subtle vitiating factor, where a party uses their influence to gain undue benefit for themselves either as a result of persuading someone to enter into a contract with them or by persuading the influenced party to enter into a contract with a third party, for their own benefit. Such contracts, induced by undue influence are voidable, and may be void.

Illegality. A contract is illegal if it contravenes a statute or common law.

Illegal contracts include those which involve the commission of a crime or tort, and those which contravene or offend against certain fundamental rules of common law or morality and collectively termed 'public policy'. Examples are those contracts which result in restraint of trade, extortionate repayment terms or sexual immorality (e.g. a 'wife swapping' contract). Contracts are also illegal if they prejudice:

- Foreign relations (e.g. a contract to carry out acts which are illegal in a foreign and friendly country).
- The administration of justice (e.g. a contract to circumvent the bankruptcy laws).
- Standards in public life (e.g. a contract to purchase a knighthood).
- The Revenue (a contract to defraud the Inland Tax Office or to avoid local government rates).

DISCHARGING OF CONTRACTS

Contracts may be discharged by:

Mutual agreement

Performance - where both parties have completely fulfilled their obligations.

Breach - where one party repudiates their liability before performance is due, or where they fail to perform the obligations they have undertaken. (The injured party is therefore able to sue for damages).

Impossibility or frustration - where circumstances alter before a hitherto entirely valid contract can be performed (e.g. outbreak of war, or a change in the law), the contract may be voided.

Operation of law - where events result in legal consequences that render the original contract discharged, e.g. the passage of time, and the operation of the Limitation Act 1980, which sets time limits for various actions (particularly 6 years in respect of torts, or of 3 years following the death or injury of a relevant party).

THE RELATIONSHIP BETWEEN PRODUCER AND VENDOR

Since the introduction of the HASAWA, legislation has more precisely focused on matters of safety in design. This has included the important contribution made by the Consumer Protection Act (CPA) 1987. The CPA amended some features of the HASAWA 1974 contained in section 6. Both the HASAWA 1974 and CPA 1987 define articles and substances for use at work, in sections 53(1) and 45 respectively.

Duties

Articles for use at work

Section 6 HASAWA 1974, as amended, imposes on any person who designs, manufactures, imports and supplies any such article (or any article of fairground equipment) a general duty to:

- Ensure, so far as reasonably practicable, it is so designed and constructed as to be safe at all times when set, used, cleaned or maintained by a person at work.
- Carry out or arrange necessary testing or examination for that purpose.

■ Ensure the provision of adequate information about design use and conditions of use (Section 6) and keep it updated (CPA 1987 Schedule 3).

Substances for use at work

Section 6 as amended by CPA 1987 Schedule 3 imposes on manufacturers, importers and suppliers of any such substance a similar general duty to that with respect to articles:

■ Ensure, so far as reasonably practicable, it will be safe at all times when used, handled, processed, stored or transported by a person at work.
■ Carry out or arrange necessary testing or examination for that purpose.
■ Ensure the provision of adequate information about risks from its inherent properties, tests and necessary conditions of use, and keep it updated.

There are additional duties under HASAWA 1974 section 6 and CPA 1987 Schedule 3 on:

■ Designers and manufacturers of articles, and manufacturers of substances, to carry out research to discover and, so far as is reasonably practicable, eliminate risks.
■ Installers of articles for use at work to ensure, so far as is reasonably practicable, safe installation.

It is important to note that importers and suppliers do not need to repeat testing, examination or research by designers or manufacturers. It is accepted that a person who designs, manufactures, imports or supplies an article for or to another person on the basis of a written undertaking of safety by that other may rely on that undertaking.

Liability of importers

It is emphasised that nothing in HASAWA 1974 relieves an importer of an article or substance from any of his duties as regards anything done (or not done) within the control of a foreign designer or manufacturer, HASAWA 1974 section 6 (8A), added by CPA 1987 Schedule 3.

Unsafe imported goods

The HASAWA 1974 gives no power to enforcing authorities to stop the supply of unsafe products at source or prevent the sale of unsafe products; so enforcing officers have been given powers to interrupt the supply/distribution chain by the use of a prohibition notice. Additionally, Her Majesty's Customs and Excise [HMCE] officers have power to:

■ Detain articles and substances (cf. HSE inspectors).
■ Transmit information to HSE about unsafe imported products; HASAWA section 25(A), added by CPA 1987 Schedule.

THE RELATIONSHIP BETWEEN VENDOR AND CONSUMER

Consumer Protection Act 1987

Part I of the Consumer Protection Act (CPA) 1987 brought into law strict product liability so that the consumer suffering damage or injury relating to defective or unsafe products no longer has to establish negligence. Provided that the claimant can prove that damage or injury was caused by the defective product then civil liability arises. Those liable include:

■ The producer or processors of the product.
■ The manufacturer of the product.
■ A person who purports to be the manufacturer (e.g. a supermarkets 'own brand' label).
■ An importer into the European Union.
■ A supplier - provided that the supplier will not provide the identity of the party that supplied the product to him.

Liability under the Act is joint and several. A defective product is defined as one where the safety of the product is not to a standard which can be reasonably expected. This is not concerned with products which are defective solely because they are of poor quality or because they have been superseded by a safer version of the product. In determining defects, the court will take all relevant circumstances into account including:

■ The way in which the product is labelled and marked.
■ The instructions and warnings given.
■ The uses that the product might be reasonably expected to be put to.
■ The time that the producer supplied the product.

Defences include:
■ Product not supplied in the course of business.
■ Defect did not exist when the product was provided.
■ Technical knowledge was such that the defect could not have been known (the development risk defence).

Any attempt to exclude liability either by contract or by notice is excluded by the Act.

The Act covers consumer goods, components and raw materials. Unprocessed agricultural products, unprocessed game and buildings are not covered; however, building materials, such as bricks, are. Action can be brought for death, injury and damage. There is a threshold limit for damage to property of £275. This is to exclude trivial claims; however, for claims over this amount, all damages are recoverable (including the first £275).

Part II of the CPA 1987 creates a "*general safety requirement*" (GSR) for products. General safety requirements are not applied to second-hand goods. Breach is a criminal offence enforceable by local authority trading standards officers. Part IV contains various powers and provisions on enforcement.

Section 10 of the CPA creates a criminal offence relating to the provision of *consumer goods* ordinarily intended for private use or consumption which fail to comply with the general safety requirement. They must be reasonably safe, having regard to all the circumstances, including:

■ The manner and purposes of marketing, any marking instructions or warning.
■ Any published standards of safety.
■ Whether it would have been reasonable for them to have been made safer.

- Any safety regulations, made by the Secretary of State, for any of the 3 general and 11 specific purposes in section 11(1) and (2).

The definition of safe is restricted to people, not property or animals or the environment.

This obligation is translated to offences. It is an offence for any person to:

- Supply any consumer goods which fail to comply with the GSR.
- Offer or agree to supply any such goods.
- Expose or possess any such goods for supply.
- Fail to comply with safety regulations.

The penalty on summary conviction is imprisonment not exceeding 6 months and/or a fine not exceeding level 5 on the standard scale.

As with other modern legislation the CPA 1987 has notices to assist with ensuring consumer protection. Under the CPA 1987 there are 3 types of notice - the Secretary of State may serve:

- A **prohibition notice** in respect of any relevant unsafe goods prohibiting supply, offer or agreement to supply, or exposing or possessing for supply.
- A **notice to warn** requiring the publication of warnings about unsafe goods; section 13.

The general safety requirements under section 10 of the Act have been largely replaced by the General Product Safety Regulations 1994 (GPS Regulations). These were introduced in order to implement the EU General Product Safety Directive into UK Law.

And an enforcement authority may serve (section14):

- A **suspension notice** prohibiting for a period not exceeding 6 months, supply, offer or agreement to supply, or exposing for supply, any goods in respect of which there is reasonable ground to suspect the contravention of any safety provision.

Failure to comply with any notice is an offence against the Act. Appeal against a suspension notice must be made to the magistrates.

Magistrates may order forfeiture and destruction of goods on application by an enforcing authority.

Specific regulations have been made for particular goods; examples include:

- Cooking Appliances (Safety) Regulations 1989.
- Toys (Safety) Regulations 1989 require toys supplied in the UK to comply with BS 5665 and to meet other safety requirements.
- Nightwear (Safety) Regulations 1985 impose flammability requirements.
- Furniture and Furnishings (Fire) (Safety) Regulations 1988 as amended in 1989, impose fire resistance requirements.
- Low Voltage Electrical Equipment (Safety) Regulations 1989.

The goods cannot legally be sold in the UK if they do not comply.

Although Part II of the Act relates to criminal sanctions, breach can be used to assist a civil claim. A claimant injured by goods which infringe the safety requirements can sue for breach of statutory duty.

Part III of the CPA 1987 is concerned with criminal liability relating to misleading price indications.

The trading standards authorities enforce the CPA 1987 in respect of defined consumer goods - regardless of to whom they are supplied. The HSE enforces the law relating to products purely used at work under section 6 of the HASAWA 1974 which was amended by the CPA 1987 **(see later summary)**.

Sale of Goods Act 1979 and Sale and Supply of Goods Act 1994

The Sale and Supply of Goods Act 1979 (as amended by the Sale and Supply of Goods Act 1994) affords civil protection to consumers in respect of the goods which they purchase. The term goods also includes items supplied under a contract for work and materials (e.g. an air filter supplied by a garage servicing a car). In essence the Act requires that goods:

- Have to fit the description given to them.
- Sold in the course of a business be of satisfactory (formerly *merchantable*) quality.
- Sold in the course of a business be fit for the requirements that the customer gives to the seller.
- Must match the description, sample or demonstration model offered for inspection by the customer.

Section 1 of the Sale and Supply of Goods Act 1994 amends the Sale of Goods Act 1979 by defining the condition that goods must be supplied in order for them to be of **satisfactory quality**. To be of satisfactory quality the goods must meet the standard expected by a reasonable person taking into account the price, any description and other relevant factors. Factors include:

- Fitness for the purpose for which the goods are commonly supplied.
- Safety.
- Durability.
- Appearance and finish.
- Freedom from minor defects.

Defects which have been brought to the purchaser's attention are not covered. Buyers are able to reject goods which are blemished etc. provided that they have not 'accepted' them. This is based on the buyer having a reasonable opportunity to examine the goods to see if they conform to the contract of sale. Prior to the Act this was time-based; however the courts are now able to ignore periods when the goods are not being used and concentrate on periods of trial by use. For example, if a person buys a computer in June as a Christmas present and then stores it until December only to find that it does not work properly, then under old law the buyer would have lost the right to reject the goods.

THE RELATIONSHIP BETWEEN CLIENT AND CONTRACTOR

Once the client has accepted a tender for work from a company/person, the contract can be drawn up. The contract can stipulate certain conditions, for example, the area the contractor is responsible for, and the time the work is meant to take.

The client cannot delegate his duty of care to the contractor nor can he state that he is not responsible for injury or death on his site. There are some duties in health and safety law that the client must retain and cannot sign over to the contractor in a contract, for example, the duties regarding his plant and equipment.

Details of the contract must be understood by both parties with nothing hidden; there must be nothing illegal; and both parties must agree without undue influence.

Relationships between client and contractor are influenced by health and safety law such as the Construction (Design and Management) Regulations (CDM) 2007.

EXCLUSION CLAUSES

The effect of the Unfair Contract Terms Act 1977

The Unfair Contract Terms Act 1977 states that the common law duty of care for death or personal injury cannot be excluded in relation to business premises. In addition loss or damage can only be excluded when it is reasonable to do so.

The Act also prevents exclusion of liability for breach of contract, or of different performance or non-performance of contract unless it is reasonable to do so.

The Unfair Contract Terms Act also renders ineffective contract clauses relating to the exclusion or restriction of manufacturer's liability in respect of loss or damage arising from defective goods used by a consumer resulting from negligent manufacture. Similarly clauses which exclude liability from duties imposed under the Sale of Goods Act 1979 (on a sale) or the Supply of Goods (Implied Terms Act) 1973 as amended (on a hire purchase transaction) are also ineffective.

Employment law in relation to health and safety

DEFINITION OF CONTRACT OF EMPLOYMENT

Section 53 of the HASAWA 1974 defines an 'employee' as an individual who works under a contract of employment. It further defines a 'contract of employment' as a contract of employment or apprenticeship (whether express or implied and, if express, whether oral or in writing). Thus a formal written contract is not necessarily required in order for someone to be considered an employee.

DISCIPLINARY PROCEDURES

The Employment Relations Act (ERA) 1999 exempts employers with less than 20 employees from the requirement to provide details of the disciplinary and grievance procedures but must provide the name of the person to whom application can be made.

Precise grievance and disciplinary procedures are therefore usually part of the contract and employers must adhere to them if they wish to avoid liability. The procedure usually comprises a series of oral and written warnings.

The ERA 1999 give workers a right to be accompanied in certain disciplinary and grievance hearings.

REMEDIES FOR UNFAIR DISMISSAL

There are many acceptable grounds for dismissing an employee including genuine redundancy, misconduct and lack of capability or qualifications. Dismissal must however be reasonable and the ERA 1999 requires the employer to give these reasons in writing. The Act also includes a test of reasonableness when determining if a dismissal was fair in relation to the 'size and administrative resources of the employer's undertaking'.

In order for an employee to claim unfair dismissal he or she must first have to be dismissed. There are two type of dismissal:

Actual. A formal dismissal of the employee by the employer either orally or in writing: and

Constructive. Where the employee is compelled to leave due to the conduct of the employer. The employer's conduct is considered to have been a fundamental repudiation of the contract of employment.

Dismissal can occur even when a fixed term contract has not been renewed. The ERA 1999 prohibits the use of waivers for unfair dismissal but not redundancy payments in fixed term contracts. Grounds for unfair dismissal include:

Health and safety dismissals and detriments. Detriment in relation to safety representatives and representatives of employee safety (e.g. loss of overtime). This category includes ordinary employees who leave or refuse to return to the workplace because of a health hazard which they reasonably thought to exist.

Dismissal in connection with trade unions. Dismissal is automatically unfair if it is principally due to membership of, or the taking part in at an appropriate time, the activities of a trades union which is independent of the employer. This applies equally to non-membership as well as membership. Under the terms of the Trade Union and Labour Relations (Consolidation) Act 1992 dismissal relating to refusal to join a trades union is automatically unfair even if there is a closed shop.

Dismissal for asserting statutory rights. Dismissal of an employee trying to enforce their employment rights under the ERA is also automatically unfair.

Unfair selection for redundancy. Where selection for redundancy has been made unfairly (e.g. trades union membership, complaints about safety standards) or where the employer has failed to comply with an agreed prior arrangement (e.g. last in - first out).

Transfer of business. If part or the whole of a business undertaking is transferred and an employee is dismissed as a result then dismissal is automatically unfair.

Dismissals in connection with pregnancy or childbirth. Where the principal reason for dismissal is that the worker is pregnant or any reason connected with childbirth.

Pressure on employer to dismiss unfairly. For example, pressure put on the employer by a worker because of a refusal to join a trade union in a closed shop. Dismissal is unfair even if there is industrial action or the threat of action. The trade union as well as the employer may be sued by the dismissed employee.

Employment Rights Act 1996

The Employment Rights Act 1996 (ERA) states that the employer must give his employee written information about the terms of employment within two months of starting work (provided that the duration of the job is more than one month). Details should include:

- The names of the employer and employee.

- The date when employment began.
- The duration of temporary contracts.
- Details of any previous employment which counts as continuous service.
- Job title or brief job description.
- Pay details (including holiday and sick pay).
- Details of working hours and conditions.
- If work outside the UK for longer than one month is required: details of duration, currency of payments, pay and benefits.
- Work location or locations.
- Collective agreements with trades unions affecting the job.
- Who to apply to in respect of disciplinary and grievance procedures.
- The disciplinary and grievance procedures.

An employee who fails to undertake all the duties agreed in the contract will be in breach of contract.

Trade Union and Labour Relations (Consolidation) Act 1992

The Trade Union and Labour Relations (Consolidation) Act 1992 prohibits employers from taking action against employees because they are member of, or take part in at an appropriate time, the activities of a trades union which is independent of the employer.

This applies equally to non-membership as well as membership. Under the terms of the Act dismissal for failing to join a trades union is automatically unfair even if there is a closed shop.

The Act also provides that any breach of contract which endangers human life or causes serious bodily injury or exposes valuable property to destruction is a criminal offence. It is also an offence to intimidate another person and prevent that person from going about their lawful business.

Trade Union Reform and Employment Rights Act 1993

Trade Union Reform and Employment Rights Act 1993 obliged trades unions to ballot its members and provide a minimum of seven days notice to the employer prior to taking industrial action. The notice, in writing, must contain the names of those employees who intend to take part in the action. Failure to comply with these obligations leaves the union open to civil action for damages. This has now been modified by the Employment Relations Act 1999.

Employees who take unofficial strike action cannot complain of unfair dismissal to an employment tribunal. A strike will be unofficial unless:

- The employee is a trade union member and the action is endorsed or authorised by the union or a responsible officer of the union.
- Other union members are participating though the employee is not personally a union member.

Schedule 5 of the Trade Union Reform and Employment Rights Act 1993 gives grounds for unfair dismissal to employees in relation to the performance of statutory functions by safety representatives and representatives of employee safety. This category includes ordinary employees who leave or refuse to return to the workplace because of a health hazard which they reasonably thought to exist.

DISCRIMINATION

Sex Discrimination Acts 1975 and 1986

The Sex Discrimination Acts of 1975 and 1986 together with the Equal Pay Act 1970 form the basis of the laws relating to sex discrimination. The 1975 Act makes it unlawful to treat anyone on grounds of sex less favourably than the opposite sex is or would be treated in the same circumstances.

There are two kinds of discrimination:

- *Direct* whereby people are treated less favourably because of their sex or because of marital status.
- *Indirect* where, for example, a supermarket advertises for shop assistants over 6 feet tall thereby disadvantaging women.

As with the Race Relations Act 1976, the 1975 Act also protects those who suffer discrimination by way of victimisation for bringing a complaint under its provisions. The Act applies equally to men as well as women. Thus, in 1996, the Labour Party was held to have unlawfully discriminated against two men through their policy of short-listing only women as prospective parliamentary candidates.

The Sex Discrimination Act of 1986 extended provision to areas such as the offering of partnerships. The law applies to all companies, partnerships and to sole traders regardless of the size of the business.

Race Relations Act 1976

The Race Relations Act deals with discrimination of racial groups on racial grounds. A *racial group* is defined as a group of persons defined by reference to colour, race, nationality, or ethnic or national origin, and racial *grounds* as colour, race, nationality, ethnic or national origins. It does not apply to religious beliefs unless that constitutes racial discrimination. Thus racial discrimination would exist if the religion was Jewish but not Protestant or Catholic since these last two are not a matter of race.

The Race Relations Acts defines the following in relation to contracts of employment:

- *Direct* discrimination where a person is treated unfairly on grounds of race.
- *Indirect* discrimination where there is a requirement or condition which, although it applies to everyone, is discriminatory.

Thus a rule that bus conductors must wear uniform caps was found to be indirect discrimination against Sikh applicants. The Act also protects those who suffer discrimination by way of victimisation for bringing a complaint under its provisions.

The Act deals with other areas of racial discrimination relating to matters such as partnerships, qualifying bodies and discrimination in education.

Disability

The Disability Discrimination Act 1995 only applies to employers who employ 15 employees or more. It does not apply to operational members of services such as the police, the fire service or the prison service.

It is unlawful to discriminate against disabled persons when deciding:

- Whom to interview.
- Whom to employ.
- The terms of offer.

The employer must make reasonable adjustments to both the working conditions and the workplace but may take cost into account when deciding on what is reasonable.

The employer is allowed the defence of believing on reasonable grounds that the nature of the disability will substantially affect the person's ability to carry out the tasks required.

A complaint to an employment tribunal must be taken within three months of the alleged discrimination.

Situations where it is lawful to discriminate

In general it is unlawful for employers to discriminate on the grounds of colour, race, nationality or ethnic or national origins, gender or marital status, disability or trades union status. The exception to this is where there is *a genuine occupational qualification* or the job is one of two held by a married couple. *Examples of lawful discrimination are outlined below*.

Race

In the case of *Panesar v Nestlé & Co Ltd [1980]* an orthodox Sikh who naturally wore a beard as part of his religious belief was refused employment on hygiene grounds. The strict rules required that no beards or excessively long hair was allowed. The claimant claimed indirect discrimination which was rejected. The Court of Appeal held that as the defendants had supported their rule with scientific evidence there was in fact no discrimination.

Sex

It is lawful to discriminate on the grounds of marital status or gender when there is a genuine occupational qualification (e.g. a fashion model), for reasons of privacy or decency (e.g. a single sex school) or where the job is one of two held by a married couple. There are some other non-occupational exceptions relating to the appointment of head teachers in schools or colleges which may be restricted to members of a religious order where this is contained in a trust deed or other founding instrument. In addition women are allowed to receive special treatment when they are pregnant.

Sex discrimination may also be lawful in the interests of safety. In the case of *Page v Freight Hire (Tank Haulage) Ltd [1981]* a 23 year old female driver was taken off a job involving the transport of chemicals which involved a risk to women of child bearing age. She brought an action under the Sex Discrimination Act 1974 (SD Act) for unlawful sex discrimination. The SD Act does not allow the employer to stop employing women at the first hint of danger; however the employer's duty under section 2 of the HASAWA 1974 takes precedence. In this case there was evidence that the chemical was dangerous to women of Mrs Page's age and the act of stopping her from carrying out the work was therefore reasonable. Thus there was no unlawful discrimination.

THE PUBLIC INTEREST DISCLOSURE ACT 1998

The Public Interest Disclosure Act 1998 (dubbed the 'whistleblowers charter'), which amended the Employment Rights Act 1996, allows employees who are penalised or dismissed for revealing workplace malpractice (including dangers to health, safety or the environment), to claim compensation or reinstatement for unfair dismissal.

With 'whistleblowing' there is a conflict of interest between the employer's legitimate interest in preserving confidentiality and the greater public interest. In the case of Initial Services Ltd v Potterill [1968], where there was disclosure of a price cartel to the press, Lord Denning said that the employee need not be confined to the disclosure of crimes but "any misconduct of such a nature that it ought, in the public interest be disclosed to others".

The amendment states that an employee must not be subject to detriment or dismissal for making a 'protected disclosure'. There is emphasis on making an initial disclosure to the employer. Dismissal is automatically unfair for 1) a protected disclosure and 2) if it is made in a way envisaged by the Act.

Protected disclosures are:

- Deliberately concealing information relating to other protected disclosures.
- Criminal offences.
- Failure or likelihood to fail to comply with a legal obligation.
- Miscarriage of justice is likely to occur.
- The health and safety of an individual is endangered.
- Any environmental harm.

The Employment Tribunal's £50,000 limit does not apply in these cases.

A7.2 - Absolute and qualified duties

CONCEPT OF ABSOLUTE AND QUALIFIED DUTIES

Statute law can place either absolute or qualified duties onto the duty-holder. These standards are defined as:

In the case of R v Gateway Foodmarkets Ltd (CA) 1997 (not listed in syllabus) the Duty Manager of a store at Broomshill fell to his death through a trap door in the floor of the lift control room. For approximately a year there had been a problem with the lift. Although this had initially been rectified by a form of outside contractors, employees at the store had been shown how to rectify the fault themselves. This meant going to the control room.

The day before the accident the contractors had undertaken routine maintenance and left open the trap door in the control room. The next day, when the lift jammed, the Manager entered the room going from bright sunlight into darkness and fell through the open trap door to his death.

It was held that both Section 2 and Section 3 (the employer's duties to persons other than his employees) of the HASAWA 1974 imposes strict liability subject to the test of reasonably practicable (i.e. the taking of all reasonable precautions by the Company on its behalf - including its servants and agents). Since there was a failure at store management level the Company was guilty of the offence under Section 2.

Definition of the terms

'ABSOLUTE'

Absolute duties require compliance regardless of technical considerations or cost *(see - John Summers & Sons v Frost [1955] - below)*. Absolute duties are expressed by using words such as "will", "must" and "shall". It is an absolute duty to undertake risk assessments under the Management of Health and Safety at Work Regulations (MHSWR) 1999.

John Summers & Sons V Frost 1955 All ER 870 AC.740, [F.A.1937 S14 (1), F.A.1961 S14 (1)]

Securely fenced (absolute duty)

Circumstances:

Mr Frost was injured whilst using a grinding wheel. His thumb was caught between the small (1cm) gap between the guard and the grinding wheel. Although the wheel was partially guarded, section 14 of the Factories Act imposed an absolute duty to guard the dangerous parts of machinery.

Decision:

The House of Lords ruled that there had been a breach of statutory duty.

Relevance:

The obligation to guard securely those parts of a machine which are dangerous must be fulfilled in such a manner, as to afford "complete protection" to the "careless or inattentive worker as well as the meticulous, careful one".

Moreover, the "dangerous part is securely fenced if and only if the presence of the fence makes it no longer dangerous.

The duty was to provide fencing which absolutely prevented any part of any person working on the premises from coming into contact with any dangerous part of the machine. This illustrates the literal interpretation of statutes that the courts are required to make - if the effect of this is to make the machine unusable then so be it.

'PRACTICABLE'

Practicable requires the duty-holder to keep up with developing technology in the light of current knowledge and invention and not to be too slow to employ it. It is a stricter standard than that of 'reasonably practicable' and may require the duty-holder to eliminate cost as a consideration *(see - Marshall v Gotham & Co Ltd [1954] - below)*. Regulation 5 of the Health and Safety (Display Screen Equipment) Regulations 1992, requires an employer to provide an eye test as soon as practicable after this has been requested.

Marshall v. Gotham Co. Ltd (1954) AC 360 HL

Metalliferous mines regulations 1938

Practicable as against reasonably practicable

Circumstances:

Mr Marshall was killed by a roof collapse whilst working in a gypsum mine. The roof had been tested; however the roof fall had been caused by an undetectable geological fault known as "slickenside". His wife claimed compensation for breach of statutory duty.

Decision:

The employer was not liable as they had taken reasonable steps to secure the roof.

Relevance:

The term 'secure' means safe against normal or likely hazards. Thus a totally unexpected or abnormal movement or fall does not prove a failure of duty. In this case the movement was caused by an unforeseeable geological fault.

In this case a comparison between the levels of duty required by the terms "practicable" and "reasonably practicable" was made.

> "If a precaution is practicable, it must be taken unless in the whole circumstances that would be unreasonable and as men's lives may be at stake it should not lightly be held that to take a practicable precaution is unreasonable."

Figure A7-1: 'practicable' and 'reasonably practicable' comparison.
Source: Lord Reid.

'REASONABLY PRACTICABLE'

Here the duty-holder is allowed to balance the quantum of risk against the cost in terms of time, trouble, money and effort when deciding on what measures to implement. ***See - Edwards v National Coal Board (1949); Martin v Boulton and Paul (Steel Construction) Ltd (1982)*** *(Not listed in syllabus)*; ***and West Bromwich Building Society Ltd v Townsend (1983)*** Not listed in syllabus. Companies have a general duty under Section 2(1) to ensure the health, safety and welfare of their employees.

Edwards v. National Coal Board (1949) [All ER 743 KB 704]

Reasonably practicable - the 'quantum of risk' test

Circumstances:

Mr Edwards was killed when a section of roadway collapsed. The NCB argued that the cost of shoring up would have been prohibitive and was not justified.

Decision:

The NCB were found liable on the basis that the cost of making this particular road section safe was not great when compared to the risk.

Relevance:

The 'Quantum of Risk' test should be applied in determining whether or not the steps that were taken in the circumstances of the incident were sufficient to satisfy the requirements of the term 'reasonably practicable' where such an obligatory term is stipulated.

"This 'Quantum of Risk' test is the analogy of a scale balance whereupon the degree of risk is placed on one pan and the sacrifice involved in the measures necessary for averting the risk (whether in money, time or trouble) is placed on the other; and that, if it be shown that there is a gross disproportion between them - the risk being insignificant in relation to the sacrifice - the defendants discharge the onus upon them."

Figure A7-2: 'Quantum of risk' test definition. Source: Lord Asquith.

A7.3 – Role of the European Union

The influence and role of the European Union as it affects UK health and safety legislation

The Council of the European Commission can, under the Treaty of Rome, issue Directives. These are to harmonise the laws of the member states, including those covering occupational health and safety.

DIRECTIVES

Representatives of the member states meet to agree on the content of the draft Directives. When they are agreed, they are presented to the European Parliament for ratification. The Directives impose a duty on each member state to make legislation to conform to the Directive and to enforce such legislation. The Directives are legally binding on the governments. Framework Directives set out the overall objectives and they are dealt with individually in the form of Daughter Directives.

REGULATIONS

In the UK the Directives are translated into Regulations. For example, we have the Working Time Directive translated into the Working Time Regulations

The Single European Act identified the need to eliminate technical barriers to trade, such as the differing legal health and safety standards throughout the Community. The approach is to develop a philosophy of essential safety requirements and harmonisation Directives that establish those essential safety requirements. Further to this, there is recognition in the Act to encourage improvements in the working environment.

This approach very much depends on the availability of European standards. They are usually prepared by the European standards bodies: the European Committee for Standardisation (CEN) and the European Committee for Electrotechnical Standardisation (CENELEC), as a result of mandates being agreed with the European Commission. CEN and CENELEC are based in Brussels and they bring together the national standards bodies of the Community and European Free Trade Association (EFTA). The UK member is the British Standards Institute (BSI).

Standards may be set by agreement on a text that has been developed or by agreeing to adopt an existing international standard as a European standard. All national members have agreed to adopt the resulting standards as their national standards and to withdraw any existing and conflicting standards. The UK adopts the standards as British Standards, for example, BS EN 292.

Composition and roles

THE MAIN INSTITUTIONS

Council of ministers

The Council (or Council of the European Union) is made up of representatives of each of the member states and represents the individual member states. This is the main decision and law making body of the European Union (EU). The relevant ministers attend specialised meetings as appropriate. For example, transport ministers meet to discuss proposed transport legislation.

At lower levels the Council is assisted by a Committee of Permanent Representatives ('Coreper') consisting of more junior national representatives from each member state. These consider the detail of proposed measures in order to forward them for Council approval.

The European Council meets twice a year and consists of heads of Member States, foreign ministers and the President of the Commission. The European Council is basically a 'super meeting' of the Council which formulates and reviews overall EU policy. They may also negotiate new treaty obligations requiring unanimity and ratification. Presidency of the Council rotates between heads of Member States and changes after each meeting.

European Commission

The Commission consists of 20 members appointed by the member governments for periods of 5 years. Once appointed the Commissioners must act independently of the member governments and of the Council. Individual members have special responsibilities (e.g. transport, agriculture) and cannot be removed by the Council. The European Parliament can, by a two thirds majority, pass a motion of censure compelling the whole group to resign. The Commission's role is:

- To initiate Community legislation and policy.
- To enact legislation where the power to do so has been delegated by the Council.
- To enforce the treaties.
- To be the executive arm of the Community.
- To initiate Community policy.
- To defend Community interests in the Council.

The Commission can also bring member states and organisations before the Court of Justice where it considers that community obligations are not being carried out (e.g. failing to implement a directive). The Commissioners are supported by a 'civil service' of over 14,000 staff most of whom are based in Brussels or Luxembourg. Each member of the Commission is responsible for one or more portfolios and has one or more of the 22 Directors General reporting to him or her.

European Parliament

Originally set up as a consultative assembly, the European Parliament has three fundamental powers:

- Legislative power.
- Budgetary power.
- Supervisory power.

It has the right to veto or amend legislation agreed by EU governments. It can also:

- Reject the EU's budget.
- Set up committees of inquiry.
- Sack the EU's executive Commission.
- Block EU expansions.
- Veto international agreements.

The Parliament holds monthly plenary sessions of one week's duration in Strasbourg. Most other activities (e.g. committee meetings) take place in Brussels. The Parliament consists of 731 Members of the European Parliament (MEPs), (situation as at 6th April 2005 for the 6th term 2004-2009). MEPs serve a five-year term and election is by direct universal suffrage. The current European Parliament is made up of:

- 99 from Germany.
- 78 each from France, Italy and the UK.
- 54 each from Spain and Poland.
- 27 from the Netherlands.
- 24 each from Belgium, the Czech Republic, Greece and Hungary.
- 23 from Portugal.
- 19 from Sweden.
- 18 from Austria.
- 14 each from Denmark and Slovakia.
- 13 each from Ireland and Lithuania.
- 9 from Latvia.
- 7 from Slovenia.
- 6 each from Estonia, Cyprus and Luxembourg.
- 5 from Malta.

The European Parliament considers and decides on legislation proposed by the commission.

European Court of Justice

The European Court of Justice (ECJ) sits in Luxembourg and comprises 28 persons in all:

- The President of the Court.
- Two First Advocates-General.
- Six Presidents of Chambers (numbered one to six respectively).
- Eleven Judges.
- Seven Advocates General.
- One Registrar.

The Single European Act empowered the Court to set up a Court of First Instance, which it did in 1988. This Court is designed to relieve the pressure on the Court of Justice. The Court of First Instance comprises of four Presidents of Chamber, ten judges and a Registrar. It deals with all direct action by citizens and firms against Community institutions (except in anti-dumping matters) and appeals against Commission Decisions in Competition cases. The Court of Justice should not be confused with the European Court of Human Rights. The Court of Human Rights' function is to interpret the European Convention for the Protection of Human Rights. The articles of the Convention provide for matters such as the right not to be subjected to inhuman or degrading treatment, and freedom of peaceful assembly.

EUROPEAN COURT OF JUSTICE

Jurisdiction and powers

The task of the Court is to ensure that interpretation of the treaties is in accordance with the rule of law. They may deal with the following actions under the Treaty of Rome:

1. Actions by the Commission against member states for failure to fulfil Treaty obligations.

2. Actions by one member state against another member state for failure to fulfil Treaty obligations.

3. Actions by a member state or an individual or a company against the Council or Commission for acting in breach of the Treaty.

4. Actions by a member state against the Council or Commission for failure to act.

The European Court of Justice issues a single judgement based on a majority decision. No dissenting views are given. The case is considered first by the Advocates General who assist the Court by giving an independent view of the case prior to the Court's decision. However the Court is not bound by these opinions. Enforcement of judgements is through the national courts of all Member States.

ECONOMIC AND SOCIAL COMMITTEE AND ADVISORY GROUPS

The Court of Auditors has existed since 1967 and has 15 members appointed by the Council after consultation with the European Parliament. Its task is to check and report on the financial management exercised by the other institutions.

There are a number of ancillary bodies in the EU. The most important of these is the Economic and Social Committee. This advises the Council and Commission on economic matters. It considers matter relating to social groups such as employers, business people, farmers and manufacturers. The committee is designed to form a link between the EU bodies formulating and making policy and those occupational groups who will be affected by such policy. It exerts a strong influence on the decision making process because of its political and technical terms of reference.

Other advisory groups include the Committee of the Regions which again has a purely advisory role. Both the Council and Commission are mandated to consult this committee in matters relating to regional education, cultural, public health, economic and social matters.

The European Agency for Safety and Health at Work has been set up in order to serve information needs with regard to health and safety at work. The Agency is located in Bilbao, Spain. Their goal is to improve the lives of people at work by stimulating the flow of technical, scientific and economic information between all those involved in occupational safety and health (OSH) issues. This includes workers, employers, safety representatives, experts, practitioners and national as well as European Community bodies.

Their Administrative Board is comprised of representatives of governments, employers and workers from all EU Member States, and of the European Commission. They carry out much of their work through a network of nationally appointed occupational health and safety institutions known as Focal Points. Internationally, they co-operate with organisations such as the International Labour Organisation and the World Health Organisation, as well as with other safety and health institutions world-wide.

The European Investment Bank provides loans and guarantees in all economic sectors to promote development in the less-developed regions. This will include such matters as the creation of new jobs and the modernisation and converting of undertakings. In addition it assists in projects of common interest to several Member States.

The status and procedures of European law

INSTRUMENTS IN EC LAW

Treaties

Treaty of Rome (overview of key articles)

Article 95 (was Article 100) of the Treaty of Rome gives the legal authority for the imposition of EC Directives on Member States.

Article 95A (was Article 100A) was added to the Treaty of Rome in order to accelerate the removal of trade barriers between Member states, many of which have safety implications.

Article 137 (was Article 118A) was added to the Treaty of Rome and deals with the harmonisation of conditions in the working environment, including the maintenance and improvement of measures to ensure health and safety.

Article 130 was added to the Treaty of Rome by The Single European Act 1987 and is primarily concerned with the environment, but does have health and safety implications.

It should be noted that these Articles have now been renumbered by the Treaty of Amsterdam (e.g. Article 137 was Article 118A). For clarity the 'new' numbering system is used in this text.

The Single European Act

This Act, which came into force on 1 July 1987, extended the Community's field of competence and brought about significant changes in relations between the institutions and in their operating rules. It also gave formal legal status to European Political Co-operation.

The Treaty on European Union (The Maastricht Treaty)

This Treaty came into force on 1 January 1993 following ratification of the provisions agreed at Maastricht in December 1991. It envisages monetary union and closer co-operation on foreign, security, justice and home affairs policies. The stated aim of the 135 page treaty is "to organise relations between the member states" and create "an ever closer union among the people of Europe".

Provisions of the Maastricht Treaty include the following:

- The EEC is renamed the European Community.
- Provision is made for certain intergovernmental structures, notably the European Central Bank in Frankfurt.
- The term "European Union" is introduced to encompass both the EC and the new intergovernmental structure.
- Common policies will be decided in Brussels.

- Qualified majority voting (QMV) is extended to more than 70 policy areas.
- The principle of "subsidiarity", first enunciated by Jacques Delors in 1989, is affirmed (i.e. the Community should only act to achieve objectives which cannot be sufficiently achieved by the member states).

Decisions

Whilst a few types of decision (e.g. those affecting taxation) still require unanimity in the Council of the European Union, most directives are now subject to one of the three procedures listed below. Each procedure can be seen as an extension of the previous one and reflects the increasing power of the European Parliament. These three procedures are:

1. The Proposal Procedure (or traditional procedure).
2. The Institutional Co-operation Procedure (Article 189c).
3. Co-Decision Procedure (Article 189b).

The default system is the proposal procedure which is used for instruments where neither the co-decision or the co-operation procedure is stated to apply.

The co-operation procedure is used primarily for matters relating to the internal market, social policy, economic and social cohesion and research and development.

The co-decision procedure relies on the ability of the Council and Parliament to agree by placing both on an equal footing. This has been used in many key areas including those relating to the free movement of workers, freedom of establishment and the freedom to provide services, the harmonisation of legislation for the operation of a single market and consumer protection.

DIRECTIVES

Co-decision procedures (article 189b)

This procedure is flow-charted on the next page.

It is the same as the consultation procedure as far as the second Parliamentary reading. However, if there is disagreement between Parliament and the Council at this stage, a Conciliation Committee is convened, and, if there is still no agreement, the proposal fails.

This procedure gave Parliament an effective veto and power-share.

The procedure applies to many important areas of legislation including free movement of workers, freedom of establishment, freedom to provide services, harmonisation of single market legislation, education, vocational training, youth, culture and health, consumer protection, some R & D and some environmental programmes.

The European Council Meeting in Amsterdam (June 1997) agreed to an extension of Co-determination (Co-decision) Procedure.

Qualified majority voting

A major problem for the European Community has always been that of reaching agreement. On the one hand, it is no easy task to get several countries to agree unanimously on any but the most pedestrian of proposals. On the other hand, it is virtually impossible for a majority to force a really recalcitrant member state to fall into line. Under the EC Treaty most Council decisions in the transitional period (1958-1965) had to be unanimous.

From January 1996, however, the intention was that Article 148 should come into force, which provided in Section 1 that "Except where otherwise provided in this Treaty, the Council's decisions shall be taken by a majority of its members."

Article 148 (Section 2) went on to provide for 'qualified majority' voting to be used in specified cases. However, these provisions proved unworkable when in 1965 France blocked decision-making on the common Agricultural Policy by 'the empty chair'. In 1966 the 'Luxembourg compromise' allowed states to veto decisions on the grounds that "very important interests" were at stake.

The Single European Act revived QMV as the normal method for reaching decisions including health and safety related issues. The Treaty of Nice (EU Enlargement) updated this, thus increasing the number of members countries from 15 to 25. Votes are distributed as follows.

Country	Votes (per country)
Germany, France, Italy, United Kingdom	29 each
Spain, Poland	27 each
Netherlands	13
Belgium, Greece, Czech Republic, Portugal, Hungary	12 each
Austria, Sweden	10 each
Slovakia, Denmark, Ireland, Finland, Lithuania	7 each
Luxembourg, Latvia, Slovenia, Estonia, Cyprus	4 each
Malta	3

Figure A7-3: Qualified majority voting. *Source: ACT.*

A "qualified majority" requires 232 of these 321 votes.

Note: the above chart will change as the EU grows in membership.

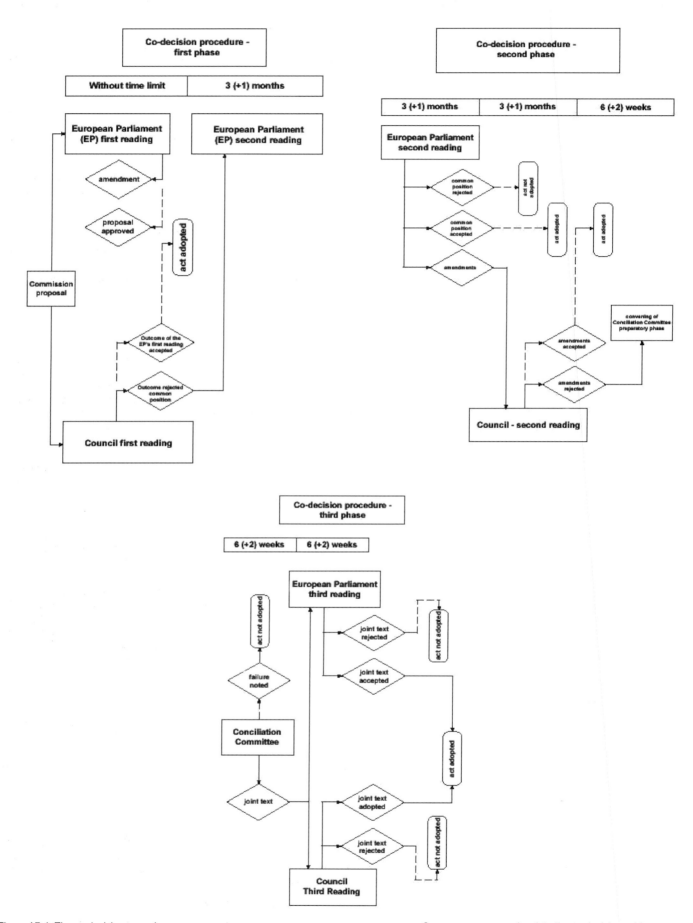

Figure A7-4: The co-decision procedure.

Distinction between directives made under article 95 and article 137 of the Treaty of Rome (formerly article 100 and article 118a respectively)

Articles 95 and 95A are concerned with the harmonisation of standards. These are important in terms of health and safety because they relate to the working environment including standards for personal protective equipment and plant and machinery. Directives issued under these Articles include:

■ The Noise at Work Directive (86/188/EEC).
■ The Approximation of Personal Protective Equipment Laws Directive (89/686/EEC).

Article 137 provides as follows:

■ The Member States shall pay particular attention to encouraging improvements, especially in the working environment, as regards the health and safety of workers, and shall set as their objective the harmonisation of conditions in this area, while maintaining the improvements.
■ In order to help achieve the objective laid down in the first paragraph, the Council, acting by a qualified majority on a proposal from the Commission and after consulting with the European Parliament and the Economic and Social Committee, shall adopt, by means of directives, minimum requirements for gradual implementation, having regard to the conditions and technical rules obtaining in each of the Member States. Such Directives shall avoid imposing administrative, financial and legal constraints in a way which would hold back the creation and development of small and medium-sized undertakings.

The provisions adopted pursuant to this Article shall not prevent each Member State from introducing more stringent measures for the protection of working conditions compatible with the Treaty.

The major health and safety directives were made under Article 137 (e.g. the 'Framework Directive'). Some regulations were derived from directives made under Article 95A. Examples include: the Noise at Work Regulations (NWR) 1989 and the Supply of Machinery Safety Regulations (SMSR) 1992.

Social responsibility

Article 118a of the Treaty is the appropriate legal basis for the adoption by the Community of measures whose principal aim is the protection of the health and safety of workers, not withstanding the ancillary effects which such measures may have on the establishment and functioning of the internal market. The aim is to ensure protection, Article 118a constitutes a more specific rule than Articles 100 and 100a, the existence of which does not have the effect of restricting its scope, and must be widely interpreted as regards the scope it gives to Community legislative action regarding the health and safety of workers. Actions may comprise measures which are of general application, not merely measures specific to certain categories of workers, and which have to be in the nature of minimum requirements only in the sense that Member States remain at liberty to adopt more protective measures.

Internal market issues

Article 8 of the Single European Act identified the need to eliminate technical barriers to trade through the harmonisation of standards for health and safety. The approach is to develop a philosophy of essential safety requirements through harmonisation Directives to establish common essential safety requirements throughout the community.

UK LAW IN RESPONSE TO EC DIRECTIVES

Most directives are implemented in the UK by regulations made under Section 15 of the HASAWA 1974. Section 15 lays down the framework which must be adhered to when making health and safety regulations. In most cases, these statutory instruments are laid (placed for members to read in the house) before Parliament for 40 days before they can come into force rather than being positively voted upon.

Regulations start life in the form of a consultative document which is distributed to any interested parties such as the CBI and TUC for comment. The consultative document outlines the background and aims of the proposed legislation together with a cost/benefit analysis (effect on society of the proposal i.e. the reduction of loss compared to the cost of implementation) as well as the draft regulations themselves. Comment is sought on the proposed regulations as well as the assumptions and costs in the cost benefit assessment. The Secretary of State must consult the HSC and when making or modifying regulations made under the HASAWA 1974. The UK is obliged to implement EU directives in full; therefore the consultative role can only have a limited effect in this instance.

THE ROLE OF THE EUROPEAN COURT OF JUSTICE

Procedure for referring cases

The High Court and the Court of Appeal have a jurisdiction to interpret Community law and they are not obliged to grant a right of appeal to the European Court of Justice (ECJ). If however the case goes to the House of Lords on appeal, the House of Lords are obliged to refer it to the European Court of Justice if either of the parties involved wishes it.

In effect the appeals to the European Court of Justice can only be made once the final court of appeal has been reached. Thus, in the UK, any court may ask the ECJ for a ruling but the House of Lords is bound to ask for a ruling if a party requests it.

How decisions of the European Court of Justice are enforced through courts of Member States

The provisions of the Treaty of Rome are enforceable in the High Court under the European Communities Act 1972. This provides that the High Court can find out from the Treaty itself what rights have been infringed. This is not always clear as the wording is very general and lacks the precision of statute law. However the ECJ is, in effect, the interpreter and enforcer of the various treaties and UK judges are obliged to take note of their decisions - even when they are in conflict with UK law.

Effect of decisions of the European Court of Justice on UK law

As stated earlier the European Communities Act 1972 requires the UK courts to take note of the provisions of the various Treaties and the decisions of the ECJ. In effect the decisions of the ECJ must be accepted by the courts of the Member States and there is no right to appeal. In effect EC law has supremacy over UK law.

A7.4 - UK legislative framework

Status and procedure for making UK Acts of Parliament, regulations, orders

ACTS OF PARLIAMENT

The functions of green and white papers

Green papers are discussion documents which precede the Bill presented before Parliament. When considering legislation the Government may publish a white paper which contains policy statements and explanations for proposed legislation. During passage through Parliament and before Royal Assent an intended Act is called a Bill.

Progression of a Bill through Parliament

A Bill goes through the following process:

House of Commons

First Reading:	Bill introduced into the House of Commons for formal reading.
Second Reading:	Discussion of the general principles and the purpose of the Bill.
Committee Stage:	Bill goes to committee for detailed consideration.
Report Stage:	Committee reports Bill to the House for any amendments.
	House amends Bill and returns it to Committee.
Third Reading:	Bill read in House of Commons and only verbal alterations may be made.

House of Lords

The Bill follows similar procedures in the Lords.

Any amendments by the Lords must be returned to the Commons for consideration.

If the Lords reject the Bill for 2 sessions, it may receive Royal Assent without the Lords agreement as the House of Lords can only delay a Bill for a maximum period of 1 year.

Royal Assent

After being passed by both Houses the Bill receives Royal Assent.

REGULATIONS

Procedure under section 15 of the HASAWA and permissible subject matter of regulations

Some Acts allow delegated legislation such as Regulations to be made by Ministers of the Crown. In some cases, these statutory instruments are laid before Parliament for 40 days before they can come into force rather than being positively voted upon. During this period a member may propose a negative affirmation to veto the statutory instrument.

The Health and Safety at Work etc. Act (HASAWA) 1974 is an "enabling" Act which allows the Secretary of State and other designated Ministers to make health and safety regulations (Section 15). Regulations should be drawn up with the aim of maintaining or improving standards of health, safety and welfare. Section 15 lays down the framework which must be adhered to when making health and safety regulations. Failure to follow this framework would allow the courts to treat the regulations as void under the legal principle of *'ultra vires'* that is, that it exceeds the prescribed limits or that it has been made without due compliance with the correct procedure.

Role of the Secretary of State

As previously discussed, the Secretary of State is empowered by Parliament, via primary legislation such as the HASAWA 1974, to make regulations. Two other bodies the Health and Safety Commission (HSC) together with the Health and Safety Executive (HSE), which are established by Section 10 of the HASAWA 1974 have a pivotal role to play in the drawing up and drafting of regulations.

Health and Safety Commission in making regulations

The general functions of the HSC/E are laid down in Section 11. They propose necessary changes to law and participate in developing appropriate standards at both national level and with European and international bodies. This includes the negotiation and implementation of EU directives and the reform of domestic health and safety legislation.

Various stages of consultation

Regulations start life in the form of a consultative document which is distributed to any interested parties such as the CBI and TUC for comment. The consultative document outlines the background and aims of the proposed legislation together with a cost/benefit analysis as well as the draft regulations themselves. Comment is sought on the proposed regulations as well as the assumptions and costs in the cost benefit assessment. The Secretary of State must consult the HSC and when making or modifying regulations made under the HASAWA 1974.

The use of socio-technical cost-benefit analysis in the economic assessment of proposed legislative/regulatory change

Socio-technical cost benefit analysis is concerned with the needs or advantages given to society by the implementation of a new technology or change, for example, the introduction into a work place of a substance to make paint for automobiles with an assigned MEL, where the desire for the product will outweigh the concern for those who may be at risk from its use. The calculation will consider the impact on society of not making the change, the technical ability to make the change, with regard to the practical prevention techniques available such as in this instance Local exhaust ventilation and personal protective equipment. Much comment is made about the use of mobile phones which use microwave (radiation) transmitters for communication, where it is argued by many that the benefit (talk to anyone, anywhere, anytime) is outweighed by the risk, namely possible risk of brain tumour. To date society has chosen to take the risk. The HSE/HSC will monitor workplace ill health and will make proposals based on such observations to change the law, and government will consult and make legislative changes based on such cost benefit calculations.

A7.5 - Structure of the Courts

The function, jurisdiction and powers of courts

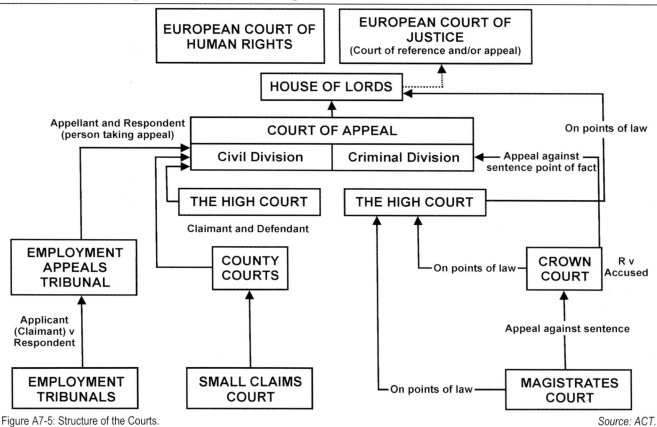

Figure A7-5: Structure of the Courts.   *Source: ACT.*

EMPLOYMENT TRIBUNALS

Functions

Employment tribunals deal with the following employment/health and safety matters:

1.   Victimisation (automatic grounds for unfair dismissal section 100 the Employment Rights Act 1996).
2.   Dismissal, actual or constructive, following a breach of health and safety law, regulation and/or term of an employment contract.
3.   Appeals against improvement and prohibition notices (Section 24 HASAWA 1974).
4.   Safety representatives and safety committees [time off, payment functions and training of representatives Safety Representatives and Safety Committees Regulations (SRSC) 1977].
5.   Representatives of employee safety [pay and time off under the Health and Safety (Consultation with Employees) Regulations (HSCER) 1996].
6.   Suspension from work for medical reasons [Employment Protection (Consolidation) Act 1978].
7.   Suspension from work on maternity grounds.

Jurisdiction

Employment Tribunals deal with complaints relating to health and safety at work matters.

Powers

They may make financial awards to employees, unlimited for issues concerning discrimination, public interest disclosure, but limited to £50000 for all other cases. They may direct that certain rights must be given to employees performing duties under specific legislation, e.g. Disputes over Appointed Trade Union Safety Representatives rights to time off to perform their duties. They can uphold, modify or amend requirements under appeal for Improvement or Prohibition notices.

An arbitration scheme involving ACAS is proposed for cases relating to unfair dismissal. Both parties must agree to the scheme and the employee must be advised by a 'relevant independent adviser' (e.g. solicitor, barrister, competent trades union officials or workers at advice centres). Any award made is binding and enforceable in the County Court.

Title

Under the Employment Rights (Dispute Resolution) Act 1998, Industrial Tribunals are to be known as Employment Tribunals.

Composition

An employment tribunal usually consists of a legally-qualified chairperson appointed by the Lord Chancellor and two lay members - one representing management interests and the other employees (e.g. one from a trades union). These are selected from panels kept by the Department of the Environment after nominations from employers' organisations and trades unions.

All hearings are heard by the chairman and either two other members or, with the consent of the parties, one other member.

Decision

When all three members of an employment tribunal are sitting the majority view prevails.

An arbitration scheme involving ACAS is proposed for cases relating to unfair dismissal. Both parties must agree to the scheme and the employee must be advised by a 'relevant independent adviser' (e.g. solicitor, barrister, competent trades union officials or workers at advice centres). Any award made is binding and enforceable in the County Court.

MAGISTRATES' COURTS

Functions

Magistrate courts are the first court to deal with all summary or indictable offences.

Magistrates' courts are mostly staffed by lay magistrates who are not legally qualified and sit part-time. Lay magistrates come from the community and are appointed by the Lord Chancellor. They are assisted by salaried clerks who must be solicitors or barristers of at least five years' standing. Stipendiary magistrates sit in large towns and are paid a stipend (a form of salary). They must be solicitors or barristers of at least seven years' standing. Lay magistrates sit two or usually three to a court, stipendiary magistrates sit alone.

Jurisdiction

County courts have criminal and some civil (e.g. matrimonial maintenance orders and questions regarding adoption) jurisdiction and deal with all offences in the first instance; summary offences are normally heard by the Magistrates. The magistrates may determine that more serious cases should be indicted to the Crown Court for trial or sentencing.

Powers

The maximum fine a magistrate can impose for most health & safety infringements is £5000. This applies to breaches of Section 7 of the HASAWA 1974 (relating to the employee), subordinate regulations and other relevant legislation.

The maximum penalty for breaches of Sections 2-6 of the HASAWA 1974 and other sections relating to breaches of improvement/prohibition notices and court remedy orders is £20,000.

In addition to this, magistrates may impose a prison sentence for an offence which required a licence to be held, such as the removal of asbestos, or failure to comply with an improvement/prohibition notice.

COUNTY COURTS

County Courts have civil jurisdiction only but deal with almost every kind of civil case arising within the local areas for which the courts are established. County Courts can hear cases in contract up to £25,000 and tort claims of up to £50,000 in the case of actions for damages relating to personal injury. They may exceed the limit with consent of both parties. In practice they deal with the majority of the country's civil litigation.

The County Court is usually presided over by a Circuit judge who will have had at least 10 years advocacy experience as a barrister in the Crown or County Court. He or she normally sits alone, although in a small number of civil cases (e.g. libel) there may be a jury. Appellants to the County Court have right of appeal to the Civil Division of the Court of Appeal.

HIGH COURT

Functions

The High Court is organised into three divisions. These are the Queen's Bench, the Chancery, and the Family Divisions. Except where other special courts have exclusive jurisdiction, the High Court can deal with any civil matter.

The High Court is staffed by judges (Justices of the High Court) who must be persons who have had right of audience in the High Court for at least ten years or a Circuit judge who has held office for at least two years. In hearing a case for the first time a High Court judge sits alone. A Divisional Court of two or more High Court judges sits to hear appeals from Magistrates' and Crown Courts.

Jurisdiction

The Queen's Bench division is presided over by the Lord Chief Justice and deals mainly with actions based on contract or tort. It also contains an Admiralty Court and a Commercial Court.

The Chancery division deals with traditional equity matters such as disputed wills, company matters, trusts and mortgages.

The Family division deals with matters of family law including divorce.

Powers

There is no upper limit to the sum that may be claimed for damages relating to personal injury in a high court.

CROWN COURT

Functions

The Crown Court is a superior court of record created by the Courts Act 1971. In theory the Crown Court is a single court; however, in practice it comprises a number of courts in large towns and cities and the Old Bailey in London. The Crown Court tries all serious (indictable) offences with a jury and hears appeals and deals with committals for sentencing from magistrates' courts. It also deals with a few types of civil cases on matters arising from the magistrates' court.

A circuit judge, a recorder, or a High Court judge may sit in the Crown Court. Sometimes lay magistrates also sit. Very serious offences, such as murder and treason, may only be heard by a High Court judge in the Crown Court. All prosecutions for indictable offences are heard by a judge with a jury of 12 persons.

Jurisdiction

All indictable offences are triable in the Crown Court. An indictment is a formal statement of a serious crime prepared by trial by jury. The Court also hears appeals from magistrates and committals for sentence from the magistrate's court.

Powers

The Crown Court may impose 'an unlimited fine', or up to two years imprisonment, or both, for each breach of health and safety law (HASAWA and subordinate regulations), Manslaughter and murder up to 25, years and life imprisonment respectively.

From the Crown Court appeal on criminal matters is made to the Criminal Division of the Court of Appeal. As with the magistrates court, an appeal on a point of law may also be made to a Divisional Court of the Queen's Bench division (High Court).

COURT OF APPEAL

Functions

The Court of Appeal is divided into Criminal and Civil Divisions. The Court consists of 35 Lords Justices of Appeal. Normally, three judges will sit together to hear appeals from county courts, the High Court and the Employment Appeal Tribunal. It does not conduct a complete rehearing of the case but reviews the record of the evidence in the lower court and the legal arguments put before it.

Jurisdiction

Hears appeals from various divisions of the County Court, the High Courts (civil), the Employment Appeals Tribunal and the Crown Courts.

Powers

The Court may uphold or reverse the earlier decision, in the County Court, the High Court, and Employment Appeal Tribunal or order a new trial. A majority decision is given and dissenting judgments are stated.

HOUSE OF LORDS

Functions

Apart from the limited jurisdiction of the Court of Justice (of the EC), the Judicial Committee of the House of Lords is the highest court of appeal in the United Kingdom. The court consists of between nine and twelve Law Lords who are life peers. A minimum of three (but normally five) Law Lords constitutes a court. A majority decision is given and dissenting judgements are stated. The Court hears appeals from both the civil and the criminal divisions of the Court of Appeal.

Jurisdiction

Civil

The Court hears appeals from the Court of Appeal (Civil Division), the Court of Session in Scotland and the Supreme Court of Northern Ireland. In all cases either the lower court or the Appeal Committee of the House of Lords must certify that a point of law of general public interest is involved.

There is a 'leapfrogging' method, whereby a direct appeal may be made from the High Court or Divisional Court to the House of Lords bypassing the Court of Appeal. All parties must consent and a point of law of general public interest has to be involved. This process is most often used for revenue appeals where the construction of statutes may be involved.

Criminal

The Court hears appeals from the Court of appeal (Criminal Division) and the Divisional Court of the Queen's Bench. As with Civil, the court will only hear a point of law of general importance. The Court is not a final appellate for Scotland, the Scottish Court of Appeal is.

Powers

The Court may uphold or reverse the earlier decision, in the High Court, the Court of Appeal and Employment Appeal Tribunal or order a new trial. A majority decision is given and dissenting judgments are stated.

EUROPEAN COURT OF JUSTICE

Functions

The European Court of Justice (ECJ) hears legal actions connected with European Union (EU) law. The ECJ has a President, two First Advocates General, 6 Presidents of Chambers, eleven judges, seven Advocates-General and a Registrar (25 persons in all), all of whom are appointed by states but act independently of the countries which appointed them. A single majority judgement is given and the views of dissenting judges are not published. The ECJ's jurisdiction is limited to that set out in the EU treaties.

Jurisdiction

The court can hear disputes between states or between the Commission and a state relating to matters covered by an EU treaty. It can also consider the legality of acts or omissions of the Council of Ministers, the European Commission or the European Parliament.

Powers

The court can also declare that any of these institutions has violated the EU treaties. It can also:

- Hear appeals by persons, for example, against fines imposed by the Commission for breaches of EU law.
- Interpret EU law when asked to do so by the final court of appeal in each state (i.e. the House of Lords in the UK).
- Give an advisory opinion on whether their proposals are compatible with existing EU law at the request of the Council of Ministers or of the European Commission.

Basic court procedures

PROSECUTIONS FOR BREACHES OF HEALTH AND SAFETY LEGISLATION

Plea in the Magistrates Court

In England and Wales an HSE Inspector may take a prosecution in a Magistrates' Court. This power is authorised under section 39 of the HASAWA 1974. For summary offences, or for those either way offences where the accused has opted for the magistrates to deal with their case, the accused will be asked to enter a plea of either guilty or not guilty to the charges. If a plea of not guilty is entered, a trial date convenient for both defence and prosecution witnesses will be fixed. The trial is usually listed for some weeks later.

The magistrates, having adjourned the case, may decide to remand the accused on bail. Effectively this means that if they did not attend court on the trial date they would have committed an offence under the Bail Act for which they may be sentenced.

Bail means the granting of freedom subject to the accused having a duty to surrender to custody or to attend court at a future date and time stated to them. This is known as unconditional bail (i.e. the only condition attached is that the accused reappears at the stated date), but it is also possible for the magistrates to grant conditional bail, which imposes further conditions.

Magistrates also have the power to grant bail to an offender who appears before them while in custody after arrest (this will therefore apply only to fairly serious offences, not summary cases where the offender is free until the date of his/her appearance in court).

Trial procedure

- Charge read out - accused pleads. If pleads not guilty, then ...
- Opening speeches by prosecution and defence.
- Prosecution witnesses - examined by prosecution, defence and possible re-examination by prosecution.
- Defence witness.
- Summary by prosecution and defence.
- Magistrates retire to reach a verdict.

A similar procedure applies in the Crown Court where trials are conducted before judge and jury:

- Judge advises and directs on points of law.
- Jury decides guilt or innocence.

Appeals

Appeals relating to sentencing and conviction by the Magistrates Court may be made to the Crown Court.

Appeals can be made to the High Court:

- On a point of law (e.g. a specific interpretation of a legal issue involved such as the meaning of a particular section of the HASAWA 1974).
- On the ground that the magistrates have acted outside their jurisdiction.

Appeals from the Crown Court to the Court of Appeal can be made on questions of law and fact, against sentence, or as a point of law.

Finally, the Court of Appeal may grant leave to appeal to the House of Lords if the case involves a legal point which is of public interest.

PURSUING CIVIL ACTIONS

See also - 'Civil Law' - Element A9

Procedures for the bringing of civil actions (civil procedures rules)

The procedures for personal injury cases were radically overhauled as a result of a review by Lord Woolf (the Woolf Report). This was done in an attempt to speed up and simplify the process as well as keeping costs within reasonable limits. The resulting new Civil Procedures Rules were introduced on 26 April 1999 and have the following aims:

- To ensure that all parties are dealt with on an equal footing so that wealthier parties do not have an unfair advantage.
- To save expense.

- To deal with cases in a way that is proportionate to the sums involved, the complexity and importance of the case and the financial position of the parties.
- To ensure that cases are dealt with expeditiously and fairly in ways which promote an open and full exchange of information.
- To allot an appropriate share of the Court's resources, while taking into account the needs of other cases.

The rules apply to both the High Court and County Court. Many of the obscure Latin phrases have been replaced and the terms used simplified. For example, the person who brought an action was called a 'plaintiff' and is now known as the 'claimant' and the term 'interlocutory applications' is replaced with 'court applications'.

Cases are managed by the Court and alternate dispute resolution (ADR) is encouraged. A new body, the Centre for Dispute Resolution (CFDR) has been formed to deal with this. This recognises that about 94% of cases are settled out of court and that it is far less expensive to engage in an, on average, two day mediation process than an eight year battle for compensation suffered by one widow relating to the death of her husband! CFDR estimates that the ADR process saves £250,000 per case in professional fees alone (averaged over 40 cases).

Expert witnesses

The role of the expert witness is to assist a party to establish the facts, assess the merits of the case and help with its preparation. The overriding duty of the expert is to the court rather than to the person who pays for his or her services. Where two parties wish to submit expert evidence, the court may direct that evidence on the particular issue be given by one expert only. The rules also allow the court to direct on matters relating to the fees and expenses paid to experts.

Pre-action protocol

The process begins with a pre-action protocol which aims to reduce the need for litigation and encourages contact between the parties prior to the action starting.

Pre-action protocols have been developed for a number of events including personal injury cases and clinical negligence. The protocol for personal injury involves a 3 stage process:

1. The letter of claim.
2. The reply.
3. The investigation.

The letter of claim

The action is started on a claim form. This contains a summary of the facts of the cases together with the details of the loss (e.g. financial; injuries suffered).

The reply

The defendant must reply within 21 days after service together with details of any insurer that he or she has.

The investigation

The defendant has a maximum of three months to investigate the claim. A reply must then be sent to the claimant (or the claimants solicitor) which:

- Admits liability.
- Denies liability in full.
- Gives a partial admission of liability.

Reasons for full or partial admission of liability must be given together with any relevant documents. These are the same documents that the defendant would have to disclose anyway under court proceedings. Thus the defendant will not be able to issue a denial of responsibility without giving reasons or to delay the decision as to whether to settle or fight.

- The claimant will be able to make a decision, based on the defendant's reply, about whether or not to proceed with the claim. If the defendant fails to make a proper reply, then the claimant will be able to start proceedings without being liable for costs.

Commencement of proceedings

Once the proceedings have been started the defence has up to 28 days to file a response. Extensions may be granted but this is rare particularly if the defendant has failed to comply with the pre-action protocol. The response consists of:

- Those facts which are admitted to.
- Those facts which are denied with reasons.
- Those facts which cannot be admitted or denied and which the claimant must therefore prove.
- The defendant's version of the events.

The statement of truth

The defendant's case must be supported by a "statement of truth" which must be signed by a senior officer of the organisation, a partner or a legal representative. The statement begins:

"The defendant believes the facts stated in this defence are true".

Although not sworn, a signatory who signs the statement without honestly believing it to be true may be held in contempt of court.

If a legal representative signs the document, then they are deemed to have briefed the organisation as to its meaning and the penalties will be the same as if the defendant had signed it originally.

Disclosure of documents

All documents that could support or adversely affect the case must be disclosed. Many of these may have been previously disclosed under the pre-action protocol procedure.

The disclosure statement

Documents sent to the opposing party must be accompanied by a formal statement of disclosure confirming that this has been done with full knowledge of the requirements and to the best of their ability.

Offers to settle

An offer to settle may be made by either party and a payment made into the court. If the other side decides not to accept, this has a bearing on the awarding of costs.

Case management

The case will be managed by the Court who will give 'directions' on how it is to be handled based on an allocation questionnaire filed by the parties involved. A summary judgement may be made after giving 14 days' notice to both parties against either the claimant or the defendant because:

- The claim has no prospect of success.
- The defence has no real prospect of success.

Claims will be dealt with according to their value:

Name	Sum	Points
Small claims	up to £5,000	
Fast-track	£5,000 - £15,000	Standard time between giving of directions and trial no more than 30 weeks. Trial date fixed at time of direction. Court discretion to limit disclosure of documents. Oral expert evidence limited to two fields of expertise and to one expert per party
Multi-track	over £15,000	Court gives directions for management of case and timetable for trial. Alternatively a Case Management and/or a Pre-Trial Review may be fixed.

Figure A7-6: Case management.   *Source: ACT.*

After allocation to the appropriate track the court will set a timetable or fix a case management conference or a pre trial review or a combination of these. Under the rules, trials must be held "as soon as is practicable".

See - "Progress of a Case" flow diagram - next page.

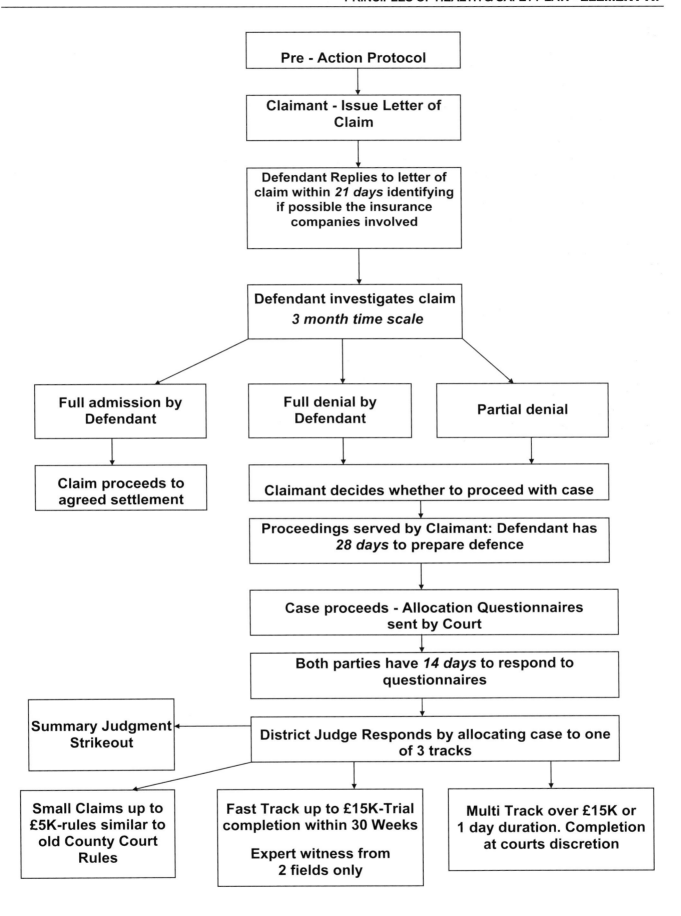

Figure A7-7: Progress of a case.

Source: ACT.

EMPLOYMENT TRIBUNALS - PROCEDURES IN MATTERS OF HEALTH AND SAFETY

Presentation of hearings

A case begins with an applicant or claimant (i.e. employee making a complaint) filing an originating application, setting out the nature of the claim and the redress sought. A copy of this document is then sent to the 'offending' employer (known as the 'respondent') who submits a defence in another document, known as a notice of appearance. If one party to the proceedings wishes to know more about allegations made against him he can request 'further particulars'; if this request is refused when such particulars are relevant to the case the tribunal can order 'discovery' of them (i.e. their production).

'Privileged' documents do not have to be made available to the other party, though their existence must be disclosed to the tribunal, e.g. documents predominantly concerned with litigation, such as counsel's opinion, solicitors'/clients' letters.

Procedure

Current law relating to procedure in employment tribunals is contained in regulations made under the Employment Tribunals Act 1996.

Importance of documents

If a party proposed to refer to a document at the hearing they should supply the other side with copies in advance (a week before the hearing), as well as the Chairman and the two lay members. Failure to do so can mean that the other party might ask for an adjournment in order to study them, especially if they are complicated. It should be borne in mind that documentary evidence at a hearing is much more important and convincing than oral evidence.

Witnesses

Persons present at all material times and occasions relating to the complaint should be available to give evidence as witnesses. Witnesses should commit to writing their recollections of events and conversations; this will facilitate answers to questions at the hearing. Witnesses cannot refer to notes when giving evidence, unless the notes were made at the time of the event or conversation. If a witness is reluctant to appear, the tribunal can order him to do so if it is felt that his evidence would be material.

Timetable

Both parties to the proceedings must be informed at least 14 days before the date fixed for the hearing. The hearing itself consists of two parts:

1. The applicant (the employee):
   - Presents the outline of the case.
   - Calls his evidence.
2. The respondent (the employer):
   - Calls his evidence.
   - Makes a closing speech.

Full hearing

Proceedings are always heard in public unless there is a good reason for not doing so, e.g. national security. In his opening speech an applicant should preferably mention:

- His role in the organization.
- The facts on which he bases his case.
- Any relevant statutes and case law.

Employers may be represented by a specialist member of management or may decide to instruct lawyers if the case is complicated. Any witnesses are then called and examined on oath. This is then repeated by the respondent. Then in a closing speech each side's representative should sum up the relevant facts and law, answering any questions raised by the other side or the chairperson or members of the tribunal.

Evidence

The strict 'hearsay' evidence rules do not apply in employment tribunals, though of course first-hand evidence of what the applicant/witnesses actually saw or heard carries much more weight.

Conclusion of hearing

After completion of the final speeches, the tribunal will give its decision - normally on the day of the hearing but if the case is difficult it can be postponed. The decision is oral, consisting of a summary of the facts and the result. At a later date the decision is set out formally.

Costs

Costs are not normally awarded to a successful party; and in order for costs to be awarded it must be shown either that:

- One party acted 'frivolously or vexatiously' (i.e. there never was a valid claim), or
- The proceedings were brought or conducted unreasonably (e.g. failure by one party to warn witnesses to attend, thereby resulting in delay).

Moreover, an order for costs would be in keeping with the ability of a party to pay; thus if a party was unemployed this would be taken into account. Applications for costs must be made either at the hearing, or within a reasonable time afterwards.

The appeals system

Review of decision

A decision of an industrial tribunal can be challenged, or 'reviewed' on the following grounds:

- The decision discloses an error on the part of the tribunal.
- A party did not receive notice of proceedings.
- The decision was made in the absence of a party entitled to be heard.
- New evidence has come to light.
- The interests of justice require a review.

(Moreover, the Divisional Court of the Queen's Bench Division of the High Court can overturn a decision of an industrial tribunal, disclosing an error of law.) For instance, if there was a relevant conflicting judgement of the Employment Appeal Tribunal (EAT) which the tribunal had not taken into account, then the tribunal can be reconvened to rectify the oversight.

Appeals against enforcement notices

Appeals are made against improvement and prohibition notices on the grounds of:

1. Time limits for compliance.
2. Substantive law involved.

Appeals against time limits

While employers are unlikely to succeed in most cases on appeals on substantive law, tribunals are more flexible about time limits. Appeals from employment tribunals lie to the Employment Appeal Tribunal (EAT), except in health and safety matters, where appeal lies to the Divisional Court of the High Court. Like the EAT, the latter can only interfere where the tribunal has erred in respect of the view of law (not facts) which it took.

A7.6 - Enforcement of health and safety law

Enforcement authorities

AUTHORITIES EMPOWERED TO ENFORCE HEALTH AND SAFETY LEGISLATION

The Health and Safety Executive has primary responsibility for enforcing health and safety law. Section 18 of the HASAWA 1974 allows the Secretary of State to make local authorities responsible for enforcement as he prescribes and to assign or transfer enforcement responsibilities between the HSE/Local Authority as necessary.

OUTLINE OF DIVISION OF RESPONSIBILITIES BETWEEN ENFORCING AUTHORITIES

The division of these responsibilities is made under the Health and Safety (Enforcing Authority) Regulations 1998. In general the HSE is responsible for enforcement in premises such as factories, fairgrounds and construction sites as well as the enforcement of specific legislation such as section 6 of the HASAWA 1974. The local authority is generally responsible for premises such as offices, launderettes, most shops and distribution premises such as warehouses.

DESCRIPTION OF POWERS OF ENFORCING AUTHORITIES AND THEIR INSPECTORS

Powers of inspectors (HASAWA 1974 Section 20 & 25)

This section grants the health and safety inspector a number of powers of enforcement. Inspectors carry a warrant which entitles them to use these powers. The powers are summarised below:-

1. The right of entry (without having to resort to a Magistrates' Court). An inspector may enter any premise which he considers to be a place of employment at any reasonable time of day or night.
2. An inspector may take with him a police constable if he/she has reasonable cause to think that there would be any serious obstruction to prevent him from carrying out his duties.
3. An inspector can also take with him any other person who has been authorised by the Health and Safety Executive/Local Authority.
4. Equipment and materials required to carry out tests etc. may also be taken into places of employment.
5. An inspector may require premises, parts of premises or anything in the premises to be left undisturbed until any examination or investigation is completed.
6. An inspector has the right to take measurements, photographs and make sound recordings as he thinks fit.
7. Section 20 allows an inspector to obtain samples of articles and substances, either in the premises or in the atmosphere, or in the vicinity of the premises.
8. An inspector may order equipment, plant, substances, etc. to be dismantled or destroyed if they are a cause of immediate danger (Section 25).
9. An inspector may take into the possession of the articles or substances.
10. An inspector has the right to require the production of, and take copies of, books and documents which are relevant to his work.
11. An inspector has the right to examine any person, either alone or with a second person, as he thinks fit, and to require that person to provide a written statement of fact.
12. An inspector may conduct legal proceedings before a Court of Summary Jurisdiction (Magistrates' Court) in England and Wales, and serve Improvement and Prohibition Notices under Sections 39, 21 and 22 respectively.

OBLIGATIONS OF ENFORCING OFFICERS

Duty to give information to employees or their representatives (HASAWA 1974 Section 2)

The duties of **Employers to their Employees**. This section of HASAWA 1974 also contains duties relating to joint consultation with Trade Union appointed Safety Representatives. The SRSC 1977 were made under the authority of section 2(4).

Section 2. (c) The provision of such information, instruction, training and supervision as is necessary to ensure, so far as is reasonably practicable, the health and safety at work of his employees.

Information may need to be given to others to ensure health and safety of employees (**R v Swan Hunter Shipbuilders Ltd**). **See - Element A8.**

Duty not to disclose information (HASAWA 1974 Section 28)

Obligations of Enforcing Authorities and their Inspectors - prevents officers disclosing confidential information.

Basically this section of the Health and Safety at Work etc. Act 1974 prevents officers appointed by the Enforcing Authorities from disclosing confidential information gained in the course of his/her duties.

The fundamental role of inspectors is summarised as follows:

1. Enforcement of legislation relating to health, safety and welfare.
2. To monitor the safety performance and accident potential of industry and other places of employment.
3. To provide general advice to industry and other places of employment on practical aspects of health, safety and welfare, and also to interpret the legislation which they enforce into practical terms which can be understood by industrialists and others affected.
4. To investigate accidents and dangerous occurrences.
5. To form links with local employers and employee's organisations and discuss health and safety problems relevant to their particular trades or activities.
6. To collect and collate statistics relating to accidents and industrial diseases, and transmit this into the headquarters organisation for analysis and publication.
7. To monitor the standards of new machinery, processes and substances, and liaise with manufacturers.
8. To conduct legal proceedings before Magistrates' Courts.
9. To become involved in the safety training activities relating to the health, safety and welfare of people at work.

Section 27 of the HASAWA 1974 empowers the HSC (with the Secretary of State's consent) to require the provision of specified information in order for the HSC/Enforcing Authority to carry out its functions. Under section 28 this information, which must only be used for the purposes of the HSC/Enforcing Authority, must remain confidential - particularly the disclosure of trade secrets. Information must not be disclosed without the consent of the person who provided it. There are, however, some exceptions including the provision of information to public bodies such as the police to enable them to carry out their statutory functions.

Inspectors are required to provide information to employees or their representatives where this is necessary in keeping them adequately informed about health and safety matters. The information the inspector is required to supply relates to both factual information regarding their workplace and any actions the inspector proposes to take in respect of their work premises. Information provided to employees must also be given to employers.

Offences and maximum penalties under the law

OFFENCES (HASAWA SECTION 33)

Section 33 of the HASAWA 1974 outlines the provisions as to offences under Health & Safety legislation. A number of other miscellaneous offences are also identified by Section 33, including:

1. Impersonation of an inspector.
2. The obstruction of an inspector.
3. Contravention of improvement and prohibition notices.
4. The prevention of an inspector from interviewing witnesses or others who may assist with his enquiries.

PENALTIES

Health and Safety (Offences) Act (HSOA) 2008

The Health and Safety Offences Act 2008 received royal assent on 16 October 2008 and came into force in January 2009 covering Great Britain and Northern Ireland. The Act does not impose additional duties upon individuals or businesses but increases the penalties for existing offences and provides courts with greater sentencing powers for those who fail to adhere to health and safety legislation.

The Act amends Section 33 of the Health and Safety at Work etc Act 1974, and raises the maximum penalties available to the courts in respect of certain health and safety offences.

The Act raises the maximum penalties that can be imposed for breaching health and safety regulations in the lower courts from £5,000 to £20,000. Imprisonment is an option for individuals prosecuted for health and safety offences in both the lower and higher courts - up to 12 months in a Magistrates Court (6 months in Northern Ireland) and 2 years in a Crown Court .

Offence	Penalty on summary conviction	Penalty on conviction on indictment
An offence under section 33(1)(a) consisting of a failure to discharge a duty to which a person is subject by virtue of sections 2 to 6.	Imprisonment for a term not exceeding 12 months, or a fine not exceeding £20,000, or both.	Imprisonment for a term not exceeding two years, or a fine, or both.
An offence under section 33(1)(a) consisting of a failure to discharge a duty to which a person is subject by virtue of section 7.	Imprisonment for a term not exceeding 12 months, or a fine not exceeding the statutory maximum, or both.	Imprisonment for a term not exceeding two years, or a fine, or both.
An offence under section 33(1)(b) consisting of a contravention of section 8.	Imprisonment for a term not exceeding 12 months, or a fine not exceeding £20,000, or both.	Imprisonment for a term not exceeding two years, or a fine, or both.
An offence under section 33(1)(b) consisting of a contravention of section 9.	A fine not exceeding £20,000.	A fine.
An offence under section 33(1)(c). To contravene any health and safety regulations	Imprisonment for a term not exceeding 12 months, or a fine not exceeding £20,000, or both.	Imprisonment for a term not exceeding two years, or a fine, or both.
An offence under section 33(1)(d). To obstruct any person in the exercise of his powers under section 14 of the Act	A fine not exceeding level 5 on the standard scale.	
An offence under section 33(1)(e) - To contravene any requirement imposed by an inspector under section 20 or 25. (f) - To prevent any person from appearing before an inspector or (g) - To contravene an improvement or prohibition notice	Imprisonment for a term not exceeding 12 months, or a fine not exceeding £20,000, or both.	Imprisonment for a term not exceeding two years, or a fine, or both.
An offence under section 33(1)(h). To intentionally obstruct an inspector	Imprisonment for a term not exceeding 51 weeks (in England and Wales) or 12 months (in Scotland), or a fine not exceeding level 5 on the standard scale, or both.	
An offence under section 33(1)(i). Failure to provide information.	A fine not exceeding the statutory maximum.	A fine.
An offence under section 33(1)(j). Disclosing restricted information.	Imprisonment for a term not exceeding 12 months, or a fine not exceeding the statutory maximum, or both.	Imprisonment for a term not exceeding two years, or a fine, or both.
An offence under section 33(1)(k) – to make a false statement. (l) – to make a false entry in a register or (m) – to forge or use forged documents.	Imprisonment for a term not exceeding 12 months, or a fine not exceeding £20,000, or both.	Imprisonment for a term not exceeding two years, or a fine, or both.
An offence under section 33(1)(n). To pretend to be an inspector.	A fine not exceeding level 5 on the standard scale.	
An offence under section 33(1)(o). Failure to comply with a court order.	Imprisonment for a term not exceeding 12 months, or a fine not exceeding £20,000, or both.	Imprisonment for a term not exceeding two years, or a fine, or both.
An offence under the existing statutory provisions for which no other penalty is specified.	Imprisonment for a term not exceeding 12 months, or a fine not exceeding £20,000, or both.	Imprisonment for a term not exceeding two years, or a fine, or both.

Figure A7-8: Summary of new structure under the Health and Safety (Offences) Act 2008.   *Source: RMS.*

OFFENCES FOR WHICH IMPRISONMENT IS, AND IS NOT, A FORM OF SANCTION

Imprisonment for health and safety offences is only possible for a limited number of offences: failure to comply with a notice; failure to have a licence where a licence is required, e.g. removal of asbestos; failure to comply with a court order. The Magistrates may give up to six months imprisonment and the Crown Court Judge may give up to two years. The prison sentence may be given as well as or instead of a fine.

Options for enforcement action

HEALTH AND SAFETY EXECUTIVE (HSE) ENFORCEMENT GUIDE

The health and safety enforcers, i.e. HSE and local authorities have a range of enforcement actions available to them and these are detailed in the Enforcement Guide.

The HSC has issued an Enforcement Policy Statement, which sets out the general principles and approach expected to be followed by the enforcing authorities (mainly HSE and local authorities). All inspectors who take enforcement action are required to follow the Statement.

Quoting from the Statement:

> The enforcing authorities have a range of tools at their disposal in seeking to secure compliance with the law and to ensure a proportionate response to criminal offences.

Figure A7-9: Enforcement action. *Source: HSE enforcement guide.*

It goes on to say that inspectors may offer duty holders advice, both verbal and in writing, which may include a warning that they are, in the inspector's opinion, not complying with the law. They may issue improvement and prohibition notices, withdraw approvals, vary licence conditions or exemptions, issue formal cautions (only in England and Wales), and they may prosecute (or report to the Procurator Fiscal with a view to prosecution in Scotland).

A formal caution is a statement by an inspector that is accepted in writing by the duty holder, that the duty holder has committed an offence for which there is a realistic prospect of conviction. A formal caution may only be used where a prosecution could be properly brought. The enforcing authorities should take account of Home Office guidelines when considering whether to offer a formal caution.

Note: this is not the same as the caution given under the Police and Criminal Evidence Act given before questioning a suspect about an alleged offence.

Quoting from the Statement regarding the purpose and method of enforcement:

> The ultimate purpose of the enforcing authorities is to ensure that duty holders manage and control risks effectively, thus preventing harm. The term 'enforcement' has a wide meaning and applies to all dealings between enforcing authorities and those on whom the law places duties (employers, the self-employed, employees and others).

Figure A7-10: Purpose and method of enforcement. *Source: HSE enforcement guide.*

PROSECUTION

Criminal offences can be categorised according to their seriousness. There are three types of offence:

- **Summary offence:** comparatively minor offences which can be tried in a Magistrates' Court.
- **Indictable offence:** serious offences which are triable in the Crown Court before a judge and jury. These cases are preliminarily investigated by the Magistrates' Court in order to establish a prima facie case.
- **Hybrid or 'either way' offence:** can be tried by a Magistrate or before the Crown Court. Cases are sent to the Crown Court if the magistrates consider they do not have sufficient powers of sentence or, where allowed by law, the accused opts for trial by jury.

There is a more positive form of action open to Inspectors, to facilitate immediate remedial action. Sections 21 and 22 of the Act empower Inspectors to utilise either improvement or prohibition notices facilitating instant action without recourse to the courts.

ENFORCEMENT NOTICES

Improvement notices (HASAWA 1974 Section 21)

This allows inspectors to use an improvement notice procedure. It is aimed at situations where there is not a serious risk, but a breach of legislation; prohibition notices may be used in employment situations which are outside the existing law. An improvement notice allows a period of time for improvements to plant, equipment, processes, etc. to be carried out. After this period has elapsed, the employer is in breach of the notice, and consequently in breach of the Act if improvements are not completed within the specified time; persons or organisations committing this breach are guilty of two offences:-

- Failing to comply with the improvement notice.
- Breach of the particular legislation in question.

The enforcing authority has the power to withdraw or amend a notice, also to extend the time period.

Prohibition and improvement notices are on a standard format, which is completed on site by the inspector. The top copy of the notice is given to the person who is, in the inspector's opinion, in breach and the carbon copy is retained.

Both forms of notice contain a schedule which provides a written description of the steps to be taken to comply with the Inspector's requirements, and in particular outlines practical guidance, relevant Codes of Practice or other accepted standards.

Prohibition notices (HASAWA 1974 Section 22)

This allows an Inspector to stop a process, machine or other activity which involves, or will involve, in the Inspector's opinion, the risk of serious personal injury. This includes injury to health.

Prohibition notices may either come into effect immediately if the risk is imminent, or alternatively be deferred, for example, to allow a continuous process to come to completion.

Grounds for appeal, appeal procedures, effect of appeal

Information included in and withdrawal of notices (HASAWA 1974 Section 23)

Defines notices and may state what may be included in them, e.g. any remedies to be taken.

Notices may be withdrawn by the inspector before the end of the specified period or extended.

Appeal (HASAWA 1974 Section 24)

Appeals are provided for by this section. If a recipient of the notice is aggrieved by the conditions of the notice, he has the right of appeal to an Employment Tribunal. Essentially appeals should be lodged within 21 days of the date of the Notice. A copy of the standard appeal form is always issued with the notice.

Effects of appeal (HASAWA 1974 Sections 21-24 and 39)

An appeal has the effect of suspending an improvement notice until a decision has been made or the appeal is withdrawn. In the case of a prohibition notice however the notice remains in force unless directed by the tribunal. Appeals against tribunal decisions are made to the Employment Appeals Tribunal (EAT).

Special duties

IMPLICATIONS OF SECTION 36 OF THE HASAWA 1974

Offences due to fault of other person (Section 36)

Section 36 provides that if any person commits an offence due to the act or default of some other person, that other person shall be guilty of the offence, and a person may be charged with and convicted of the offence, whether or not proceedings are taken against the first-mentioned person.

Thus, if someone with a duty to comply with a specific regulation is in breach of the regulation due to the fault of someone else then the other person can be prosecuted. The first person may be a corporate body and another person may be a local manager within the company, an architect of another company or even a health and safety consultant.

In other words, if someone with authority over others, e.g. a supervisor or a manager, tells an operator to operate a machine without a guard, then that supervisor or manager could be prosecuted for the offence, possibly under section 7 of HASWA 1974, of operating the machine without a guard whether or not the operator is charged.

IMPLICATIONS OF SECTION 37 OF THE HASAWA 1974

Offences by Body Corporate (Section 37)

Section 37 provides that, where an offence has been committed by a body corporate and is proved to have been committed with the consent or connivance of, or to have been attributable to any neglect on the part of, any director, manager, secretary of the body corporate or a person who was purporting to act in any such capacity, he as well as the body corporate shall be guilty of that offence and shall be liable to be proceeded against and punished accordingly.

Thus, if a Company, Local Authority or other corporate body is in breach of a health and safety requirement, then if it can be proved that the breach of the requirement was due to a Director, Manager or Company Secretary, etc. consenting (allowing something wrong to take place or continue), conniving (turning a blind eye) or neglecting (failing to take care of health and safety) then he as well as the corporate body can be prosecuted for the same offence.

Proof and defence in criminal proceedings

IMPLICATIONS OF SECTION 40 OF THE HASAWA 1974

Onus of proof (Section 40)

In any proceedings for an offence under any of the relevant statutory provisions involving a failure to comply with a duty or requirement to do something so far as is practicable, reasonably practicable or to use the best means to do something, it shall be for the accused to prove that it was not practicable, or not reasonably practicable to do more than was in fact done to satisfy the duty or requirement, or that there was no better practicable means than was in fact used to satisfy the duty or requirement.

The onus of proof is thought by many to mean that the accused is guilty until he proves himself innocent. This appears to go against the basic principle in law that the accused is innocent until proved guilty.

However, the proof laid on the defendant is less onerous than that on the prosecutor as regards proving the offence and can be done by satisfying the court as to the probability of what the defendant has to prove. The High Court of Judiciary stressed, "Once there is a prima facie case against the accused in that he has not ensured the health, safety and welfare at work of his employees then the onus under section 40 is on the accused. Thus the Crown does not have to prove that it was reasonably practicable to comply with the Act." (Redgrave Fife & Machin 1993).

This burden of proof was tested in the Court of Appeal (Criminal Division) in the case R. v Davies (David Janway) 2002. Davies, the owner and occupier of a plant hire yard and workshop appealed against his conviction for a breach of duty under HASAWA 1974 section 3 (1) and section 33 by failure to ensure that people not in his employment were not exposed to danger. A self-employed subcontractor had been crushed to death in Davies's yard by a reversing JCB. The trial judge ruled that section 40 of HASAWA 1974 imposed a legal burden of proof on a defendant to show, on the balance of probabilities, that it would not have been reasonably practicable for him to have done more to satisfy the duty to ensure safety. Davies appealed on the grounds that a reverse burden of proof under section 40 of the Act was incompatible with the presumption of innocence enshrined in the Human Rights Act 1998.

The appeal was dismissed stating that section 40 is compatible with the Human Rights Act 1998 as it is justified. It was said that HASAWA 1974 was motivated by the need to protect public safety and its regulatory nature meant that those operating within it had to conform to certain standards. It was acceptable in health and safety to impose absolute duties on employers and it did not follow that a reverse burden of proof, within reasonable limits, would infringe Article 6 (2) of the 1998 Act.

IMPLICATIONS OF REGULATION 21 OF MHSWR 1999

Provisions as to liability and defence

Employers cannot submit a defence in criminal proceedings that contravention was caused by the act or default either of an employee or the competent person appointed under Regulation 7. *See also - the case of Armour v Skeen - below.*

ARMOUR V. SKEEN (1977) IRLR 310 [HSWA 1974 SECTION 37 AND SECTION 2]

Personal liability -Criminal controlling mind of a company

Circumstances

A workman fell to his death whilst repairing a road bridge over the River Clyde. The Strathclyde Regional Council and its Director of Roads (Mr Armour) were both prosecuted. The basis of Mr Armour's prosecution under section 37 of the HASAWA 1974 was that the duty of supervising the safety of council workmen on the roads was his. He had failed to formulate a sound safety policy.

Mr Armour claimed in his defence to have no personal duty to carry out the council's statutory obligations (one of which was the formulation of a detailed safety policy for the roads department).

Decision

He was convicted of the offences and the conviction was upheld on appeal. The fact that section 2 of HASAWA 1974 imposes a duty on the employers to provide a safe system of work did not mean that there was no duty on his part to carry out that duty. Section 37(1) refers to 'any neglect', not to the neglect of a duty imposed. The offences were committed by the body corporate, but were due to his neglect. Further, although his title as 'Director of Roads' did not mean he was a 'director' within the meaning of section 37 (1), he was within the meaning of the words "manager or similar officer".

Relevance

The case gives guidance as to those who may be considered as the "directing mind" of the organisation who therefore are liable under section 37 of the HASAWA 1974. This includes persons who purport to act as directors, manager's secretaries or other similar officers: all may be equally liable. Anyone who acts in a managerial capacity must be held liable under section 37 (1) whatever the title he or she may have. If the affairs of the body corporate are being managed by its members (e.g. a workers' co-operative), then the acts of the member which are in connection with his managerial functions are within the meaning of this section (section 37 (2)).

For a person to be convicted under section 37, it must be shown that he or she has some responsibility for the making of management decisions, and be in a position of responsibility. In R v Boal, the accused was the assistant general manager of Foyle's bookshop. He had been given no management training, in particular, none in health and safety matters, or fire precautions. He was, however, in charge of the shop while the general manager was away on a week's holiday. During this period, the premises were visited by officers from the local fire authority, who discovered there were serious breaches of the fire certificate which had been issued. Foyle's and the accused were charged with a number of offences under the Fire Precautions Act (FPA) 1971 - Foyle's as the 'body corporate' and the accused because the 1971 Act provides that:

" ... *where an offence committed by a body corporate is proved ... to be attributable to any neglect on the part of any director, manager, secretary or other similar officer of the body corporate ... he as well as the body corporate shall be guilty of that offence ... ".*

Foyle's were convicted on 11 counts, and were fined. The accused pleaded guilty to 3 counts, and was found guilty of 7 others. He was sentenced to 3 months' imprisonment, suspended for 12 months. He then appealed against the conviction on the ground that he was not "... a manager or similar officer ... "within the meaning of the Act.

The Court of Appeal (Criminal Division) allowed his appeal. A person was "a manager" if he had the power of "... the management of the whole of the affairs of the company ..." or was, "... entrusted with power to transact the whole of the affairs of the company ..."or was "... managing in a governing role the affairs of the company itself ...". The Court further thought that the intended scope of section 23 of the Fire Precautions Act was "... to fix with criminal liability only those who are in a position of real authority, the decision makers within the company who have both the power and responsibility to decide corporate policy and strategy. It is to catch those responsible for putting proper procedures in places; it is not meant to strike at underlings."

R V BRITISH STEEL PLC [1995] IRLR 310 [STATUTE REF. HEALTH AND SAFETY AT WORK ETC ACT 1974, SECTION 3 (1)]

Circumstances

In 1990, at its Sheffield plant, British Steel planned to reposition a section of steel platform. This involved cutting the platform free and using a crane to move it to its new position.

The repositioning work was carried out by contractors on a labour only basis with British Steel providing supervision and equipment. The two men supplied by the contractors cut the platform free, but they neglected to secure it. The platform collapsed and killed one of the men.

British Steel was convicted of an offence under section 3(1) for failing to discharge its duty under that section.

The company appealed to the Court of Appeal on the grounds that, it argued, section 3(1) allowed a company to avoid liability if, at the level of directing mind it had taken reasonable care. The Court of Appeal was asked to infer that the words, "through senior management" appeared in section 3(1) immediately after the word "employer". (That is: "It shall be the duty of every employer "through senior management" to conduct his undertaking in such a way as to ensure, so far as is reasonably practicable, that persons not in his employment who may be affected thereby are not thereby exposed to risks to their health and safety".)

Decision

A corporate employer was not able to avoid liability for an offence under section 3(1) on the basis that the company at "directing mind" or senior management level was not involved, having taken all reasonable care to delegate supervision.

It was accepted that Parliament considered it necessary for the protection of public health and safety to impose absolute criminal liability, subject to the defence of reasonable practicability. It would drive a juggernaut through the legislative scheme if companies could avoid criminal liability where the potentially harmful event was committed by someone who was not the directing mind of the company.

If the appellant's submissions were accepted, it would be particularly easy for large companies, engaged in multifarious hazardous operations to escape liability on the basis that the company, through its directing mind or senior management was not involved. That would emasculate the legislation.

The appeal should be dismissed.

R V NELSON GROUP SERVICES (MAINTENANCE) LTD [1998] ALL ER 420 [STATUTE REF. HASAWA 1974 SECTION 3(1)]

Circumstances

Nelson Group Services (Maintenance) Ltd (N Ltd) installed, maintained and serviced gas appliances and employed a large number of gas fitters. A fitter employed by the company had been properly trained to enable him to carry out his work competently and safely. While removing a gas fire from a house, the fitter left the gas fittings in a condition which exposed the occupier of the house to health and safety risks.

N Ltd was prosecuted under section 3(1) of the HASAWA 1974. At first instance, N Ltd was convicted. At the Crown Court trial the judge directed the jury on the issue of reasonable practicability, saying that in the circumstances the defence of reasonable practicability was not available.

The company appealed to the Court of Appeal on the basis that:

- It was accepted that gas fittings had been left in such a state that the occupants of houses had been exposed to risk to their health and safety.
- The question was whether this alone made N Ltd guilty of an offence under section 3, or whether,
- The negligent act by the fitter was not the employer conducting its undertaking for the purposes of section 3.
- The fitter's negligent act or omission did not prevent N Ltd from showing that it had done all that was reasonably practicable to ensure that the occupants were not exposed to risk.

Decision

The fact that an employee has done work carelessly does not preclude an employer from establishing a defence of reasonable practicability.

The question of what is reasonably practicable is a question of fact for the jury depending on the circumstances of the case, for example, that an employee had safe systems of work, the appropriate skill and instruction, and had been provided with safe plant and equipment.

The appeal succeeded.

Application of manslaughter and corporate manslaughter to work related incidents

MANSLAUGHTER

There are three categories of homicide: murder, manslaughter and causing death by dangerous driving. Manslaughter is a crime where the offender has caused a death, but the act itself falls short of murder. Manslaughter can be voluntary or involuntary.

Voluntary manslaughter. Where the accused has, or could be, charged with murder but can demonstrate the defence of diminished responsibility or provocation

Involuntary manslaughter. Where the accused had no intention of either seriously harming or killing the victim (i.e. there was no malice or aforethought).

Strictly speaking, involuntary manslaughter is called Gross Negligence. It is a failure in Common Law and is a Common Law Crime.

The proof is similar to Negligence, but involves a death:

- A duty of care was owed to the individual.
- There was a gross failure to fulfil that duty.
- That failure resulted in a death.

CORPORATE MANSLAUGHTER

The body of law relating to the criminal prosecution of a corporate body has been slow to develop. This was because it was thought that a company, not being a human being, did not have the capacity to commit a crime. The mental element (e.g. motive) is important in proving manslaughter and it was not thought possible to demonstrate corporate manslaughter because companies do not have minds. This changed in the 1940s when companies came to be regarded as being like a person. Those who control the company are considered to be its body and mind and are 'identified' with the company. They speak and act as, rather than for, the company.

A category of involuntary manslaughter is that of 'gross negligence' on the part of the accused. Where an individual causes death through gross negligence then a criminal offence has been committed which may be considered to be a criminal variation based on the civil tort of negligence; negligence to such an extent that it results in a death.

Lord Mackay stated in a 1995 House of Lords Judgement of **R v ADOMOKO [1995] 1 AC 171**

> *"The ordinary principles of the law of negligence apply to ascertain whether or not the defendant has been in breach of a duty of care towards a victim who has died. If such a breach of duty is established the next question is whether the breach of duty caused the death of the victim. If so, the jury must go on to consider whether the breach of duty should be characterised as gross negligence and therefore is a crime. This will depend on the seriousness of the breach of duty committed by the defendant in all the circumstances in which the defendant was placed when it occurred. The jury will have to consider whether the extent to which the defendant's conduct departed from the proper standard of care incumbent upon him, involving as it must have done a risk of death to the [person] was such that it could be judged criminal."*

Figure A7-11: Statement from R v Adomoko 1995 House of Lords Judgement.   Source: Lord Mackay.

Lord Mackay's statement is based on the fundamental proof above, i.e. there was a breach of the duty of care towards the victim who has died as a result and the death was caused by the breach.

Currently corporate liability for manslaughter is difficult to establish as the jury must be satisfied that at least one individual who is part of the 'directing mind' of the company caused the victim's death by gross negligence. However, the Corporate Manslaughter and Corporate Homicide Act 2007, which received Royal Assent on 26 July 2007 and comes into force on 6 April 2008, will allow for an organisation to be prosecuted for corporate manslaughter by looking at the wider organisational issues. It is not dependent on finding the individual controlling mind.

The following cases show why it was seen as necessary to introduce the new Act: i.e. it is easier to find the grossly negligent controlling mind in a small organisation than in a large one, therefore successful prosecutions for corporate manslaughter are more likely in the small organisations and extremely unlikely in large ones.

SUCCESSFUL AND UNSUCCESSFUL MANSLAUGHTER CASES

The first recorded prosecution for corporate manslaughter was in 1927 against Cory Bros Ltd. In this case, a person was killed in a trap set for trespassers. As this was before the changes in the law in the 1940's, the company was acquitted because an 'artificial entity' could not commit violence.

R V OLL Ltd (Peter Kite and Joseph Stoddart) 1994 - Lyme Bay (March 1993)

Four teenagers, taking part in a canoeing trip organised by OLL Ltd (formerly Active Learning and Leisure Ltd), died. They were in a group accompanied by a schoolteacher - all were novice canoeists - and two unqualified instructors who had only basic proficiency skills.

The group was swept out to sea, capsizing frequently. The centre had neither provided distress flares, nor informed the coastguard of the expedition. Despite cold sea temperatures, the victims wore only swimming suits under their wetsuits. Although the rescue boat had set out at midday to look for the group when it did not return, the centre manager did not call the coastguard until 3pm.

OLL Ltd's managing director, Peter Kite, and the centre's manager, Joseph Stoddart were charged with gross negligence manslaughter.

The court heard that the children would have survived if their lifejackets had been fully inflated. Although the instructors had not told them to inflate the jackets, the prosecution alleged that the blame lay with the regime which allowed these instructors to be sent on such an expedition. Numerous criticisms were made, e.g. there was no system for alerting the authorities within a given time of an expedition being overdue.

Kite argued that he delegated safety matters to the centre manager. But, the prosecution countered, this did not absolve him from his duty to put in place a system to protect those in his care from foreseeable risk. The judge suggested that the letter meant he was under an even stricter duty than he might otherwise have been to monitor and supervise safety.

The jury found the steps that Peter Kite had taken to discharge his responsibilities were sufficiently negligent as to amount to a criminal neglect of duty. He was sentenced to three years' imprisonment. This was reduced to two years on appeal. The centre manager, Joseph Stoddart, was acquitted.

Kite admitted that he was one of the company's "driving forces". He was clearly part of its controlling mind and, when he acted as managing director, he also acted as the company. Accordingly, the company was also found guilty of manslaughter, and fined £50,000.

R V Jackson Transport (Ossett) Ltd 1996

James Hodgson died after cleaning out a tanker containing residues of a dangerous chemical (parachloro-orthocresol), with a steam pressure cleaner while wearing only a boiler suit and a baseball cap. He had been injured three months earlier when similarly exposed to a dangerous tank cleaning operation. In the subsequent trial, the court heard that the director Alan Jackson had failed to provide first aid facilities, a trained first aider or protective clothing.

The jury decided that both the company and Mr Jackson were guilty of manslaughter. The company was fined £15,000 for manslaughter and £7,000 for breaches of the HASAWA 1974. The director was fined a total of £1,500 and jailed for one year.

Once again in this case the controlling mind of the company was easily identifiable.

Tebay Rail Deaths 2004

In February 2004, four men were working on a railway line at Tebay, Cumbria, when a wagon ran out of control. The brakes had failed and the rail workers had no warning that the wagon was running toward them out of control. The four men were all killed.

Mark Connolly, the boss of MAC Machinery Services had deliberately disconnected the hydraulic brakes on two wagons because it was cheaper than repairing the wagons properly. The hydraulic systems were in such a bad way that they would not work properly in conjunction with a crane.

MAC Machinery had been contracted by Carillion to replace track on the West Coast Main Line. Connolly's employee, Roy Kennett was using a crane to load steel rails onto two flat-bed wagons. Because the hydraulic brakes were in such a bad way with the hydraulic fluid having leaked out, Connolly disconnected them. He then filled the hydraulic brake cables with ball bearings, giving the impression that they were filled and in working order and that all was well. Kennett had placed pieces of wood under the wagons' wheels as a makeshift brake. One of the wagons rolled over the chocks acting as brakes, careered down a hill for three miles and collided with a gang of workers who were carrying out track maintenance. Four of the men were killed by the 19-tonne wagon and another three were injured.

Connolly was charged with health and safety offences and gross negligence (manslaughter) at Newcastle Crown Court. He was found guilty of four charges of gross negligence (manslaughter) and three counts of breaches of health and safety law. He was sentenced to nine years imprisonment for the manslaughter charges. Kennett, who had continued to use the wagons even though he knew they were faulty, was also imprisoned for two years for manslaughter charges.

The Prosecutor told the court that Connolly was "grossly negligent" in his actions and had "scant regard" for railway safety.

It is interesting to note that TUC General Secretary Brendan Barber said that the case "must be contrasted with the failure to prosecute the directors of large companies following other deaths". This is indeed shown in the cases that follow.

P&O European Ferries (Dover) Ltd 1991- Herald of Free Enterprise (6 March 1987)

Less than half an hour after the ferry Herald of Free Enterprise sailed from Zeebrugge harbour for Dover, it capsized with the loss of 188 lives.

The subsequent inquiry revealed that the Herald capsized because it went to sea with the bow doors open. The assistant boatswain had a duty to close the doors, but had fallen asleep and failed to attend for duty when the ship left harbour. The chief officer had been on deck at the time, but failed to ensure that the assistant boatswain had reported to work. His certificate of competence was later suspended as a result.

The inquiry report found severe fault with the system which allowed the capsizing to happen:

"The underlying or cardinal faults lay higher up in the company… All concerned in management, from the members of the board of directors down to the junior superintendents, were guilty of fault in that all must be regarded as sharing responsibility for the failure of management. From top to bottom the body corporate was infected with the disease of sloppiness."

Figure A7-12: Fault with the system quote.   Source: Herald of Free Enterprise inquiry.

The tragedy was caused by:

"The faults of [the assistant boatswain, the chief officer, the captain and the company] at all levels from the board of directors through the managers of the marine department down to the junior superintendents".

Figure A7-13: Cause of tragedy quote.   Source: Herald of Free Enterprise inquiry.

The inquest jury decided 188 victims had been unlawfully killed. Subsequently, the company and seven employees were charged with manslaughter. Those charged included the Assistant Boatswain and the Chief Officer. Five senior staff were also charged and, as one or all of the five were thought to represent the company's directing mind, it too was charged.

Despite the damning conclusions of the inquiry and inquest, the prosecution failed to prove its case against any of the five and therefore had no case against the company. The judge discontinued their trials, and the prosecution then dropped charges against the chief officer and assistant boatswain

The cases failed for lack of evidence that the conduct of the accused fell below the standard to be expected, i.e. what was common practice in the industry. The prosecution failed to show that a reasonably skilled person in the same line of work would have behaved differently to any of the senior officers.

This meant that if no single senior officer was sufficiently at fault, then neither was the company. This was because of an earlier court ruling that it was not possible to aggregate the faults of more than one individual and say that, together they amounted to such a high degree of fault as to be sufficient to convict the company, although not the individuals, of manslaughter.

R V Great Western Trains Company - Southall Train Collision (19 September 1997)

A high speed Intercity 125 train, operated by Great Western Trains (GWT), collided with an empty freight train killing 7 and injuring a further 147 passengers.

The subsequent inquiry heard that the passenger train passed two amber warning signals 'at or very near its top speed of 125 mph' then ran a red light before the collision. The AWS (Automatic Warning System) system fitted in the driver's cab had been turned off because of a fault on the previous day. The AWS gives the driver an audible warning, when a signal is passed. The train and the track were installed with a system of ATP (Automatic Train Protection) as part of a pilot scheme introduced by BR following the Hidden Report into the accident at Clapham Junction in 1988. However this ATP system had been switched off because the driver had not been trained in its use.

Manslaughter charges were made against both the driver of the train, Larry Harrison, and GWT. In dismissing the seven charges of manslaughter against GWT the judge (Mr Justice Scott-Baker) held that the prosecution must, in order to establish their case, identify GWT's negligent controlling mind. The Court of Appeal later upheld this principle, which is known as attribution or identification. The only candidate for this was the managing director Richard George who had ultimate responsibility for safety. Responsibility for safety is not however enough to charge a person with manslaughter. The judge concluded that if the Crown thought it could charge Mr George with manslaughter it would have done so.

Mr Justice Scott Baker said that:

"It is still necessary to look for …a directing mind and identify whose gross negligence it is that fixes the company with criminal responsibility."

Figure A7-14: R V Great Western Trains Company.   Source: Mr Justice Scott Baker.

In making his decision the judge said that the lack of action since the publication of the Law Commission's report was regrettable but it was for Parliament to decide if it wished to change the law to remove the present obstacle to prosecuting large corporations for manslaughter.

Following this ruling, the prosecution dropped the charge of manslaughter against Driver Harrison. This was said to be in part because of the psychiatric reports that suggested he had been damaged by the accident.

Great Western Trains were fined a record £1.5 million under section 3 of the HASAWA 1974. In doing so the judge followed the Howe sentencing criteria.

If the driver had been prosecuted for gross negligence (manslaughter), it would not have enabled the body corporate employer to be prosecuted for corporate manslaughter as the driver is not the 'controlling mind' of the body corporate.

The law will change in this respect with the Corporate Manslaughter and Corporate Homicide Act 2007, making it possible for the body corporate employer to be prosecuted for corporate manslaughter without having to find a person who is a 'controlling mind' to prosecute first. The change in the law required a statute to be made to do this, rather than rely on change through judicial precedent in common law.

Corporate Manslaughter and Corporate Homicide Act 2007

The Act creates the statutory offence of "corporate manslaughter" in England, Wales and Northern Ireland and of "corporate homicide" in Scotland. It addresses the difficulty of the lack of successful prosecutions against large companies. Companies and government bodies will be found guilty of the offence if their failure to manage their activities has resulted in a person's death. The failings by senior management would amount to a gross breach of the duty of care owed to employees, the public or other individuals. The courts will be able to look at the wider picture of collective actions and failings of the senior management.

Senior management is defined in the Act as those persons who play a significant role in the decision making process about how the company's activities are managed and organised.

The Act is not concerned with increasing the liability of individuals. They can still be held to account by the existing common law crime of manslaughter by gross negligence and health and safety legislation. The Act is about prosecuting companies where the failures of management have resulted in death and should be able to deal with these prosecutions more effectively than the common law does.

It is hoped that the possible resulting penalties following a successful conviction under the Act will also be an incentive to companies to improve their standards and make the working environment safer for employees and third parties.

Penalties following a successful conviction include an unlimited fine, remedial orders and publicity orders.

A remedial order requires an organisation to take specific steps to remedy any management failing that led to death. This may be any deficiency in health and safety matters in the policies, systems or practices. The relevant enforcement authority or authorities must be consulted on this.

A publicity order requires the organisation to publicise in a specified manner: the fact that it has been convicted of the offence; the specified particulars of the offence; the amount of fine imposed; and the terms of any remedial order made. Again, the court must ascertain the views of the relevant enforcement authority or authorities.

Failure to comply with a remedial order or a publicity order is an offence, and liable on conviction on indictment to a fine.

Crown bodies are not immune from prosecution under this Act and are to be treated as owing the same duties of care they would owe if they were corporations that were not servants or agents of the Crown.

Criminal law

Learning outcomes

The intended learning outcomes are that the student will be able to:

A8.1 discuss the status and role relevant acts, regulations, approved codes of practice, and guidance in their application to health and safety at work

A8.2 state and explain the defences available in criminal health and safety and manslaughter cases

Contents

This page is intentionally blank

A8.1 - The Health and Safety at Work etc. Act 1974 and associated legislation

APPLICATION OF MAIN SECTIONS OF THE HASAWA

The Health and Safety at Work etc. Act (HASAWA) 1974 covers all employment activities, apart from private domestic workers. Consequently, when the Act came into force some years ago, it brought, for the first time, twelve million people under the protection of health and safety legislation. These included laboratories, academic institutions, research establishments and many other areas which did not comply with the definition of a "factory" given in Section 175 of the Factories Act, which basically required manual labour or gain, and the manufacture of articles and substances.

HASAWA applies to employers, self-employed persons, subcontractors, visitors to places of employment, members of the public affected by the employer's activities, designers, suppliers, importers, employees, directors and managers. It also provides the enforcers, i.e. the Health & Safety Executive inspectors and the Local Authorities' environmental health officers with various enforcement powers. Sections 2 - 6 and 9 are the duties on the employers and others, Section 7 is the duty on the employee and Section 8 is the duty on the person. Section 2 (1) Is the general duty on the employer to his employees and Section 2, subsections (2), (3) (4-7) are the more specific duties. The duties are expressed in general terms so that they apply to all workplaces and work activities. *(Further discussion can be found later in this element).* The absolute duties placed on the employer are qualified by "so far as is *reasonably practicable*" and the duty on the employee is to take *reasonable care*.

Section 15 allows for regulations to be made to stricter standards than the reasonably practicable ones provided for in HASAWA 1974. Thus the employers' duty to make an assessment under the Control of Substances Hazardous to Health Regulations (COSHH) 2002 is absolute and amplifies the general duty of the employer to make arrangements to ensure that substances and articles can be used, handled, stored and transported safely under Section 2.

Due to the very general nature of the duties under the HASAWA 1974 it should be noted that failure to comply with Sections 2-7 or breach of Section 8 confer no right of action in civil proceedings (Section 47 of HASAWA 1974 excludes civil liability). HASAWA 1974 is therefore primarily criminal law.

Management of Health and Safety at Work Regulations 1999

DUTIES PLACED ON EMPLOYERS

The Management of Health and Safety at Work Regulations (MHSWR) 1999 extend the general duties placed on employers by HASAWA 1974. In particular the regulations require that suitable and sufficient risk assessments are carried out. Risk assessments should give particular consideration to pregnant employees and young people and children. Following the risk assessment appropriate control measures must be put in place. This might include the development of emergency procedures and the provision of information to those who could be affected. In order to manage health and safety successfully, employers must be able to plan, organise, control, monitor and review the management arrangements. Furthermore, when deciding control measures and developing arrangements, employers must have access to competent advice.

DUTIES PLACED ON EMPLOYEES

Similarly, the general duties placed on employees by sections 7 and 8 of HASAWA 1974 are extended by regulation 14. All employees are required to:

a) Use tools, materials, substances, etc. in accordance with any training or information that has been given.

b) Report those things that may reasonably be considered to be a danger to health and safety and also, any shortcomings in the employer's arrangements for managing health and safety.

DUTIES PLACED ON OTHERS

The regulations require that employers jointly occupying a worksite, such as a construction site or office block, should co-operate and co-ordinate their activities. Areas where co-operation and co-ordination may be necessary are health and safety training, emergency procedures and welfare provision. The regulations require liaison between a host employer and temporary employment businesses to ensure that the workers placed with the host employer receive relevant information.

It should be noted that the regulations are accompanied by an Approved Code of Practice (ACOP) and guidance. *See also - '8.3 ACOPs and Guidance' - later in this element.*

Relevant decided cases

R V SWAN HUNTER SHIPBUILDERS LTD AND ANOTHER [1982] 1 ALL ER 264

HASAWA Section 2. Contractors who are ignorant of the dangers involved can pose a risk to employees. Employers have a duty to give information to contractors when required in order to ensure the health and safety of their own employees.

Section 2(2)c HASAWA (criminal prosecution) provision of information to third parties.

Circumstances A fire broke out during the building of HMS Glasgow in 1976. The fire was caused by sub-contractors (Telemeter Installations) who failed to disconnect a hose from the oxygen supply at the end of the shift. This resulted in an overnight build up of oxygen. Eight Swan Hunter employees were killed and two firemen hospitalised. The subsequent investigation showed that although Swan Hunter's employees had been given information and training about the danger of oxygen enrichment, Telemeter's employees had not.

Decision Swan Hunter was found guilty and fined £3,000. The Court of Appeal upheld the conviction on the basis that Swan Hunter had endangered their own employees because they had failed to provide information and instruction to their contractors (persons other than their employees).

Relevance If the ignorance of another company's employees places its own employees at risk, then it is the company's duty for the protection of its own employees to inform the employees of another, of any special risks within its knowledge.

The conviction underlined the need to communicate and adequately inform non-employees of special risks that may be created in order to protect one's own employees, because pertinent information, effectively imparted, would diminish such risks.

R V ASSOCIATED OCTEL CO LTD [1996] 4 ALL ER 846

HASAWA Section 3. The duty to prevent exposure to risks arising from the conduct of the undertaking includes the activities of independent contractors carrying out the works of cleaning, repair and maintenance of plant, machinery and buildings that are necessary for the conduct of the employer's business or enterprise.

Section 3(1) of HASAWA 1974 liability for the safety of persons affected by the undertaking

Circumstances In June 1990 Associated Octel had closed down its production processes at its Ellesmere Port chemical plant for pre-planned annual maintenance. The repair of the lining of a tank in the chlorine plant was carried out by a specialist contractor Resin Glass Products Ltd (RGP). During the maintenance, one of RGP's employees was badly burned when the bulb of the lamp he was holding shattered, igniting vapour from the acetone - a highly inflammable solvent - that he was using to clean the surface. The contractor RGP was convicted under Section 2 of the Act and Associated Octel was prosecuted under Section 3.

Decision Associated Octel was fined £25,000, with £60,000 costs. They appealed to the Court of Appeal and then to the House of Lords, both of whom rejected the appeal.

Relevance Section 3(1) stipulates that "It shall be the duty of every employer to conduct his undertaking in such a way as to ensure, so far as is reasonably practicable, that persons not in his employment who may be affected thereby are not exposed to risks to their health and safety".

This includes the activities of independent contractors carrying out the works of cleaning, repair and maintenance, which were necessary for the conduct of the employer's business or enterprise.

Health and Safety at Work etc Act 1974

ARRANGEMENT OF ACT

Preliminary

1) Preliminary.

General duties

2) General duties of employers to the employees.
3) General duties of employers and self-employed to persons other than their employees.
4) General duties of persons concerned with premises to persons other than their employees.
5) [Repealed].
6) General duties of manufacturers etc. as regards articles and substances for use at work.
7) General duties of employees at work.
8) Duty not to interfere with or misuse things provided pursuant to certain provisions.
9) Duty not to charge employees for things done or provided pursuant to certain specific requirements.

The Health and Safety Commission and the Health and Safety Executive

10) Establishment of the Commission and the Executive.
11) General functions of the Commission and the Executive.
12) Control of the Commission by the Secretary of State.
13) Other powers of the Commission.
14) Power of the Commission to direct investigations and Inquiries.

Health and safety regulations and approved codes of practice

15) Health and safety regulations.
16) Approval of codes of practice by the Commission.
17) Use of approved codes of practice in criminal proceedings.

Enforcement

18) Authorities responsible for enforcement of the relevant statutory provisions.
19) Appointment of inspectors.
20) Powers of inspectors.
21) Improvement notices.
22) Prohibition notices.
23) Provisions supplementary, Sections 21 and 22.
24) Appeal against improvement or prohibition notice.
25) Power to deal with cause of imminent danger.
26) Power of enforcing authorities to indemnify their inspectors.

Obtaining and disclosure of information

27)   Obtaining of information by the Commission, the Executive, enforcing authorities etc.

28)   Restrictions on disclosure of information.

Special provisions relating to agriculture

29-32)   [repealed].

Provisions as to offences

33)   Offences.

34)   Extension of time for bringing summary proceedings.

35)   Venue.

36)   Offences due to fault of other person.

37)   Offences by bodies corporate.

38)   Restriction on institution of proceedings in England and Wales.

39)   Prosecutions by inspectors.

40)   Onus of proving limits of what is practicable etc.

41)   Evidence.

42)   Power of court to order cause of offence to be remedied or, in certain cases, forfeiture.

Financial provision

43)   Financial provisions.

Miscellaneous and supplementary

44)   Appeals in connection with licensing provisions in the relevant statutory provisions.

45)   Default powers.

46)   Service of notices.

47)   Civil liability.

48)   Application to Crown.

49)   Adaptation of enactments to metric units or appropriate metric units.

50)   Regulations under the relevant statutory provisions.

51)   Exclusion of application to domestic employment.

52)   Meaning of work and at work.

53)   General interpretation of Part I.

54)   Application of Part I to Isles of Scilly.

OUTLINE OF KEY POINTS

Section 2 - duties of employers to employees

Section 2 (1) general duties

An employer shall ensure, so far as is reasonably practicable, the health, safety and welfare of all employees at work. The Act also specifies five areas that in particular are covered by the employer's general duty. The fact that these five areas are specified does not mean that they are the only issues with which the employer should be concerned. This Section places requirements on the employer as follows.

Section 2 (2) specific duties

Without prejudice to the above statement of intent the duty is extended to the following particular matters:

- Provide and maintain plant and systems of work that are safe and without risk to health.
- Make arrangements to ensure that substances and articles can be used, handled, stored and transported safely.
- Provide information, instruction, training and supervision, to ensure the health, safety and welfare of employees.
- Maintain the place of work in a safe condition and without risk to health, and to ensure that means of access and egress to and from the place of work are provided and maintained in a safe condition.
- Provide and maintain a safe and healthy working environment and provide adequate welfare facilities.

Section 2 (3) safety policies

An employer must prepare, and revise when necessary, a written statement of policy with respect to health and safety at work and, in particular, outline the organisation and arrangements which have been implemented to ensure that the policy is being carried out. Such a statement should be drawn to the attention of the employees. Under separate regulations, employers with fewer than five employees are exempt from having a written policy statement.

Section 2 (4) appointment of safety representatives

Allows the Secretary of State to make regulations dealing with consultations between employers and recognised trade unions and their method of representation. This led to the Safety Representatives and Safety Committee Regulations (SRSC) Regulations 1977.

Section 2 (5) repealed

Section 2 (6) consultation

Duty of employer to consult recognised trade union representatives (under SRSC Regulations 1977).

Section 2 (7) safety committee

Duty of employers to establish a safety committee if requested to do so by recognised trade union representatives (in accordance with SRSC Regulations 1977).

Section 3 - duties of employers and self-employed to persons other than employees

Section 3 (1) general duty

Employers have a duty to conduct their undertakings in such a way as to ensure, so far as is reasonably practicable, that persons not in his employment who may be affected thereby are not thereby exposed to risks to their health and safety.

Section 3 (2) self-employed

Similarly, self-employed persons should conduct their undertakings so that neither themselves, nor others, are affected by their activities and exposed to health and safety hazards. The above are qualified by "reasonably practicable".

Section 4 - premises

Anyone in control of premises or plant used by persons not in their employment must:

- Ensure safe access and egress to premises and plant.
- Ensure that plant or substances in the premises, or provided for their use, are safe and without risk to health.

Both are tempered by the reasonable practicability of this exercise.

Section 4 (3) tenancies

The obligations under Section 4 are transferred to the tenant, or person under contract, if the terms of the agreement are related to maintenance and repair of premises, access or egress there from, safety of plant or substances and any health risks arising from these.

Section 5 repealed

Section 6 duties of those who manufacture etc.

The duties of those who make, supply, design or import anything for use at work to ensure, so far as is reasonably practicable, that the article is so designed and constructed, that it will be safe and without risks to health at all times when it is being set, used, cleaned or maintained by a person at work; additionally there is a duty:

- To carry out any necessary testing and examination to ensure the duty imposed by the preceding paragraph.
- To take any necessary steps to provide adequate information about the safe use and to ensure safe dismantling and disposal.
- To revise provided information if it becomes known that anything gives rise to a serious risk to health or safety.

This section was substantially altered by the Consumer Protection Act 1987 in order to incorporate fairground equipment into the scope of the Act.

Section 7 - employees' duties

These sections place general obligations upon all employees. Briefly, the general duties require that employees should:

- Take reasonable care of their own health and safety and that of others who may be affected by their acts or omissions.
- Co-operate with the employer so as to ensure that the employer can comply with his statutory obligations.

Note: Regulation 14 of the MHSWR 1999 also places additional duties on the employee.

Section 8 - duties of person

No person shall intentionally and recklessly misuse or interfere with anything provided under the HASAWA 1974 and other legislation in the interests of health, safety or welfare.

Section 9 - employer not to charge

Employers must not levy, or permit to be levied, any charges for anything done or provided for by health and safety legislation. This includes, for example, personal protective equipment (PPE) and safety equipment such as fire extinguishers.

Management of Health and Safety at Work Regulations 1999

ARRANGEMENT OF REGULATIONS

1) Citation, commencement and interpretation.
2) Disapplication of these Regulations.
3) Risk assessment. *- for employees, others, young persons.*
4) Principles of prevention to be applied. *hierarchy - hand-out.*
5) Health and safety arrangements.
6) Health surveillance. *also in COSHH + Noise.*
7) Health and safety assistance.
8) Procedures for serious and imminent danger and for danger areas.
9) Contacts with external services.
10) Information for employees.
11) Co-operation and co-ordination.
12) Persons working in host employers' or self-employed persons' undertakings.

13)   Capabilities and training.

14)   Employees' duties.

15)   Temporary workers.

16)   Risk assessment in respect of new or expectant mothers.

17)   Certificate from a registered medical practitioner in respect of new or expectant mothers.

18)   Notification by new or expectant mothers.

19)   Protection of young persons.

20)   Exemption certificates.

21)   Provisions as to liability.

22)   Exclusion of civil liability.

23)   Extension outside Great Britain.

24)   Amendment of the Health and Safety (First-Aid) Regulations 1981.

25)   Amendment of the Offshore Installations and Pipeline Works (First-Aid) Regulations 1989.

26)   Amendment of the Mines Miscellaneous Health and Safety Provisions Regulations 1995.

27)   Amendment of the Construction (Health, Safety and Welfare) Regulations 1996.

28)   Regulations to have effect as health and safety regulations.

29)   Revocations and consequential amendments.

30)   Transitional provision.

Schedule 1.   General principles of prevention.

Schedule 2.   Consequential amendments.

OUTLINE OF KEY POINTS

MHSWR 1999 set out some broad general duties that apply to all workplaces. They are aimed at improving health and safety management. You may already be familiar with broad health and safety law of this kind - as it is the form taken by HASAWA 1974. The Regulations work in a similar way, and in fact they can be seen as a way of fleshing out what is already in HASAWA 1974. The 1999 Regulations replace the Management of Health and Safety at Work Regulations 1992, the Management of Health and Safety at Work (Amendment) Regulations 1994, the Health and Safety (Young Persons) Regulations 1997 and Part III of the FPWR 1997.

Regulation 3 - risk assessment

The regulations require employers (and the self-employed) to assess the risk to the health and safety of their employees and to anyone else who may be affected by their work activity. This is necessary to ensure that the preventive and protective steps can be identified to control hazards in the workplace. A hazard may be defined as something with the potential to cause harm and may include machinery, substances or a work practice. A risk may be defined as the likelihood that a particular hazard will cause harm. Consideration must be given to the population, i.e. the number of persons who might be exposed to harm and the consequence of such exposure.

Where an employer is employing or about to employ young persons (under 18 years of age) he must carry out a risk assessment that takes particular account of:

■   The inexperience, lack of awareness of risks and immaturity of young persons.
■   The layout of the workplace and workstations.
■   Exposure to physical, biological and chemical agents.
■   Work equipment and the way in which it is handled.
■   The extent of health and safety training to be provided.
■   Risks from agents, processes and work listed in the Annex to Council Directive 94/33/EC on the protection of young people at work.

Where five or more employees are employed, the significant findings of risk assessments must be recorded in writing (the same threshold that is used in respect of having a written safety policy). This record must include details of any employees being identified as being especially at risk.

Regulation 4 - principles of prevention to be applied

Regulation 4 requires an employer to implement preventive and protective measures on the basis of general principles of prevention specified in Schedule 1 to the Regulations. These are:

■   Avoiding risks.
■   Evaluating the risks that cannot be avoided.
■   Combating the risks at source.
■   Adapting the work to the individual, especially as regards the design of workplaces, the choice of work equipment and the choice of working and production methods, with a view, in particular, to alleviating monotonous work and work at a predetermined work-rate and to reducing their effect on health.
■   Adapting to technical progress.
■   Replacing the dangerous by the non-dangerous or the less dangerous.
■   Developing a coherent overall prevention policy that covers technology, organisation of work, working conditions, social relationships and the influence of factors relating to the working environment.
■   Giving collective protective measures priority over individual protective measures.
■   Giving appropriate instructions to employees.

Regulation 5 - health and safety arrangements

Appropriate arrangements must be made for the effective planning, organisation, control, monitoring and review of preventative and protective measures (in other words, for the management of health and safety). Again, employers with five or more employees must have their arrangements in writing.

Regulation 6 - health surveillance

In addition to the requirements of specific regulations such as COSHH 1999 and Asbestos regulations, consideration must be given to carry out health surveillance of employees where there is a disease or adverse health condition identified in risk assessments.

Regulation 7 - health and safety assistance

The employer must appoint one or more competent persons to assist him in complying with the legal obligations imposed on the undertaking (including Part II of the Fire Precautions (Workplace) Regulations (FPWR) 1997). The number of persons appointed depends on the size of the establishment and the range and severity of the risks. If more than one competent person is appointed, then arrangements must be made for ensuring adequate co-operation between them. The competent person(s) must be given the necessary time and resources to fulfil their functions. This will depend on the size of the undertaking, the risks to which employees are exposed and the distribution of those risks throughout the undertaking.

The employer must ensure that competent person(s) who are not employees are informed of the factors known (or suspected) to affect the health and safety of anyone affected by business activities. Competent people are defined as those who have sufficient training and experience or knowledge and other qualities to enable them to perform their functions. Persons may be selected from among existing employees or from outside. Where there is a suitable person in the employer's employment, that person shall be appointed as the 'competent person' in preference to a non-employee.

Regulation 8 - procedures for serious and imminent danger and for danger areas

Employers are required to set up emergency procedures and appoint competent persons to ensure compliance with identified arrangements, to devise control strategies as appropriate and to limit access to areas of risk to ensure that only those persons with adequate health and safety knowledge and instruction are admitted.

Regulation 9 - contacts with external services

Employers must ensure that, where necessary, contacts are made with external services. This particularly applies with regard to first-aid, emergency medical care and rescue work.

Regulation 10 - information for employees

Employees must be provided with relevant information about hazards to their health and safety arising from risks identified by the assessments. Clear instruction must be provided concerning any preventative or protective control measures including those relating to serious and imminent danger and fire assessments. Details of any competent persons nominated to discharge specific duties in accordance with the regulations must also be communicated as should risks arising from contact with other employer's activities (see Regulation 11).

Before employing a child (a person who is not over compulsory school age) the employer must provide those with parental responsibility for the child with information on the risks that have been identified and preventative and protective measures to be taken.

Regulation 11 - co-operation and co-ordination

Employers who work together in a common workplace have a duty to co-operate to discharge their duties under relevant statutory provisions. They must also take all reasonable steps to inform their respective employees of risks to their health or safety which may arise out of their work. Specific arrangements must be made to ensure compliance with fire legislation (i.e. the FPWR 1997).

Regulation 12 - working in host employers' or self employed persons' undertakings

This extends the requirements of regulation 11 to include persons working as sole occupiers of a workplace under the control of another employer. Such persons would include those working under a service of contract and employees in temporary employment businesses under the control of the first employer. The controlling employer has a duty to give relevant information to the employer of the persons. The second employer has a duty to give that information to his employees.

Regulation 13 - capabilities and training

Employers need to take into account the capabilities of their employees before entrusting tasks. This is necessary to ensure that they have adequate health and safety training and are capable enough at their jobs to avoid risk. To this end consideration must be given to recruitment including job orientation when transferring between jobs and work departments. Training must also be provided when other factors such as the introduction of new technology and new systems of work or work equipment arise.

Training must be repeated periodically where appropriate; be adapted to take account of any new or changed risks to the health and safety of the employees concerned; and take place during working hours.

Regulation 14 - employees' duties

Employees are required to follow health and safety instructions by using machinery, substances, transport etc. in accordance with the instructions and training that they have received.

They must also inform their employer (and other employers) of any dangers or shortcomings in the health and safety arrangements, even if there is no risk of imminent danger.

Regulation 15 - temporary workers

Consideration is given to the special needs of temporary workers, in particular to the provision of particular health and safety information such as qualifications required to perform the task safely or any special arrangements such as the need to provide health screening.

Regulation 16 - risks assessment in respect of new or expectant mothers

Where the work is of a kind that would involve risk to a new or expectant mother or her baby, then the assessment required by regulation 3 should take this into account. If the risk cannot be avoided, then the employer should take reasonable steps to:

- Adjust the hours worked.
- Offer alternative work.
- Give paid leave for as long as is necessary.

Regulation 17 - certificate from a registered medical practitioner in respect of new or expectant mothers

Where the woman is a night shift worker and has a medical certificate identifying night shift work as a risk then the employer must put her on day shift or give paid leave for as long as is necessary.

Regulation 18 - notification by new or expectant mothers

The employer need take no action until he is notified in writing by the woman that she is pregnant, has given birth in the last six months, or is breastfeeding.

Regulation 19 - protection of young persons

Employers of young persons shall ensure that they are not exposed to risk as a consequence of their lack of experience, lack of awareness or lack of maturity. No employer shall employ young people for work which:

- Is beyond his physical or psychological capacity.
- Involves exposure to agents that chronically affect human health.
- Involves harmful exposure to radiation.
- Involves a risk to health from extremes of temperature, noise or vibration.
- Involves risks which could not be reasonably foreseen by young persons.

This regulation does not prevent the employment of a young person who is no longer a child for work:

- Where it is necessary for his training.
- Where the young person will be supervised by a competent person.
- Where any risk will be reduced to the lowest level that is reasonably practicable.

Regulation 20 - exemption certificates

The Secretary of State for Defence may, in the interests of national security, by a certificate in writing exempt the armed forces, any visiting force or any headquarters from certain obligations imposed by the Regulations.

Regulation 21 - provisions as to liability

Employers cannot submit a defence in criminal proceedings that contravention was caused by the act or default either of an employee or the competent person appointed under Regulation 7.

Regulation 22 - exclusion of civil liability

Civil liability is no longer excluded under these regulations except for non-employees. (This change was made in 2003).

Regulations 24-29 revocations and amendments

Modern regulations are generally goal setting, which means they give the employer a series of goals to achieve without telling him how to achieve them. They place duties on the employer for requirements, for example, that are "*suitable and sufficient*" or "*suitable*". This may leave the employer wondering what he has to do and how far he has to go to ensure that the provisions are suitable and sufficient or suitable. Further help then is given in the form of Approved Codes of Practice (ACOPs) and Guidance.

WITH REFERENCE TO THE MANAGEMENT OF HEALTH AND SAFETY AT WORK REGULATIONS 1999

Purpose

The Management of Health and Safety at Work Regulations 1999 have both an ACOP and Guidance. The ACOP is called "*Management of Health and Safety at Work*". The ACOP is an interpretation of the legal requirements and states how the duty holder can comply with the law. The guidance gives more practical help in fulfilling the legal requirements.

Role

The ACOP is used to help in the understanding of how to comply with the law. This can be demonstrated by looking at regulation 3, Risk assessment. Regulation 3 (1) states: Every employer shall make a suitable and sufficient assessment of ...

The ACOP explains what this entails and describes what suitable and sufficient means in respect of a risk assessment. The stages of a risk assessment are considered in detail: Identifying the hazards; Identifying who might be harmed and how; Evaluating the risks from the hazards; Recording; and Review and revision. These details are further produced by HSE in a guidance leaflet entitled "5 steps to risk assessment". The format for a risk assessment is not discussed in the ACOP.

Structure and application

The "Management of health and safety at work" is the publication that contains the Management of Health and Safety at Work Regulations 1999, the ACOP and the guidance. The regulations are numbered sequentially, each followed by the appropriate ACOP and guidance, sometimes just the ACOP and sometimes just the guidance. For example, *regulation 3, Risk assessment* has only ACOP information, while *regulation 4, Principles of prevention to be applied* has both ACOP and guidance information.

The information is colour coded in columns and boxes down the left hand side of the page. The regulations have white columns and boxes, the ACOP has pale green and the guidance has darker green. Furthermore, the regulations are written in italics, the ACOP in standard font, but in bold and the guidance in standard font. This clear visual differentiation makes it easier to follow and to see at a glance whether a requirement is a legal duty, an interpretation of a legal duty or a practical way to comply with a legal duty.

At the end of the regulations there are 2 schedules, references for further reading and a select index. **Schedule 1** relates to **regulation 4, General principles of prevention**, and because this schedule is referred to in regulation 4, it is part of the regulation. **Schedule 2, Consequential amendments** shows where the Management Regulations have amended other regulations or where other regulations should be updated with the new version.

Status of ACOPs

Approved Codes of Practice (ACOPs) are provided for in several Acts of Parliament such as the HASAWA 1974 and the FPA 1971. They are instruments intended to give people more detailed information on compliance with their duties under the law. While failing to follow an ACOP is not in itself an offence, the accused would have to show that the measures he took were at least as effective. It is, therefore, strongly advisable to follow the provisions of an ACOP where they apply. An ACOP is "quasi-law", which means although it is not law, it may be used as a defence to show that the defendant did comply with the law. Section 40 of HASAWA 1974 allows for the defendant to prove that he did everything that was practicable or reasonably practicable, and he can do this by showing that he did everything in the ACOP.

ACOPs relating to health and safety are formulated by the Health and Safety Executive (HSE) and then approved by Health and Safety Commission (HSC) with the consent of the Secretary of State for Employment. This mechanism is provided for in Section 16(1) of the HASAWA 1974. The ACOP was drawn up following consultation between the Confederation of British Industry (CBI), the Trades Union Congress (TUC), local authorities, other interested parties, and HSE.

Status of HSE guidance material

Guidance notes, and other advisory literature, are published by the HSE in order to advise on best practices. They are not mandatory; however, if an offence were committed, compliance with these notes would tend to demonstrate good practice to a court. Guidance material is also published by other organisations such as the Institute of Electrical Engineers (e.g. IEE Requirements) and the Paintmakers Association.

WITH REFERENCE TO THE WORKPLACE (HEALTH, SAFETY AND WELFARE) REGULATIONS 1992

Purpose

Employers have a general duty under Section 2 of HASAWA 1974 to ensure, so far as is reasonably practicable, the health, safety and welfare of their employees at work and in Section 2 (2) (d) and (e) to provide a safe place of work including access and egress and a safe environment and welfare facilities. People in control of non-domestic premises have a duty under Section 4 of the Act towards people who are not their employees but use their premises for work activities. The Workplace (Health, safety and welfare) Regulations (WHSWR) 1992 expand on these duties and are intended to protect the health and safety of everyone in the workplace, and ensure that adequate welfare facilities are provided for people at work. These regulations have an ACOP and guidance.

Role

These Regulations aim to ensure that workplaces meet the health, safety and welfare needs of all members of a workforce, including people with disabilities. Several of the Regulations have requirements that must be 'suitable'. Regulation 2(3) makes it clear that things should be suitable for anyone. This includes people with disabilities. Where the workforce includes people with disabilities, it is important to ensure the workplace is suitable for them, particularly traffic routes, toilets and workstations. The ACOP interprets the legal requirements to show what would be considered 'suitable'.

Structure

The ACOP for the Workplace Regulations, which is called "Workplace health, safety and welfare", contains the regulations, the ACOP and guidance. The regulations are written in italics and have a blue-edged white box to the left of them. The ACOP is written under each regulation and has a pale blue box to the left side. The guidance is noted by a deeper blue box. Like the Management Regulations ACOP and guidance, this colour coding makes it easier to see which is the law, which the interpretation of the law and which the practical advice.

There are twenty-seven regulations, two schedules and two appendices: Schedule 1 Provisions applicable to factories which are not new workplaces, extensions or conversions; Schedule 2 Repeals and revocations; Appendix 1 References; and Appendix 2 Extracts from relevant health and safety legislation.

Regulation 21 can be used as an example of how the ACOP works. This regulation states that suitable and sufficient washing facilities shall be provided…. The ACOP shows in tabular form the minimum numbers of facilities: number of people at work, number of water closets and number of washstations. There is also information on the provision of facilities for remote workplaces and temporary work sites; and information on ventilation, cleanliness and lighting. The guidance associated with this refers to other Regulations and publications, e.g. Control of Substances Hazardous to Health and the associated ACOPs, in particular the ACOP dealing with the risk of Legionnaires' disease.

Application

The Regulations apply to most workplaces with Regulation 3 stating where they don't apply, e.g. on a ship, in a mine, etc.

The Regulations have to be very general and goal-setting to apply to the vast array of workplaces, each with their different layouts and requirements. The ACOP allows employers of these differing workplaces to comply with the law in ways that are relevant to them. The guidance refers to other guidance, which allows practical help to be available for specific situations.

A8.2 - Defences available in criminal law

GROSS NEGLIGENCE (MANSLAUGHTER)

The individual being charged in the criminal court with gross negligence (manslaughter) would have to show that they were not grossly negligent. They fulfilled their common law duty of care and the death was not due to negligent behaviour. Their behaviour was not reckless and all reasonable care was taken.

The defence would need to show that there was reasonable doubt that the defendant had acted in a reckless way. The defendant would have to show that his conduct did not depart from the standard of care incumbent upon him.

Corporate manslaughter could not be brought without the prior successful prosecution for gross negligence (manslaughter) of a person(s) considered to be the controlling mind of the corporate body. However, this will change from 6 April 2008 when the Corporate Manslaughter and Corporate Homicide Act 2008 comes into force. Then it will have to be shown that the corporate body's activities were organised and managed and its conduct was what could be reasonably expected of it. The compliance with relevant health and safety legislation can also be taken into account.

ABSOLUTE DUTY/QUALIFIED DUTY - PRACTICABLE AND REASONABLY PRACTICABLE

An absolute duty is difficult to defend. For example, if an employer failed to ensure that his power presses were inspected and thoroughly examined in the times stated in the part of the Provision and Use of Work Equipment Regulations (PUWER) 1998 devoted to power presses, then he would have committed an offence by being in breach of those regulations. He cannot defend himself by saying that it was disproportionately expensive to have it done or any other excuse. He was either in compliance with the requirements of the regulation or he was not. That is the nature of an absolute duty.

An absolute duty that is qualified by practicable can be defended by the duty holder showing that he could not have done more than he did, because there is no way known in modern technology for it to be done otherwise. For example, under regulation 11 of PUWER 1998 the duty to safeguard machinery is absolute, qualified by practicable. Safeguarding machinery must be as good as modern technology allows. If someone gets hurt on a circular saw, the duty holder would need to show that the circular saw had standard guarding that all well-guarded circular saws have. This would not always prevent someone being hurt as it is, for now (in the light of current knowledge and invention), not possible to guard the blade completely and still use the saw.

An absolute duty qualified by reasonably practicable can be defended by showing that it was not reasonably practicable to do more than what was done. If that risk is realised and someone does get hurt, the employer would have to show that the time, trouble and money spent had been reasonably practicable. In practice this would mean that the risk had been assessed and evaluated and controls to reduce that risk to an acceptable or tolerable level had been put in place. Their efficacy had been monitored and reviewed. The cost was in proportion to the risk.

In HASWA 1974 section 2 (1), the employer 'shall ensure so far as is reasonably practicable' the health, safety and welfare of all employees at work. If the employer is prosecuted because he is in breach of that section, s.40 gives him the right to defend himself by showing he did everything that was reasonably practicable.

S.40 Onus of Proof says the defendant will need to show that he did everything so far as is practicable or reasonably practicable. This will be judged by the court on the 'balance of probabilities'.

> The burden of proof laid on the defendant is less onerous than that resting on the prosecutor as regards proving the offence, and may be discharged by satisfying the court of the **probability** of what the defendant is called on to prove.

Figure A8-1: Burden of proof.   *Source: Redgrave's Health and Safety all editions, HASWA 1974, paragraph 3.87.*

FAULT LAY WITH SOMEONE ELSE

It may well be the case that the defendant could show that the fault lay with someone else, but this someone cannot be one of his employees or competent persons. For example, the employer cannot state as a defence that it is the risk assessor's fault for not having carried out all the risk assessments, if the employer is being prosecuted for breach of regulation 3 of the Management of Health and Safety at Work Regulations. This is stated in regulation 21 of the same regulations.

It is difficult for the duty holder to blame someone else when he has the duty to ensure something is done.

NOT GUILTY DUE TO A TECHNICALITY

It may be shown that the accused is not guilty because he was not the duty holder at that time. It would be a defence to show that the duty holder was the employer, who had duties to his employees, but the person who, for example was involved in an accident was not an employee. Therefore, he was not guilty of failing to ensure the safety of his employees.

This page is intentionally blank

Civil law

Learning outcomes

The intended learning outcomes are that the student will be able to:

A9.1   explain the duties owed in civil law by an employer to his employees and others and describe the standards to be achieved in discharging the duties

A9.2   describe the breach of duty, the main defences available and the procedure for assessment of damage under civil law

A9.3   outline the main duties owned by the occupiers of premises

A9.4   outline the differences between public, private and statutory nuisances

Contents

This page is intentionally blank

A9.1 - Civil liability for negligence

The tort negligence

THE TERM NEGLIGENCE

The tort of negligence together with action for breach of statutory duty is the most common cause of action for injury at work. Negligence was defined in the case of Blyth v Birmingham Waterworks 1856. Here the plaintiff (now claimant) alleged that the water company had failed in their duty of care by laying a water pipe at too shallow a depth in the ground, which, as a result, became frozen in winter.

> "Negligence is the omission to do something which a reasonable man guided upon those considerations which ordinarily regulate the conduct of human affairs would do, or doing something which a prudent and reasonable man would not do."

Figure A9-1: Definition of negligence.   *Source: Baron Alderson, Blyth v Birmingham Waterworks [1856].*

Thus negligence is failing to do something a reasonable person would do or doing something that a reasonable person would not do (i.e. an act or omission) in the same circumstances. The "man on the Clapham omnibus" is often cited as representing the reasonable person. Ultimately it is the Judge who will decide what is reasonable based on the facts of the case. The Judge will take into account precedents established in prior cases. Thus the law of torts relating to negligence is being continually developed with old cases being applied to new situations.

> "The categories of negligence are never closed". In effect, the standard of "reasonableness" changes with the changing morals and attitudes of Society as a whole."

Figure A9-2: Development of term negligence.   *Source: Lord Macmillan said in Donoghue v Stevenson [1932].*

In order to prove negligence, the claimant must show that:-

- The defendant owed him a duty of care.
- The defendant was in breach of that duty.
- That the claimant had suffered an actionable loss as a result of the breach.

DUTY OF CARE OWED

Thus, before negligence is proved, it must first be established that a duty of care is owed by the defendant to the claimant. Donaghue v Stevenson (1932)

> "You must take reasonable care to avoid acts or omissions which you can reasonably foresee would be likely to injure your neighbour. Who then, in law, is my neighbour? The answer seems to be - persons who are so closely and directly affected by my act that I ought reasonably to have them in contemplation as being so affected when I am directing my mind to the acts or omissions which are called into question."

Figure A9-3: The neighbour principle.   *Source: Lord Atkin.*

BREACH OF THE DUTY OF CARE THROUGH NEGLIGENCE

A breach of the duty of care is required when proving negligence. This depends on the standards of care that may be expected from the "reasonable person".

CAUSAL LINK BETWEEN THE BREACH AND THE LOSS SUFFERED

The injury (loss) was a result of the breach. The injury or loss must be as a consequence of the breach. Generally the injury must be "reasonably foreseeable". It is, however, no defence to show that an injured person was unforeseeably weak ("the thin skull" rule). The loss must not be too remote from the breach and there must be a direct causal link established by the facts of the case.

CONCEPT OF RES IPSA LOQUITOR

Normally the burden of establishing that the defendant has broken the duty of care rests with the claimant. In some instances the facts that the claimant establishes (obvious to the court that there is negligence) are such that 'the thing may speak for itself' *res ipsa loquitur*. Here there is a presumption that the defendant has been negligent. Effectively, but not in fact, the burden then shifts to the defendant to establish that the damage occurred without their negligence. It is up to the defendant to prove that the accident could have occurred without his negligence.

In *Cassidy v Ministry of Health (1951)*, for example, the Court of Appeal was of the view that the very fact that the claimant emerged from treatment in a hospital with a paralysed hand raised a presumption that the defendant hospital had been negligent. The presumption may arise when the claimant has satisfied the court as to what has occurred but has not been able to show exactly how it occurred. For the presumption to arise the situation must have been under the control of the defendant; thus it is particularly likely to arise where an accident has occurred on premises under the control of the defendant.

The principle of *res ipsa loquiter* was established in *Scott v London and St Katherine Docks Co (1865)*. Here the defendants dropped a bag of sugar from a crane onto the plaintiff (now claimant), causing him injury. The claimant satisfied the court on this fact. The Court of Exchequer (now the High Court) was then prepared to find that the claimant had raised a presumption that the defendant had been negligent. In the judgement the rule is stated as:

> "There must be reasonable evidence of negligence, but where the thing is shown to be under the management of the defendant, or his servants, and the accident is such as, in the ordinary course of things, does not happen if those who have the management of the machinery use proper care, it affords reasonable evidence, in the absence of explanation by the defendant, that the accident arose from want of care."

Figure A9-4: Res ipsa loquitur.   *Source: Erle Court Judge (CJ), Scott v London and St Katherine Docks Co [1865].*

It should be noted that *res ipsa loquitur* is a rule of evidence rather than a defence.

The concept of 'duty of care'

TO WHOM A DUTY IS OWED (THE 'NEIGHBOUR TEST')

In the case of Donoghue v Stevenson [1932], the claimant, Ms Donoghue, became ill when she drank a bottle of ginger beer which contained a decomposed snail. The bottle was opaque and she had no reason to believe that it contained anything other than ginger beer. She sued the manufacturer.

As it was Ms Donoghue's friend who had purchased the ginger beer, the manufacturer claimed that there was no contract between them.

Damages were awarded to the claimant. The House of Lords held that a duty of care was owed and determined the extent of that duty known as the "neighbour principle".

The question was asked, "To whom is this duty of care owed?"

said:

> *"You must take reasonable care to avoid acts or omissions which you can reasonably foresee would be likely to injure your neighbour."*

Figure A9-5: The neighbour principle.   *Source: Lord Atkin, Donoghue v Stevenson [1932].*

Who is my neighbour, in the legal sense?

> *"Persons who are so closely and directly affected by my act that I ought reasonably to have them in contemplation as being so affected when I am directing my mind to the acts or omissions which are called in question."*

Figure A9-6: Clarification of term neighbour.   *Source: Lord Atkin, Donoghue v Stevenson [1932].*

In other words, my neighbour is someone who is affected by what I do.

THE DUTY OF CARE OF VARIOUS CATEGORIES OF PERSON

Designers, manufacturers and suppliers to customers/users

The duty of care owed by designers, manufacturers and suppliers to customers/users follows on from the Donoghue v Stevenson case.

At common law a manufacturer has a duty of care to both industrial and domestic users of his product (including servicemen and repairers) in respect of defects. He has a duty to the *"end user"*.

In order for an action for negligence to succeed, the claimant must show that the defect:

- Was caused by lack of reasonable care on the manufacture's part; and
- Was foreseeably likely to cause injury, and loss occurred; and
- Existed at the time that the product left the manufacturer; and
- Was not one which a legitimate intermediary (e.g. the retailer) or the user could be expected to discover and modify.

Manufacturers and suppliers are not automatically liable for injuries caused by a product. They will be liable if they fail to take reasonable care. For example by:

- Failing to consult available technical information.
- Failing to give suitable warnings or clear instructions.
- Poor ergonomic details in, for example, instrumentation leading to user error.
- Defective insulation in an electrical appliance.

The seller as well as, or instead of, the manufacturer may be liable for negligence if they failed to make reasonable enquiries about the use and purpose of the product in relation to its safety or suitability.

The supplier's liability can be offset or reduced if, for example:

- The user (e.g. employer) is expected to test the goods himself.
- Where the goods are put to a purpose for which they are not intended.
- They are not maintained in accordance with the manufacturer's instructions.
- The user uses the equipment knowing it is defective.

In recent years product liability has moved from the need to establish negligence towards strict liability. The sale and supply of goods is regulated by statutes with both civil and criminal liability under the Consumer Protection Act 1987 (CPA) and the Sale and Supply of Goods Act (SASGA) 1994.

Occupiers of premises to those using or visiting the premises

Under the Occupiers' Liability Act (OLA) 1957, an occupier owes a "common law duty of care" to all visitors. The duty is to take such care as is reasonable (given the circumstances) to see that visitors are reasonably safe in using the premises for the purposes for which they are invited or permitted to be there.

A visitor is usually extended an 'area of invitation' in which they are expected to stay and to which the duty applies. If a visitor strays outside this area then they become uninvited. A visitor going off to search for toilets, however, is likely to receive special sympathy from the courts.

The OLA 1957 reminds the employer (or occupier) that they must be prepared for children to be less careful than adults. They must also take care that 'allurements' such as attractive poisonous berries or machines are considered. The occupier may be liable even if the child is a trespasser as far as the allurement itself is concerned.

Under section 2(1) of the OLA 1957 the occupier may exclude or restrict liability by giving adequate warning or by contract. The Unfair Contract Terms Act (UCTA) 1977 states that the common law duty of care for death or personal injury cannot be excluded in relation to business premises. In addition loss or damage can only be excluded when it is reasonable to do so.

In determining whether the occupier of premises has discharged the common duty of care to a visitor, regard is to be had to all the circumstances, so that (for example):

- Where damage is caused to a visitor by a danger of which he had been warned by the occupier, the warning is not to be treated as an excuse absolving the occupier from liability, unless in all the circumstances it was enough to enable the visitor to be reasonably safe.
- Where an injury arises through the defective work of a contractor, the occupier can avoid liability provided that the contractor was selected with reasonable care.

The common law duty of care does not impose on an occupier any obligation to a visitor in respect of risks willingly accepted by that visitor. The question whether the visitor accepted a risk is a matter for the court to decide using the same principles as in other cases in which one person owes a duty of care to another. However, an occupier may expect that persons, in the exercise of their calling, will appreciate and guard against any special risks ordinarily incident to that calling. An employer (or occupier) cannot be prosecuted for a breach of their duties under the OLA 1957, but if a visitor is injured, the occupier may be liable to pay compensation for the injury.

Persons who enter premises for any purpose in the exercise of a right conferred by law (e.g. HSE inspector, Customs & Excise Officer) are to be treated as permitted by the occupier to be there for that purpose, whether they have his permission or not.

The position towards non-visitors is governed by the Occupiers' Liability Act (OLA) 1984. Prior to the OLA 1984 certain duties of common humanity were owed under common law by an occupier to those other than lawful visitors - for example, to trespassers or ramblers The OLA 1984 extended the rules of common law (see British Railways Board v Herrington (1972)) and defines under what circumstances a duty is owed. In particular, occupiers owe a duty if:

- They are aware of a danger.
- They know (or should know) that a person may put themselves at risk.
- The risk is one which the occupier might reasonably be expected to do something about.

The extent of the duty is as follows:

- The occupier must take such care as is reasonable in the circumstances of the case, to see that the other person does not suffer injury.

The Act provides that the duty may be discharged by:

- Giving warning of the danger.
- Discouraging people from putting themselves at risk in the first place (e.g. by making it more difficult for trespassers, etc. to enter the premises).

As with the OLA 1957, the duty is greater towards children. What constitutes a reasonable warning for an adult may not do so for a child. If the occupier, knowing that children trespass onto his land, fails to take action (e.g. by repairing fences) this might be taken as evidence of implied permission and an injured child would therefore be considered a visitor.

Contractors to clients and vice versa

Under the neighbour principle espoused in Donoghue v Stevenson, a reciprocal duty of care exists between clients and contractors. The duty owed by a client to visiting contractors is that laid down by the Occupiers Liability Act (OLA) 1957 *(see above)*. That is, the client must have safe premises and take reasonable care of the contractor's safety. In return, the client may assume that the contractor will take all precautions reasonable to his trade and the client is not expected to tell a highly skilled workman how to do his job. If the client (occupier) is involved in supervising operations, however, then they have to ensure that adequate safety arrangements have been made.

Clients are, however, liable for risks that are peculiar to the premises but are not occupational hazards. For example, a client could not expect a contractor such as a telephone engineer to deal with working on an unusually fragile roof as part of his normal expertise.

The client would not be liable under English civil law for the dangers created by contractors on or near his premises - provided they have taken reasonable care in selecting them. The exception to this is if the injured person is the client's own employee (a strict liability exists for the reasonable care of employees which cannot be delegated to a contractor). It should be noted however that there might be criminal liability under the HASAWA 1974 for exposure to risks arising from the employers' undertaking *(see R v Swan Hunter and R v Associated Octel).*

EXTENT OF DUTY

Remoteness

This is the principle that the damage or loss is not sufficiently connected to the defendant's breach of duty of care. The principle of a new act intervening (novus actus interveniens) is an extension of the defence of remoteness of damage. To succeed it must be shown that the chain of causation is broken by an extraneous act. This principle was the defence in Scot v Shepherd [1773]. Here the defendant lit a squib at a market fair and threw it onto a stall (A). The stallholder A threw it onto another stall (B) where, in turn, it was thrown onto another stall (C) where it exploded and injured C. This defence was unsuccessful and the defendant was held liable because there was a direct chain of causation that was not broken by the acts of A and B.

The chain of causation can also be broken if the claimant acts unreasonably by, for example, taking an avoidable and foreseeable risk of injury himself, if this act can be seen to break the chain then this might be enough to establish a complete defence for the defendant (if this action is not seen to break the chain the defence will fail; however the claim may be reduced due to contributory negligence).

In some cases, the loss may be too remote where there is a sequence of physical cause and effect without human intervention. This is illustrated by The Wagon Mound [1961] case that involved the negligent spilling of oil into the sea by a ship in Sydney Harbour. The oil drifted to a wharf 200 yards away where a ship was being repaired. The owner of the wharf on seeing the oil ordered welding to cease due to the fire risk. He was later advised that the risk of fire from sparks was unlikely and accordingly allowed welding to continue albeit with additional safety precautions. A spark fell onto a piece of floating cotton waste and ignited the oil causing damage to the wharf. The charterers of the Wagon Mound were sued by the owners of the wharf. The claim failed based on the test of reasonable foresight in that pollution was a foreseeable risk; however the fire was too remote from the cause.

Note. Cases involving ships are usually referred to by the ship's name. The Wagon Mound case was brought on appeal to the Judicial Committee of the Privy Council from Australia. It has persuasive precedent in a court in England and Wales.

Reasonableness

What is meant by reasonable care will be decided by the judge in the light of contemporary knowledge and thinking. For example, what was considered reasonable conduct in the 1960s will not necessarily be seen as reasonable many years later. As in the case of Blyth v Birmingham Waterworks [1856], what is reasonable is doing something a reasonable person would do in the same circumstances. Who then is the reasonable man? The "man on the Clapham omnibus" is often cited as the representing the reasonable person. This does not mean that the average prudent person has a low standard of care. Most people behave unreasonably from time to time and it is no defence to say that we are usually reasonable people.

Ultimately it is the Judge who will decide what is reasonable based on the facts of the case.

Reasonableness could include the making of decisions for controlling a risk being based on the foreseeability and remoteness of a risk causing loss and the level of risk involved.

Foreseeability

The more likely or probable an accident is, the greater the duty to guard against it. If there is only a remote possibility of loss, the need for precautions is usually much reduced. Indeed it may not be reasonable to take any precautions at all against very unlikely events. In Latimer v AEC [1953], a flash flood was unforeseeable and the company could not have been expected to guard against it.

A car driver knows that even though he exercises due care while driving on a normal road surface, his tyres may conceivably throw a stone against the windscreen of the car behind and so cause a serious accident. The only way he could ensure that it did not happen would be to drive at 10 mph or not drive at all.

The law does not of course require such drastic precautions in normal road conditions and so it would not make him liable in these circumstances. If the road had recently been re-surfaced and stones were all over the road surface, it is foreseeable that a stone be thrown up and loss result. It then becomes reasonable to drive at a reduced speed - particularly when warning signs have been displayed.

In Millard v Serk Tubes Ltd [1969] a worker was using a power drill with his hand resting on the guard. A piece of swarf thrown out from the work-piece wound around the worker's hand and drew it into the drill causing injury. The Court of Appeal rejected the employer's defence that, although the drill was inadequately guarded, the accident itself was unforeseeable. They could not escape liability for injury on the grounds of unforeseeability when there was a duty under the Factories Act to fence the dangerous parts of machinery. Thus the defence of reasonable foresight might succeed in respect of an action for common law negligence and fail when applied to a claimant suing for breach of statutory duty.

In Doughty v Turner Manufacturing Co [1964] an asbestos cement lid accidentally fell into a vessel containing sodium cyanide at 800°C. There was an explosion due to a chemical reaction which was previously unknown to science. The defendant was injured by the molten liquid ejected by the explosion rather than the splash caused by the lid falling into the cauldron. His claim failed because splashing by sodium cyanide was foreseeable but the explosion was not.

Thus in summary the defendant is only liable for damages in respect of both events and loss that can be reasonably foreseen.

Duties owed by employers to employees and others

The common law duty of care owed by an employer may be summed up as:

■   The employer must take reasonable care not to subject his employees to unnecessary risk.

The elements of this duty were established by the case of Wilsons & Clyde Coal Company v. English in 1938. Here the House of Lords held that the employer must provide:

■   Proper and safe plant and appliances.
■   Safe systems of work (with adequate supervision and instruction).
■   Safe premises (this includes safe access and egress).
■   A competent staff of fellow employees.

It was also held that the duty owed was a personal one, which could not be delegated to an agent. Employers have no liability for risks that a reasonable employer could not have foreseen. Reasonable steps for employees' safety can only be taken if the employer knows of the danger. Employers have a duty to keep themselves abreast of the latest developments within their sphere of activity. Thus ignorance of a danger can be reasonable provided that a reasonable effort has been made to keep up to date with developments.

A SAFE PLACE OF WORK AND SAFE ACCESS AND EGRESS

An employer has a duty to ensure that the place of work is safe together with safe access and egress. The extent of the duty is to guard against foreseeable risks, not for those which are transient and exceptional *(see Latimer v AEC [1953])*. The duty to ensure safe access and egress extends beyond the duty to clear snow and ice from around the workplace but also to ensure, for example, that someone working at height can reach and leave their place of work safely.

As with all elements of the employers' duty, the duty is to take reasonable steps. In *Markwell v Suffolk Coastal District Council* an employee slipped on a patch of ice 18 inches in diameter. His claim failed because the judge considered that, when taken as a whole, the yard was reasonably safe. In contrast in Bath v BTC [1954] a man worked on a narrow ledge at the top of a dock, without any edge or fall protection to prevent death or serious injury if he slipped. He did so and the employer was held liable for failing to provide a rail or a net in a dangerous place. The judge held that the fact that the fall may have been the employee's fault was unimportant. The required precautions would undoubtedly be expensive and have ramifications throughout the industry; however these were justified due to the risk.

SAFE SYSTEMS OF WORK

The employers' duty to take reasonable steps to prevent injury to employees reaches every aspect of the employer's undertaking. The provision of a safe system of work encompasses the working environment, the work equipment, the way in which the job is carried out and the provision of the colleagues that the employer gives employees to work with. Thus it relates not so much to the place or the work equipment but to the way in which they are used. The law does not require employees to be treated as though they are children. The employer should be able to assume that employees can deal with routine and straightforward operations.

> "An experienced workman must know the ordinary risks of the work he is employed to do. In doing that work he is expected to take ordinary routine precautions common to it and should not expect to be told by his employers of every danger which might arise and of every step that should be taken to counteract that danger."

Figure A9-7: Ordinary risks and precautions.   Source: The judge, Ferner v Kemp [1960].

It is the employer's duty to reduce risks as far as is reasonably practicable. If the job cannot be made absolutely safe, the employer must do all he can to make it as safe as can be reasonably expected in the circumstances. The extent of the duty to provide a safe system of work has progressed over the years to more than just the prevention of physical injury. The duty also extends to the provision of reasonable care to take steps to ensure that employees' mental health is not adversely affected by overwork or stress at work (as was the case in Walker v Northumberland County Council [1994], where damages were awarded to a social worker for the mental stress caused by overwork).

SAFE PLANT, EQUIPMENT AND MATERIALS

The employer has a duty to provide safe and proper plant and equipment that must be suitable for the task being undertaken. This applies to machinery, apparatus, goods, vehicles and the like used by employees. As previously stated the precautions taken by the industry or in the trade provides important evidence that the appropriate standard of care has been taken in any particular case. A general industry practice which ignored hazards that are inherent to the job, or treated an occupational disease as something about which very little can be done (when precautions are appropriate) would be rejected by the court.

In Bradford v Robinson Rentals, the employer failed to provide suitable equipment when a van without a heater had to be used for travel on behalf of the company, resulting in the driver contracting frostbite. Frostbite is usually associated with mountain climbing or suffering extreme cold if lost in the open countryside in the depths of winter, not driving a van. Looking at the foreseeable risks associated with driving a van would not normally include the driver getting frostbite. However, this was not deemed to be the point. The fact was that the employer had not provided suitable equipment for use at work, i.e a van without a heater for use in winter, and this resulted in the claimant's loss. The nature of the loss was not relevant. The only time the nature of the loss would be relevant would be when an amount of compensation was awarded for that loss. The nature of the loss had nothing to do with the point of law, i.e. the employer failed to provide suitable equipment and this caused the claimant's loss.

There must also be a suitable system for the testing, inspection and maintenance of equipment. A suitable system should take reasonable steps to detect both obvious and non-obvious causes of defects. In Bell v Arnott and Harrison (1967) the employer bought a new Black and Decker electric hand drill. After a year without inspection a screw came loose and a bush flew out injuring an employee. The employer argued that they had a reasonable right to assume that equipment supplied by a reputable manufacturer was safe. This argument failed as the judge held that the equipment should have been subjected to regular checks.

INSTRUCTION, TRAINING AND SUPERVISION

The employer must take reasonable steps to ensure that adequate instruction, training and supervision is provided to employees in order to take reasonable steps to ensure their safety. Training is relevant to all levels and may take many different forms. To quote some previous judges' remarks:

> "The employer must remember that men doing routine tasks are often heedless of their own safety, and may become careless about precautions. He must by his foreman keep them up to the mark and not tolerate any slackness".
>
> "The defendants having given these lectures and prescribed the right method did what reasonable and careful employers could do in order to institute a safe and effective system of work."
>
> "If an employer…put a young girl in charge of such a machine, they are under a duty of giving special instructions to her."

Figure A9-8: Comments on instruction, training and supervision.   Source: Various judges.

The level of duty is dependent on the person and the circumstances. Young people and inexperienced workers for example require more training and supervision than that of an adult, experienced, employee. Clearly one-to-one supervision cannot be provided at all times and the law does not require it particularly where experienced employees are concerned.

COMPETENT FELLOW EMPLOYEES

The provision of competent fellow employees applies to all levels within the hierarchy of an organisation. In simple terms this means that the employer should select employees who have both the mental and physical capabilities required to perform their duties in a manner which is safe to both themselves and others. The term employee usually encompasses everyone from the chief executive, managing director etc. through to newly recruited trainees. An incompetent manager can have a significant effect on those who are affected by his or her decision-making - even though they may be remote from that manager's direct influence. It should be noted, that while the duty to provide competent employees rests with the employer as a corporate entity, there can be a personal liability. A manager assigned with responsibility for the safety of their department is not personally liable for an accident unless there is a personal failure to take reasonable care.

This duty extends beyond competence through to behaviour in the workplace. An employee who is known to engage in practical jokes and horseplay could constitute a hazard, which the employer would be expected to deal with. In Hudson v Ridge Manufacturing [1957] an employee was a known practical joker who had made a nuisance of himself over the previous 5 years. Examples of his behaviour included tripping people from behind. Although this was done for fun, and without malice or intent to bully, injury was inevitable sooner or later. In one incident an employee broke his wrist in an effort to break his fall after being gripped around the neck and pulled back by the practical joker. The employer was held liable in the resulting case on the basis that they had failed to take steps to curb his horseplay. It was held that the duty of the employer is to provide safe colleagues to work with.

In this case the employer's duty was to take steps by reprimand, discipline and, if necessary, dismiss the practical joker in order to remove the risk of injury to other employees.

A9.2 - Breach of duty, defences and damage

The main defences to claims of negligence

DENIAL

The first defence is one of a denial of liability. This may be based on a variety of grounds:

NO DUTY OWED

The defendant did not owe the claimant a duty of care. This is unlikely to apply in an action for damages between an employer and an employee as the duty of care relationship is well established. The employer could however claim that the claimant was not an employee and was working for another company *(see Mersey Docks and Harbour Board v Coggins & Griffiths [1946])*.

NO BREACH OF DUTY

Foreseeability

The risk and loss were not foreseeable, as in Latimer v AEC where there was a flash flood. No reasonable person could have foreseen this occurrence.

Reasonableness

Everything that could reasonably have been done was done.

BREACH DID NOT LEAD TO DAMAGE

There may have been a failure to fulfil the common law duty of care, but that was not what led to the loss. The employer may have failed to provide training on manual handling, but the claimant hurt his back reaching over to pick up his pen.

REMOTENESS OF DAMAGE

In some cases, the loss may be too remote where there is a sequence of physical cause and effect without human intervention. *This is illustrated by The Wagon Mound [1961] case above.*

This is the principle that the damage or loss is not sufficiently connected to the defendant's breach of duty of care. The principle of a new act intervening (novus actus interveniens) is an extension of the defence of remoteness of damage *(see Scot v Shepherd [1773])*.

The chain of causation can also be broken if the claimant acts unreasonably by, for example, taking an avoidable and foreseeable risk of injury himself, that breaks the chain (if it does not then the claim may be reduced due to contributory negligence).

VOLENTI NON FIT INJURIA

Where a person has agreed either expressly or by implication to accept the risk of injury, he cannot then recover damages for loss caused to him by that risk.

Volenti non fit injuria - translated from Latin this means 'to one who is willing no harm is done'. This is a complete defence to negligence by the defendant, and is used where the claimant agreed to run the risk of accidental harm.

In the case of Smith v Baker & Sons Ltd, the claimant, who was a railway navvy, was working in a cutting. A crane, used for removing stones, passed its load directly over a workman's head and he had made several complaints. When stones fell on him he claimed damages. The employer claimed the defence of *volenti non fit injuria* as they deemed that the navvy had accepted the danger by continuing to work.

The House of Lords found that even though he knew of the danger; and still continued to do the work, there was no evidence that he had volunteered for the risk of injury.

> *"…the duty of taking reasonable care to provide proper appliances and maintain them in a proper condition and so to carry on his operations as to not subject those employed by him to unnecessary risk."*

Figure A9-9: Duty of care to employees.   Source: Lord Hershell, Lord Atkin, Donoghue v Stevenson [1932].

An allowance should be made for the fact that most workers cannot afford to terminate their employment. After this case, the courts have rarely found that an employee has accepted the risk of injury at work.

This true consent must be freely given and has been used in connection with spectators injured in the course of events with inherent risks, for example, motor racing. In Hall v Brooklands Auto Racing [1933] a spectator paid for a ticket to watch car races. During a race two cars collided which resulted in one of them spinning off the track, through the barriers and into the stands injuring Mr Hall. He lost his subsequent claim for negligence as the precautions were deemed to be adequate (this was the first time such an incident had happened). By purchasing his ticket, the claimant was held to have assumed the risk from such an accident.

This principle can also apply to minors. In Murray v Harringay Arena Ltd (1951), a 6 year old boy was taken by his parents to watch an ice hockey match. He was sitting in the front row when he was hit in the eye by the ice hockey puck. He was unsuccessful in his claim for damages as it was held that the claimants had voluntarily undertaken the risk. The defendants had provided protection by means of a wooden barrier and netting. Had the protection been more substantial then it would have seriously interfered with the spectator's view.

An employee, however, does not consent to abnormal or unnecessary risks merely by accepting the job or continuing to do it *(see Smith v Baker & Sons [1891])*. The 'volenti' defence may, however, be successful where employees conspire to breach statutory duty against the employer's specific instructions.

In ICI Ltd v Shatwell [1964] two brothers, who were certified shot blasters, were injured whilst testing electrical circuitry used to detonate explosives. They did so in the open, contrary to the Quarries (Explosives) Regulations 1959 which required them to be in a position of safety. The resulting claim for damages against the employer was unsuccessful on the basis that they had voluntarily accepted the risk of each other's negligence and breach of statutory duty by defying the employer's instructions and breaching the Regulations which were well known to them. The volenti defence, however, will not normally succeed in cases where there is a direct breach of common law or statutory duty by the employer.

This defence is unlikely to succeed when defending claims made by rescuers who volunteered for the risk in order to safeguard others, whether or not the rescuers are members of the public or public service employees. In Haynes v Harwood [1935], for example, it was held that the defences of volenti and contributory negligence did not apply when a policeman was injured by a runaway horse and van in a crowded street. Similarly, it was held that the defence of volenti did not apply in the case of Baker v T E Hopkins and Sons Ltd [1959] where a local doctor died trying to rescue two men who had been overcome by a lethal concentration of carbon monoxide fumes when working in a well.

THE PRINCIPLE THAT A BREACH OF STATUTORY DUTY MAY GIVE RISE TO CIVIL LIABILITY

A breach of statutory duty (failing to comply with the obligations imposed by statute law) may also be a cause for a civil claim for compensation in cases that result in personal injury or loss. In order to establish a claim for breach of statutory duty, the claimant must establish the following:

- The defendant was in breach of the statute.
- This breach caused the injury.
- The claimant was of a class of person the statute was intended to protect.
- The type of injury was one the statute was intended to prevent.

It should be noted that the injured person might sue for both negligence and breach of statutory duty (double-barrelled action).

There is nothing to prevent a claimant basing his case on both breach of statutory duty and negligence, the former having a limited interpretation but affording ready proof of liability, and the latter being capable of wide interpretation but being more difficult to prove.

MAIN DEFENCES TO CLAIMS OF A BREACH OF STATUTORY DUTY

The first defence to a claim of breach of statutory duty (BOSD) could be that the statute was barred. In other words, the chosen statute is one that is not allowed to be used in a civil claim.

Statute barred

Section 47 of the HASAWA Act 1974

There are some statutes that cannot be used in a civil claim. These are said to be "statute barred". The Health and Safety at Work etc. Act (HASAWA) 1974, s.47 states that civil liability is excluded for sections 2-7 or any contravention of section 8, which in effect means that the Act has only criminal liability.

Construction (Design and Management) Regulations 2007

Generally, CDM 2007 exclude action under civil law. There are though some exceptions. For example 9(1)(b) the duty placed on the client to ensure that adequate welfare facilities are provided, 13(6) the duty placed on contractors to ensure that reasonable steps have been taken to prevent access by unauthorised persons to that site and 22(1)(l). The duty placed on the principal contractor to take reasonable steps to prevent access by unauthorised persons to the construction site.

No breach of duty

There was no breach of duty under the statute. Everything that must be done was done or was done so far as is practicable or reasonably practicable, or was suitable and sufficient, whatever the statute required.

Injured party not within the class of persons protected by the statute

The claimant was not one of the class of persons that the statute was there to protect. For example, if a visitor was the claimant and the duties under the statute were to the employee then the visitor would fail in his claim.

Harm not of the type that the statute was designed to prevent

If the harm done to the claimant were not the type the statute was there to prevent, the claim would fail. For example, suddenly sneezing and hitting your head on the side of a machine would not be a Provision and Use of Work Equipment Regulations issue.

No causal connection between the breach and the loss suffered

This defence is where the breach of statute is admitted, but the breach did not lead to the loss.

In the case of McWilliams v Sir William Arrol & Co Ltd [1962] the breach was under the Factories Act and stated as failing to provide safety harnesses for the steel erectors and thus Mr McWilliams fell to his death. The defendant agreed they were in breach, but claimed that it did not lead to the loss, as even if they had provided harnesses, the employees (including Mr McWilliams) would not have worn them. The defendant showed that they had once provided harnesses, but as nobody would wear them, they took them away again. The claimant failed, as the judge decided that the breach did not lead to the loss.

See also Corn v Weirs Glass (Hanley) Ltd [1960] for a further example of the breach not leading to the loss.

Description of damage for which tortfeasor is liable

LIMITATIONS ON ACTIONS

The Limitations Act (LA) 1980 places a time limit on actions in respect of tort of six years. Damages for personal injuries and death in respect of negligence, nuisance, and breach of statutory duty must be started within three years from the date of the claimant becoming aware of the injury, or three years from the medical diagnosis of occupational ill-health.

At common law personal actions did not survive the person: if either plaintiff or defendant died the right to litigate was lost. This principle was changed with the introduction to the Fatal Accidents Act 1846. This allowed the wrongdoer to be sued to maintain the income for the deceased's dependants at the level which the deceased had been providing.

The Fatal Accident Act (FAA) 1976 gives rights to certain persons to sue for negligence that has resulted in death. The objective of the FAA is to provide compensation for relatives who have been deprived of maintenance due to death. The claimants must have suffered financial loss because of the death and must have been financially dependent on him. Classes of persons include husband, wife, children, grandchildren, parents, grandparents, brothers, sisters, aunts, and uncles, and their issue. The relationship may be traced through step-relatives, adoption or illegitimacy, and relatives through marriage have the same rights as the deceased's own relatives. Any person who was living with the deceased for two or more years prior to death may also claim (e.g. an unmarried co-habitant).

A single action must be brought on behalf of all eligible dependants and damages apportioned according to dependency. The action may be bought by a personal representative(s) of the deceased. However, if there are none or if they fail to bring an action within six months of the death, the dependants may bring it themselves.

The three year rule under the 1980 Limitations Act still applies; however the court has discretionary powers. If the claimant dies before the limitation period has expired, the three years starts from the date of death or the date of the personal representative's knowledge of the cause of action (whichever is the later).

RELEVANCE OF DAMAGE OF FORESEEABLE TYPE

A tortfeasor is defined as someone who has carried out a tort. Tortfeasors are liable for damages that occurred while they were in breach of duty. In *Thomson and others v Smiths Ship Repairers (North Shields Ltd [1984])*, relating to a claim for damages for occupational deafness, it was held that damages should be apportioned to all previous employers. It was, however recognised that most of the damage from noise occurs in the early years of exposure, and that subsequent employers may be liable for a smaller portion of the claim. *See also the later section on joint tortfeasors.*

Damage might also be for psychological injury. Employers are normally entitled to assume that employees can withstand the normal pressures of a job. However, there have been successful claims for psychological injury, in particular occupational stress. In the case of *Sutherland v Hatton and others [2002]* the Court set out a number of practical propositions for future claims concerning workplace stress. This precedent was set to "close the floodgates" on claims for stress.

DATE OF KNOWLEDGE OF RISK

As previously stated employers have a duty to keep themselves abreast of the latest developments within their sphere of activity. Thus ignorance of a danger can be reasonable provided that a reasonable effort has been made to keep up to date with developments. The concept of date of knowledge of risk is illustrated by the *Thomson and others v Smiths Ship Repairers (North Shields Ltd)* case outlined above. Here it was held that employers were deemed to have first known about the risk of noise induced hearing loss when the publication "Health and Safety booklet 25 'Noise and the Worker' " was first published in 1963 by the Department of Employment. Similarly it has been held that industry should have been aware of the risk of vibration white finger in relation to certain processes involving the use of vibration inducing machinery since 1976. Employers are not, however, expected to change overnight and, in one case, the judge allowed three years from this date of knowledge for employers to make modifications to reduce vibration (Shepherd v Firth Brown [1985] unreported).

FACTORS TO BE CONSIDERED IN THE ASSESSMENT OF DAMAGES

In deciding the amount of damages awarded the Judge will take many factors into account including:

- Loss of actual and future earnings.
- Pain and suffering.
- Loss of amenities (i.e. enjoyment of life).

Damages are categorised as follows:

Special damages

Special damages represent the losses that can be proved to have occurred up to the date of the hearing of the claim, i.e. the tangible losses, (e.g. loss of earnings prior to the trial).

General (or ordinary) damages

General damages cover less tangible items such as pain and suffering both before and after the hearing of the claim and include any future loss of earnings.

Other damages

Exemplary or aggravated damages: intended to punish the defendant and to deter others. The House of Lords ruled that these could only be awarded where the defendant is calculated to make more money from his tort than he would have to pay in damages; where a government official acts oppressively, arbitrarily or unconstitutionally, or where statute allows this.

Nominal damages: where the claimant has suffered injury but no real loss, a small sum (i.e. a few pounds) may be awarded. For example, the defendant has trespassed onto the claimant's land without causing any damage.

Contemptuous damages: where the court has no sympathy for the action (case) that the defendant has brought (i.e. damages of one pence).

Liquidated and unliquidated damages: liquidated damages are those which result from breach of contract which are fixed by the terms of the contract. Unliquidated damages occur when a contract has been breached; however damages are not fixed by the contract. These are awarded by the court based on the evidence relating to the loss that the claimant has suffered as a result of the breach. Liquidated damages do not normally apply in the law of tort.

From the above list it can be seen that special and general damages are the most significant factors in many cases. In general terms the aim of the award is to place the injured person back to where he or she was prior to injury - as far as this can be achieved with money.

There is no exact table of awards to be paid according to the type of injuries; however certain kinds of injury should fall within a "bracket" of awards. The judge will normally explain the factors he or she considered when making the award. The claimant should however not be materially better off because of the injury. *Some factors are given below*. For example, factors relating to loss of earnings include:

- Estimated annual earnings.
- Length of working life.
- How much the injury has affected earning/working capacity.
- Life expectancy.

In making the award the judge has to consider some quite complex factors that can overlap and contradict each other. In one case of injury to "a strong, confident mentally stable and physically fit man of 40 ... reduced to a shadow of himself, a pathetic piece of human wreckage" by an accident on the docks; the judge considered that:

"Whilst the claimant is denied the satisfaction of a docker's life, he is also spared its rigours. In view also of his acute awareness of his inability to look after his wife and his family the very substantial sum coming to the claimant by way of damages for loss of earnings past and future, will be a great source of consolation for the claimant ... because he will realise that the sum, plus the additional figure to be awarded to him for general damages, really makes his family's economic future perhaps more secure than it has ever been. It is also necessary of course to have due regards to the interests and well-being of the other side's insurance company."

Figure A9-10: Damages. *Source: Ambiguous.*

Fletcher v Autocar [1968]

In recent times there has been increasing concern about the perceived low levels of damages awarded. In 1999 the Law Commission recommended that damages be increased by between 50% and 100%. The move towards higher awards has however been resisted by both the insurance industry and the NHS (which self insures). In March 2000 five judges of the Court of Appeal (including the Master of the Rolls Lord Woolf) heard submissions relating to eight test cases. The claimant's lawyers argued that the current level of damages was too low in respect of the amounts awarded for pain, suffering and loss of amenity (PSLA), and general damages. The Court ruled that such damages should be increased by as much as one third. The judges did not want to see the 'daunting' levels found in the US but thought that a 'modest increase' that recognised factors such as increased life expectancy and increases in standards of living. They held that, as damages were the only available remedy, they should be fair, even though they cannot compensate for injury. There should be a consistency so that everyone knows what to expect and so as to facilitate settlements. The Court ruled that:

- Damages at the top end of the scale should be increased by one-third.
- That there should be no increase in awards below £10,000.
- There should be a tapering increase between the above points so that the largest increases occurred at the most serious end.

As a result of one of the above test cases the Court of Appeal increased the damages awarded to:

- A woman and a man who died of asbestos-induced mesotheliomia - from £45,000 to £50,000 and from £40,000 to £44,000 respectively.
- A woman, who suffered severe multiple injuries and brain damage in a road traffic accident, from £110,000 to £138,000.

The Court of Appeal said that this process of review should not be repeated unless there was real reason to suspect that damage awards had fallen behind the times.

CONTRIBUTORY NEGLIGENCE AND ITS EFFECTS

This was a complete defence until the law was reformed in 1945. Now contributory negligence is a partial defence whereby the claimant is held partly responsible for his own injury or loss. Any damages awarded are reduced by a corresponding percentage.

In Uddin v Associated Portland Cement Mfrs Ltd [1965], Mr Uddin was injured by falling in to the top of a machine, which had guards round the perimeter, but not across the top. He was in an area of the factory he should not have been, chasing a pigeon, which was not his job. Technically, the employer was in breach of his statutory duty because he had not "securely fenced all dangerous parts of all machinery", but the claimant had contributed to his own accident. It was found that he had contributed by 80% and therefore received only 20% of the damages.

Strict liability

DEFINITION OF STRICT LIABILITY

Strict liability is defined as:

"a liability which is independent of wrongful intent or negligence".

Examples of strict liability include:

- The employers' vicarious liability for the torts of employees committed during the course of their employment.
- The employers' liability for employees' injuries caused by defective equipment issued for use at work.
- Occupier's liability under the Rylands v Fletcher rule.

STRICT LIABILITY FOR DEFECTIVE EQUIPMENT

Prior to the Employers' Liability (Defective Equipment) Act (ELDEA) 1969, liability for an employee's injury or loss due to defective equipment lay with the supplier or manufacturer. Thus in Davie v New Merton Board Mills (1958) an employee failed to gain compensation from his employer when injured by a defective drift tool. The employer could not be reasonably expected to know that a tool obtained from a reputable supplier was defective.

The position was changed by the ELDEA, which places liability on the employer where an employee is injured by defective work equipment provided by the employer. This liability is strict and applies even where the defect is attributed wholly or in part to a third party (whether that party is identifiable or not). Of course there is nothing to prevent the employer, having paid compensation to the employee, from obtaining redress either in whole or in part from the supplier who was at fault.

The word equipment includes any plant and machinery, vehicle, aircraft and clothing. This is a wide ranging definition of the word 'equipment' is illustrated by such cases as:

- Knowles v Liverpool City Council (1992): employer liable for injury caused by a 'green' concrete flagstone.
- Coltman v Bibby Tankers Ltd (1987), owners of the MV Derbyshire, which sank off the coast of Japan, liable for deaths due to defects in the ship.

It should be noted that the law relating to contributory negligence in relation to an employee's injury is not affected by this Act.

STRICT LIABILITY - THE RYLANDS V FLETCHER RULE

> *"Where a person for his own purposes brings and keeps on land in his occupation anything likely to do mischief if it escapes, he must keep it at his peril, and if he fails to do so, he is liable for all damage which is a natural consequence of the escape."*

Figure A9-11: Strict liability - Rylands and Fletcher rule.   *Source: Rylands and Fletcher [1868].*

Strict liability exists for tort arising during circumstances depicted by 'the Rylands v Fletcher rule'. The rule was established by a decision of the House of Lords when considering the Rylands v Fletcher case. The rule has been held to apply to beasts, water, filth and stenches and fire. This 'strict liability' rule can apply to all persons (corporate or individual) and a claimant does not have to prove negligence. *(See Decided cases: Rylands v Fletcher [1868]).*

Following Rylands v Fletcher, in Emanuel v Greater London Council (1970), a contractor negligently lit a fire and sparks escaped onto the claimant's land damaging buildings and goods. The GLC as the client were held liable despite the fact that they had not been negligent.

Strict liability usually has a limited number of defences. The defences available for strict liability under the Rylands v Fletcher rule are more than most:

- Act of God - e.g. an unusual and extraordinary rainfall causes an ornamental lake to overflow and water to escape.
- Wrongful act of a stranger - the escape was caused by the unlawful act of a third party over whom the defendants had no control.
- Default of the claimant - the escape of the dangerous thing was caused by the default of the claimant (e.g. failing to repair a boundary fence).
- Consent of claimant (common benefit) - where the claimant consented to the presence or existence of the dangerous thing (e.g. fire extinguishers, water pipes, cisterns used for common benefit).
- Statutory authority e.g. a local authority, gas or electricity company may escape liability if there are clear terms in a relevant statute.
- Not foreseeable.

The later defence of foreseeability was introduced subsequent to the Rylands v Fletcher case. This was developed in 1994 in the case of Cambridge Water Co. Ltd v Eastern Counties Leather plc where the court held that a prerequisite for the liability to exist was that the specific type of damage in the event of an escape must be foreseeable. This illustrates the development of common law with regard to strict liability and is said to weaken the Rylands v Fletcher rule considerably. *(See Decided cases: Cambridge Water Co v Eastern Counties Leather plc [1994]).*

The concept of vicarious liability

CIRCUMSTANCES IN WHICH EMPLOYER IS VICARIOUSLY LIABLE FOR NEGLIGENCE OF EMPLOYEE

The two major principles regarding liability at tort are that:

- A person is only responsible for the loss or damage caused by his or her own acts and omissions.
- A person is only liable if he or she is at fault.

The doctrine of the employer's vicarious liability in respect of employees appears to go against these principles and may be stated as:

> *"the employer is vicariously liable for the torts of the employee provided that they are committed during the course of employment and where a third party is hurt."*

Figure A9-12: Vicarious liability.   *Source: Ambiguous.*

It has been argued that justice is served because, if the employer chooses to employ a careless employee, then that employer should be liable for the losses caused by that employee's torts. More usually the case given is that the employee is acting on the employer's behalf. Effectively this liability is paid for by all employers, all of whom are obliged to take out insurance under the Employers' Liability (Compulsory) Insurance Act (ELCIA) 1969. The employer is only liable if there has been fault. A driver who has a sudden and unexpected heart attack cannot be said to be to blame for a resulting accident and therefore the employer would not be vicariously liable. The second proviso is that the action must be within the course of employment. If the wrongful act is done purely for the employee's own benefit, then he alone is responsible for it. Acting for his own benefit, the negligent employee is said to be "off on a frolic of his own".

Acts within the scope of his employment

As has been stated, an employer can be liable for the torts of the employee where that employee has acted improperly or has broken the rules laid down by the employer. This is logical and will often be the case. Negligent acts do not usually occur when employees are doing only the things that they have been told to do - or are supposed to do.

In Century Insurance Co Ltd v Northern Ireland Transport Board (1942) a tanker driver lit a cigarette and threw away a match whilst delivering petrol. An explosion resulted and the employer was found to be liable for the negligence of the driver. In this case the driver was said to have acted improperly in the course of employment. The employee was still basically engaged in the work of unloading petrol. In other words he was acting within his employment.

Acts beyond the scope of his employment

As indicated, the employer is not liable for acts that are personal to the employee. For example, if an employee working in a shop has a fight with a customer, then that would be regarded as being beyond the scope of his employment unless the employee is required to use force as part of his job (e.g. the employer could be liable if a bouncer at a night club used excessive force to eject a troublemaker).

In Twine v Bean's Express Ltd (1946) the driver of a van gave a lift to a third person against the specific instructions that were displayed on a sign in the van. When the third person was killed due to the driver's negligent driving, the employer was not held vicariously liable because the driver acted beyond the scope of his employment. The passenger was a trespasser and, in offering a lift, the driver was not acting in the course of his employment.

Similarly, if an employee is on a jaunt of his own then the employer is not liable for any negligence. Thus when a brewer's deliveryman took a van without permission in order to deliver a neighbour's coffin, the brewers were not held liable for a person who was injured on the return journey. Similarly, if a vehicle driver took a new and independent journey for his own purposes then the employer is unlikely to be liable. If, however, it was a minor deviation (e.g. a slightly longer road) then this would not be considered to be outside the scope of employment. If an employer lends a vehicle to an employee entirely for his own use then the employer would not be vicariously liable.

VICARIOUS LIABILITY FOR ACTIONS OF CONTRACTORS

As a general rule, a client is not liable in civil law for the torts of an independent contractor. This is provided that the client has fulfilled the common law duty to select his contractor with reasonable care. There are some exceptions, however, where the law imposes strict liability on someone in the client's position. This is based on the idea that the client is in breach of a primary duty. These include:

- Where the client is negligent in that he has failed to select his independent contractor with reasonable care or has given the contractor imperfect instructions or information.
- Where the client authorises or ratifies the tort of the contractor (e.g. the employer turns a blind eye or condones an illegal activity such as fly-tipping).
- The client's duty to his employees under health and safety legislation (e.g. the duty to prevent access to dangerous parts of machinery could not be delegated to a contractor).
- Where the work requires extra precautions, for example.
- Where the work is on, or adjacent to, the public highway.
- Where the work is particularly hazardous.
- Where a person brings and keeps anything on the land likely to do mischief, he is liable if it escapes (the Rylands v Fletcher rule). The liability cannot be avoided by employing an independent contractor.
- Where the liability for the tort is strict, responsibility cannot be delegated. The duty of an employer to prevent access to the dangerous part of a machine is laid down by statute and cannot be delegated to an independent contractor.

LIABILITY FOR EMPLOYEES OF ANOTHER COMPANY

The general principle established by Wilsons and Clyde Coal Company v English is that the employer's liability in respect of injury cannot be delegated. This is a well-developed point of common law. In McDermid v Nash Dredging and Reclamation Company Ltd [1987] Nash entered into a joint venture with a Dutch company, Sevin, to dredge a Swedish fjord. Mr McDermid, a deckhand, was employed by Nash but seconded to a vessel belonging to Sevin under the control of a Dutch captain. Nash was seriously injured when his leg became entangled in a mooring rope. The House of Lords, in upholding the award of damages against Nash, ruled that it was the employer's responsibility to devise and operate a safe system of work. They could not delegate this responsibility to the Dutch Captain.

Another key principle is that the employer is vicariously liable for the torts committed by the employee during the course of employment. This liability may still exist even where the contract of employment is temporarily transferred. The case of Mersey Docks and Harbour Board v Coggins and Griffiths (Liverpool) Ltd [1946] illustrates the point. Coggins, a firm of stevedores, hired a crane and driver (Mr Newall) from Mersey Docks and Harbour Board. Mr Newall negligently operated the crane thereby injuring a third party, Mr McFarlane. The hire contract stipulated that Mr Newall was to be a temporary employee of Coggins for the duration of the agreement. The House of Lords held that Coggins were not liable, as they, as stevedores, did not have the skill or experience to direct how the crane was to be operated. Mersey Harbour Board were therefore held vicariously liable even though Newall was a temporary employee of Coggins.

LIABILITY FOR THE LOSSES CAUSED BY CRIMES AND FOR CRIMINAL ACTS

It should be noted that the principle of vicarious liability can be extended to include civil liability in respect of a crime - provided that it was committed during the course of employment. In Nahhas v Pier House [1984] an employer was held liable for the losses caused by thefts committed by a resident porter who had been entrusted with their tenant's keys. The employer is not however liable for criminal acts merely because the work enabled the act to be committed (e.g. a cleaner making unauthorised telephone calls or a docker stealing goods whilst unloading a ship).

Vicarious liability can also extend to an employer being prosecuted and convicted for the acts of employees under criminal law. This is designed to ensure that the organisation does not routinely delegate their criminal responsibilities to individual employees. For example, food shops are required to sell food that is fit for human consumption. If they were able to delegate this responsibility to individual shop assistants, they would have no incentive to ensure that only wholesome food was sold.

In order to defend such a case, the employer would have to demonstrate that they had done everything appropriate to ensure that the employee was both fully instructed and that arrangements were in place to see that these instructions were carried out. In other words, they had acted with "due diligence".

RECOVERY OF COSTS

The employer can claim redress against the negligent employee. This happened in Lister v Romford Ice and Cold Storage (1957). Here one employee injured another through careless driving. The employer, acting on behalf of the insurance company, successfully claimed indemnity against the negligent driver. The modern practice, however, is only to make such a claim where there has been wilful misconduct or there is evidence of collusion. The negligent employee also risks dismissal where there has been a breach of contract of employment (subject to the provisions of employment law).

Concept of joint tortfeasors

A tortfeasor is defined as someone who has carried out a tort. Where two (or more) people acting together commit a tort then they are joint tortfeasors.

MEANING OF JOINT AND SEVERAL LIABILITIES

Each individual has liability for his own torts, but in some cases he may be liable for his own and others. The liability of joint tortfeasors is said to be joint and several. This means that the claimant can sue them both together or may recover the full amount from just one of them. Where one joint tortfeasor is successfully sued, he can, under the Civil Liability (Contribution) Act (CLCA) 1978, claim a contribution from the other to the extent of his liability. Where joint tortfeasors are sued together, damages are divided according to the degree of responsibility that the court considers each party to have.

RECOVERY OF DAMAGES FROM JOINT TORTFEASOR

As previously stated, a claimant can recover damages in full from just one of the joint tortfeasors. Prior to the law being reformed, there was no right for one joint tortfeasor to claim contribution from another. Now, where a joint torfeasor is sued as an individual, he may claim a contribution from the fellow tortfeasor(s). The amount recoverable is left to the discretion of the court on the principle of a just and equitable division of responsibility.

The law was further developed by the Law Reform (Husband and Wife) Act 1962. This treats spouses as separate parties when considering the liability for damages of joint tortfeasors. For example a wife is injured in a car accident due to the joint negligence of her husband and a third party. If the wife then successfully gains damages from the third party, then that third party can claim a contribution from the negligent husband.

A joint tortfeasor must bring the action for recovery of contribution within two years from the date that that liability was admitted or a judgement against him was made.

Civil procedures rules (Woolf Report)

THE WOOLF REPORT

The procedures for personal injury cases were radically overhauled as a result of a review by Lord Woolf (the Woolf Report). This was done in an attempt to speed up and simplify the process as well as keeping costs within reasonable limits. The resulting Civil Procedures Rules were introduced on 26 April 1999 and have the following aims:

- To ensure that all parties are dealt with on an equal footing so that wealthier parties do not have an unfair advantage.
- To save expense.
- To deal with cases in a way that is proportionate to the sums involved, the complexity and importance of the case and the financial position of the parties.
- To ensure that cases are dealt with expeditiously and fairly in ways which promote an open and full exchange of information.
- To allot an appropriate share of the Court's resources, while taking into account the needs of other cases.

The rules apply to both the High Court and County Court. Many of the obscure Latin phrases have been replaced and the terms used simplified. For example, the person who brought an action was called a 'plaintiff' is now the 'claimant' and the term 'interlocutory applications' is replaced with 'court applications'.

Cases are managed by the Court and alternate dispute resolution (ADR) is encouraged. A new body, the Centre for Dispute Resolution (CEDR) has been formed to deal with this. This recognises that about 94% of cases are settled out of court and that it is far less expensive to engage in an, on average, two day mediation process than an eight year battle for compensation suffered by one widow relating to the death of her husband! CEDR estimates that the ADR process saves £250,000 per case in professional fees alone (averaged over 40 cases).

EXPERT WITNESSES

The role of the expert witness is to assist a party to establish the facts, assess the merits of the case and help with its preparation. The overriding duty of the expert is to the court rather than to the person who pays for his or her services. Where two parties wish to submit expert evidence, the court may direct that evidence on the particular issue be given by one expert only. The rules also allow the court to direct on matters relating to the fees and expenses paid to experts.

PRE-ACTION PROTOCOL

The process begins with a pre-action protocol which aims to reduce the need for litigation and encourages contact between the parties prior to the action starting.

Pre action protocols have been developed for a number of events including personal injury cases and clinical negligence. The protocol for personal injury involves a 3 stage process:

- The letter of claim.
- The reply.

- The investigation.

The letter of claim

The action is started on a claim form. This contains a summary of the facts of the cases together with the details of the loss (e.g. financial; injuries suffered).

The reply

The defendant must reply within 21 days after service together with details of any insurer that he or she has.

The investigation

The defendant has a maximum of three months to investigate the claim. A reply must be then be sent to the claimant (or the claimant's solicitor) which:

- Admits liability.
- Denies liability in full.
- Gives a partial admission of liability.

Reasons for full or partial admission of liability must be given together with any relevant documents. These are the same documents that the defendant would have to disclose anyway under court proceedings. Thus the defendant will not be able to issue a denial of responsibility without giving reasons or to delay the decision as to whether to settle or fight.

The claimant will be able to make a decision, based on the defendant's reply, about whether or not to proceed with the claim. If the defendant fails to make a proper reply, then the claimant will be able to start proceedings without being liable for costs.

COMMENCEMENT OF PROCEEDINGS

Once the proceedings have been started the defence has up to 28 days to file a response. Extensions may be granted but this is rare particularly if the defendant has failed to comply with the pre-action protocol. The response consists of:

- Those facts which are admitted to.
- Those facts which are denied with reasons.
- Those facts which cannot be admitted or denied and which the claimant must therefore prove.
- The defendant's version of the events.

The statement of truth

The defendant's case must be supported by a "statement of truth" which must be signed by a senior officer of the organisation, a partner or a legal representative. The statement begins - "The defendant believes the facts stated in this defence are true". Although not sworn, a signatory who signs the statement without honestly believing it to be true may be held in contempt of court. If a legal representative signs the document, then they are deemed to have briefed the organisation as to its meaning and the penalties will be the same as if the defendant had signed it originally.

Disclosure of documents

All documents that could support or adversely affect the case must be disclosed. Many of these may have been previously disclosed under the pre-action protocol procedure.

The disclosure statement

Documents sent to the opposing party must be accompanied by a formal statement of disclosure confirming that this has been done with full knowledge of the requirements and to the best of their ability.

Offers to settle

An offer to settle may be made by either party and a payment made into the court. If the other side decides not to accept, this has a bearing on the awarding of costs

Case management

The case will be managed by the Court who will give 'directions' on how it is to be handled based on an allocation questionnaire filed by the parties involved. A summary judgement may be made after giving 14 days notice to both parties against either the claimant or the defendant because the claim has no prospect of success or the defence has no real prospect of success.

Name	Sum	Points
Small claims	up to £5,000	
Fast-track	£5,000 - £15,000	Standard time between giving of directions and case hearing no more than 30 weeks. Hearing date fixed at time of direction. Court discretion to limit disclosure of documents. Oral expert evidence limited to two fields of expertise and to one expert per party.
Multi-track	over £15,000	Court gives directions for management of case and timetable for case to be heard. Alternatively a Case Management and/or a Pre-Trial Review may be fixed.

Figure A9-13: Case management.

Source: ACT.

After allocation to the appropriate track the court will set a timetable or fix a case management conference or a pre case heard review or a combination of these. Under the rules, cases must be held "as soon as is practicable". The usual criteria for deciding which court hears a case still applies *(See also - 'Progress of a Case' flow diagram - Element A7)*. For example, fast track cases would find themselves in the County Court. Multi-track claims, would be heard by the High Court.

Relevant decided cases

Adsett v K & L Steelfounders & Engineers Ltd (1953) 1 All ER 97 and 2 All ER 320

[Meaning of practicable]

Statute   Factories Act (FA) 1937, s.47; later Factories Act (FA) 1961, s.63

Facts Mr Adsett contracted pneumoconiosis in a foundry. The main cause was inhalation of silica dust, which became airborne as he shovelled various casting sands and compounds through a grate onto a conveyor below. To control this, the employers installed a dust extractor near the conveyor. This was done as soon as they thought of it, but it was well after the onset of Mr Adsett's disease and too late to save him from disablement.

Decision The question concerned the meaning of the word 'practicable' in section 47 of the Factories Act (FA) 1937, which required employers to take all practicable measures to protect employees from inhalation of dust, etc. Dictionary definitions said, 'possible to be accomplished with known means or resources', 'capable of being carried out in action' and 'feasible'. 'Practicable' is a stricter standard than 'reasonably practicable' so the question of cost should be eliminated. No measure could be 'practicable' if it was not within current knowledge and invention. The employers were held not to have been in breach of statutory duty.

Note There was an appeal, as it was argued, on behalf of Mr Adsett, that the technology to install an extractor did exist, but that the employers (and everyone else in the industry) had not thought of this particular application for an extractor. It was said that the employers could not escape liability just because they did not think of this particular use for an extractor. The appeal was rejected on the grounds that 'practicable' meant that a measure had to be known for its application by people in the industry and especially by the experts.

Armour v Skeen (1977) IRLR 310

[Responsibilities of senior management Section 37 HASAWA 1974]

Statute HASAWA 1974 section 37 and section 2 Personal Liability - Criminal

Facts A workman fell to his death whilst repairing a road bridge over the River Clyde. The Strathclyde Regional Council and its Director of Roads (Mr Armour) were both prosecuted. The basis of Mr Armour's prosecution under section 37 of the HASAWA 1974 was that the duty of supervising the safety of council workmen on the roads was his. He had failed to formulate a sound safety policy.

Mr Armour claimed in his defence to have no personal duty to carry out the council's statutory obligations (one of which was the formulation of a detailed safety policy for the roads department).

Decision He was convicted of the offences and the conviction was upheld on appeal. The fact that section 2 of HASAWA 1974 imposes a duty on the employers to provide a safe system of work did not mean that there was no duty on his part to carry out that duty. Section 37(1) refers to 'any neglect', not to the neglect of a duty imposed. The offences were committed by the body corporate, but were due to his neglect. Further, although his title as 'Director of Roads' did not mean he was a 'director' within the meaning of section 37 (1), he was within the meaning of the words "manager or similar officer".

Relevance The case gives guidance as to those who may be considered as the "directing mind" of the organisation who therefore are liable under section 37 of the HASAWA 1974. This includes persons who purport to act as directors; company secretaries or other similar officers are equally liable. Anyone who acts in a managerial capacity must be held liable under section 37 (1) whatever the title he or she may have. If the affairs of the body corporate are being managed by its members (e.g. a workers' co-operative), then the acts of the member which are in connection with his managerial functions are within the meaning of this section (section 37 (2)).

Note For a person to be convicted under section 37, it must be shown that he or she has some responsibility for the making of management decisions, and be in a position of responsibility. In R v Boal, the accused was the assistant general manager of Foyle's Bookshop. He had been given no management training, in particular, none in health and safety matters, or fire precautions. He was, however, in charge of the shop while the general manager was away on a week's holiday. During this period, the premises were visited by officers from the local fire authority, who discovered there were serious breaches of the fire certificate which had been issued. Foyle's and the accused were charged with a number of offences under the Fire Precautions Act (FPA) 1971 - Foyle's as the 'body corporate' and the accused because the 1971 Act provides that:

" ... where an offence committed by a body corporate is proved ... to be attributable to any neglect on the part of any director, manager, secretary or other similar officer of the body corporate ... he as well as the body corporate shall be guilty of that offence ... "

Figure A9-14: Liability as well as the body corporate.   Source: Section 37 HASAWA.

Foyle's were convicted on 11 counts, and were fined. The accused pleaded guilty to 3 counts, and was found guilty of 7 others. He was sentenced to 3 months' imprisonment, suspended for 12 months. He then appealed against the conviction on the ground that he was not " ... a manager or similar officer ... "within the meaning of the Act.

The Court of Appeal (Criminal Division) allowed his appeal. A person was "a manager" if he had the power of " ... the management of the whole of the affairs of the company ..." or was, " ... entrusted with power to transact the whole of the affairs of the company ..." or was " ... managing in a governing role the affairs of the company itself ...". The Court further thought that the intended scope of section 23 of the Fire Precautions Act was ... to fix with criminal liability only those who are in a position of real authority, the decision makers within the company who have both the power and responsibility to decide corporate policy and strategy..". It is to catch those responsible for putting proper procedures in places; it is not meant to strike at underlings. The case was overturned at appeal.

Baker v T E Hopkins & Sons Ltd. [1959] 1 WRL 966

[Non-application of Volenti non-fit injuria where aid given to co-employee or third party]

Facts It was held that the defence of volenti did not apply in the case of Baker v T E Hopkins and Sons Ltd [1959] where a local doctor died trying to rescue two men who had been overcome by a lethal concentration of carbon monoxide fumes when working in a well.

The defendants used a petrol engine to clean out a well. Two employees were told not to start the engine until the manager arrived. They ignored the instruction and were overcome by carbon monoxide fumes.

The claimant, who was a doctor, attempted to rescue them, but all three died.

Decision The defendant Company was negligent in not warning the employees of the danger.

It was foreseeable that a rescue attempt would be made if employees were in difficulties. The claimant was not reckless in attempting to save life and was therefore owed a duty of care.

Barkway v South Wales Transport Co Ltd [1950] 1 All ER 392 HL

[Employers duty to maintain work equipment]

Facts The defendant's bus mounted the pavement and then went down an embankment. The claimant's husband, a passenger was killed. Evidence showed a defective tyre had burst.

Decision The principle of res ipsa loquitur did not apply and the claimant had to establish negligence. She did this by showing the system of inspecting the tyres was inadequate, being only twice a week, when the tyres suffered unduly harsh treatment from being driven over kerbstones and other obstacles. There should have been a reporting system to record incidents of heavy blows to the tyres. The defendant did not take these reasonable steps and therefore was negligent.

Bradford v Robinson Rentals Ltd [1967] All ER 267

[Employers duty to provide necessary equipment]

[Reasonable steps: working environment: cold conditions]

Common law duties

Facts A radio service engineer for Robinson Rentals was sent out on a journey of about 450 miles to change an old van for a new one. Neither van had a heater. After hearing very bad weather reports on the radio, he asked his employers if he could delay the journey, but they refused. He told them that the AA was warning people not to make unnecessary journeys. He was told to make the journey nevertheless. Due to the severe cold, the engineer was affected by frostbite. He claimed damages.

Decision It was held that though frostbite was unforeseeable in England, some injury was foreseeable due to the extreme cold which the employers had been told about and the lack of heating in the van. It made no difference that the precise type of injury was not foreseen. It is still the general type of injury that could be expected to occur from these conditions. The employers should either have not sent the engineer out or they should have ensured that he would have been adequately protected against the cold.

British Railways Board v Herrington (1971) 1 All ER 897

[Duty of common humanity in relation to trespassers]

Facts A six year old boy wandered onto a railway line and was seriously injured when he came into contact with a live electrified rail. The defendants knew that the fence alongside the line was in a state of disrepair and had taken no remedial action - despite previous reports of children being seen on the line. There was clear evidence of the presence of trespassers (likely to be children) since the path was worn from the broken fencing to the railway line.

Decision The defendants were found to be liable as they had shown a reckless disregard for the safety of the claimant. Although prior to this case an occupier owed only a limited duty of care towards trespassers, they should have acted humanely.

The duty is directed towards a 'simple' rather than an 'aggravated' trespasser. If the occupier "knew before the incident that there was a substantial probability that a trespasser would come, I think that most people would regard as culpable, failure to give any thought to their safety", L J Salmon.

Note The Occupiers' Liability Act (OLA) 1984: Occupiers' duty in respect of trespassers.

Cambridge Water Co v Eastern Counties Leather plc [1994] 2 WLR 53

[Further to decision in Rylands v Fletcher (later in this element), liability does not apply retrospectively in absence of forseeability of harm]

Facts Cambridge Water Company owned a borehole at Sawston from which it pumped water into the public supply. The water company bought the land in 1976 for the purposes of constructing the borehole to supply water to its customers. The pumping house was commissioned in 1979.

As part of its operations in the 'industrial village' of Sawston, Eastern Counties Leather plc used organochlorines, one of which was perchloroethylene (PCE), a solvent used for degreasing skins. Until about 1976, the chemical was delivered to the site in drums, kept in storage there and when needed, tipped into the reservoir supplying the degreasing machine. This transfer led inevitably to spillage, which over the years filtered through the ground into the aquifer. The degreaser is volatile and easily evaporated, and Eastern Counties might have considered that it evaporated before it could pass through the ground.

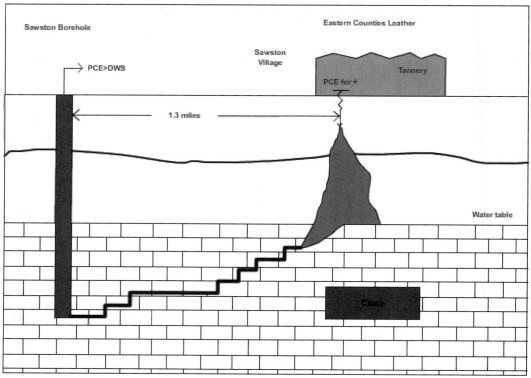

Figure A9-15: Sawston borehole.   *Source: ACT.*

In 1980 the EC drinking water directive was issued and became effective in 1985. This Directive included maximum permissible concentrations of organochlorine compounds. Tests by Cambridge Water showed that supplies from the borehole were in excess of those limits and as a result Cambridge Water had to stop pumping and find an alternative supply. This cost something in excess of £900,000.

Cambridge Water Company sued Eastern Counties Leather under the Rylands v Fletcher Rule.

Decision The High Court held that, as Sawston is an industrial village, the creation of employment by the defendants was clearly for the benefit of the community. The storage of chemicals on the land was therefore a natural use of the land.

The Court of Appeal reversed this decision and held that Easter Counties Leather were liable under Rylands v Fletcher. The storage of chemicals on the land could not be regarded as a natural use.

The House of Lords found that the defendants were not liable for the damages of £2 million awarded to Cambridge Water. Lord Goff explained that although the fact that a defendant had taken all reasonable care will not exonerate him or her from liability in nuisance, "it by no means follows that the defendant should be held liable for damage of a type which he could not reasonably foresee". This means that strict liability would only apply if damage could be reasonably foreseen. Lord Goff also commented that the storage of large amounts of chemicals should be considered a non-natural use of land.

Thus the House of Lords agreed that this was an almost classic case of non-natural use; however they reversed the Court of Appeal decision based on the principle of foreseeability of consequences. Eastern Counties could not have foreseen the consequences of the spillage or the maximum permissible levels in the EC directive, therefore they were not liable.

Note This case illustrates the development of common law as well as extending the defences to strict liability imposed by the Rylands v Fletcher rule. The defence of the consequences of an escape being unforeseeable is now available to defendants.

It should be noted that the House of Lords doubted whether the fact that Eastern Counties gave employment could lead to the conclusion that keeping chemicals on land was a natural use.

Corn v Weirs Glass (Hanley) Ltd [1960] 2 All ER 300

[A successful claim of tort of breach of statutory duty requires loss to be a consequence of a breach of statute]

Statute   Breach of Statutory Duty Reg. 27 of Building [Safety, Health and Welfare] Regulations 1948 [then in force].

Facts A glazier carrying a large sheet of glass with both hands fell on a stairway and was injured. He sued for breach of statutory duty because no handrail was provided. It was shown that, as he needed both hands to carry the glass, the hand-rail would have been of no use to him.

Decision Even though there was a breach of statute by the employer, the claim failed. In order to prove breach of statutory duty the claimant must demonstrate:

- The statute was broken.
- This breach caused the injury.
- The claimant was of a class of person the statute was intended to protect.
- The type of injury was one the statute was intended to prevent.

In this case, although there was a breach of duty, it did not cause the injury, thus the claim failed.

Davie v New Merton Board Mills Limited [1958] 1 All ER 67

[Employer not liable where injury results from latent defect in tools or equipment; led to, and remedied by, Employer's Liability (Defective Equipment) Act 1969]

Facts Prior to the Employers' Liability (Defective Equipment) Act 1969, liability for an employee's injury or loss due to defective equipment lay with the supplier or manufacturer. Thus in Davie v New Merton Board Mills (1958) an employee failed to gain compensation from his employer when injured by a defective drift tool. The employer could not be reasonably expected to know that a tool obtained from a reputable supplier was defective.

Relevance This case highlighted the problem of the employee who is injured trying to find the manufacturer in order to claim damages from him. The judge remarked that the manufacturer may be based abroad making it virtually impossible for the ordinary working man to pursue his claim.

The position was changed by the Employers' Liability (Defective Equipment) Act (ELDFA)1969 which places liability on the employer where an employee is injured by defective work equipment provided by the employer. This liability is strict and applies even where the defect is attributed wholly or in part to a third party (whether that party is identifiable or not). Of course there is nothing to prevent the employer, having paid compensation to the employee, from obtaining redress either in whole or in part from the supplier who was at fault.

Donoghue v Stevenson [1932] AC 562

[Reasonable care and the neighbour principle; duty of manufacturer to end user]

Facts The claimant (Ms Donoghue) was ill when she drank a bottle of ginger beer which contained a decomposed snail. The bottle was opaque and she had no reason to believe that it contained anything other than ginger beer. She sued the manufacturer.

As it was Ms Donoghue's friend who had purchased the ginger beer, the manufacturer claimed that there was no contract between them.

Decision Damages were awarded to the claimant. The House of Lords held that a duty of care was owed and determined the extent of that duty ("the neighbour principle").

Relevance Extent of duty of care: to whom is this duty owed?

As per:

> *"You must take reasonable care to avoid acts or omissions which you can reasonably foresee would be likely to injure your neighbour".*
>
> *Who is my neighbour in the legal sense?*
>
> *"Persons who are so closely and directly affected by my act that I ought reasonably to have them in contemplation as being so affected when I am directing my mind to the acts or omissions which are called in question."*

Figure A9-16: The neighbour principle.   *Source: Lord Atkin, Donoghue v Stevenson [1932].*

Edwards v National Coal Board [1949] 1 All ER 743

[Meaning of reasonably practicable]

Facts Mr Edwards was killed when a section of underground roadway collapsed. The NCB argued that the cost of shoring up would have been prohibitive and was not justified.

Decision The NCB were found liable on the basis that the cost of making this particular road section safe was not great when compared to the risk.

Relevance The 'Quantum of Risk' test should be applied in determining whether or not the steps that were taken in the circumstances of the incident were sufficient to satisfy the requirements of the term 'reasonably practicable' where such an obligatory term is stipulated.

This 'Quantum of Risk' test is the analogy of a scale balance whereupon the degree of risk is placed on one pan and the sacrifice involved in the measures necessary for averting the risk (whether in money, time or trouble) is placed on the other; and that, if it be shown that there is a gross disproportion between them - the risk being insignificant in relation to the sacrifice - the defendants discharge the onus upon them. (Lord Asquith).

Ferguson v Dawson and Partners Ltd [1976] IRLR 376, CA

[Self employed workers may be regarded as employees]

Facts Ferguson, a labourer, joined the company "on the lump", which was the basis they hired labourers. To avoid tax, Ferguson gave a false name. He and the company argued that he was self-employed.

He fell off a roof while removing some scaffolding boards. He claimed damages against Dawson for breach of statutory duty relying on the Construction (Working Places) Regulations (CWPR) 1966. The duty would only be owed if the claimant were an employee of Dawson.

Decision It was held that, despite the fact that both parties labelled Ferguson a "self-employed labour only contractor", the relationship was in fact that of employer-employee.

Relevance A contract of employment was said to exist because: the employer directed the manner in which the work was to be done; the worker was not allowed to use his discretion; he was an integral part of the employer's business; the worker was not allowed to employ others to assist him; and the worker was not in business on his own account.

General Cleaning Contractors v Christmas [1953] 2 All ER 1110

[Employer's duty to provide a safe system of work]

Facts Mr Christmas was a window cleaner. To save time, a method had been adopted in the trade of climbing onto the window sills instead of using ladders and hold onto the window frames. Although there was some danger, it was accepted that if a proper routine were followed, it could be done safely. It was also accepted that the use of ladders was unduly restrictive and impracticable.

Mr Christmas pulled the upper half of a sash window down a little so he could hold on to the top bar of the bottom frame. The top frame slipped down and trapped his fingers. He let go and fell to the ground suffering injury. He claimed damages, alleging negligence against his employer in the way the method of work was organised.

Decision The House of Lords held the employer liable. It was held that it was the employer's duty to go to the site, assess the risks and work out a safe method of doing the work. In this case it would have been relatively easy to devise wedges or some other system to prevent the window frames slipping. This measure would have made the work reasonably safe.

Note 'Where a practice of ignoring an obvious danger has grown up I do not think that it is reasonable to expect an individual workman to take the initiative in devising and using precautions. It is the duty of the employer to consider the situation, to devise a suitable system, to instruct his men what they must do, and to supply any implement that may be required such as in this case wedges or objects to be out on the window sill to prevent the window from closing' (Lord Reid).

Hudson v Ridge Manufacturing Co. Ltd [1957] 2 All ER 229

[Employer's duty to provide competent fellow employees; issue of horseplay at work]

Facts In Hudson v Ridge Manufacturing [1957] an employee was a known practical joker who had made a nuisance of himself over the previous 5 years. Examples of his behaviour included tripping people from behind. Although this was done for fun and without malice or intent to bully, injury was inevitable sooner or later. In one incident an employee broke his wrist in an effort to break his fall after being gripped around the neck and pulled back by the practical joker. This duty extends beyond competence through to behaviour in the workplace. An employee who is known to engage in practical jokes and horseplay could constitute a hazard which the employer would be expected to deal with.

Decision The employer was held liable in the resulting case on the basis that they had failed to take steps to curb his horseplay. It was held that the duty of the employer is to provide safe colleagues to work with. In this case the employer's duty was to take steps by reprimand, discipline and, if necessary, dismiss the practical joker in order to remove the risk of injury to other employees.

ICI v Shatwell [1965] AC 656

[Volenti non-fit injuria and sole fault of claimant as defences in employers' liability cases]

Facts In ICI Ltd v Shatwell [1964] two brothers, who were certified shot blasters, were injured whilst testing electrical circuitry used to detonate explosives. They did so in the open, contrary to the Quarries (Explosives) Regulations 1959 which required them to be in a position of safety.

Decision The resulting claim for damages against the employer was unsuccessful on the basis that they had voluntarily accepted the risk of each other's negligence and breach of statutory duty by defying the employer's instructions and breaching the Regulations which were well known to them. The 'volenti' defence can be successful where employees conspire to breach statutory duty against the employer's specific instructions.

Note The volenti defence, however, will not normally succeed in cases where there is a direct breach of common law or statutory duty by the employer.

Knowles v Liverpool County Council [1993] 1 WLR 1428

[Employers' Liability (Defective Equipment) Act 1969 extends to materials used at work]

The word equipment includes any plant and machinery, vehicle, aircraft and clothing. This is a wide ranging definition of the word 'equipment' as illustrated by such cases as:

Knowles v Liverpool City Council (1992) where the employer was held liable for injury caused by a 'green' concrete flagstone.

Mr Knowles was employed by the appellant Council as a labourer flagger. Whilst repairing a pavement a flagstone he was handling broke causing injury to his finger.

The breakage occurred because the manufacturer had not cured the flagstone properly.

The House of Lords held that the flagstone which the respondent was handling in the course of his employment was equipment provided by his employer for the purpose of the employers' business within the meaning of the Employers' Liability (Defective Equipment) Act (ELDEA) 1969 Section 1 (1) (a) and consequently his employer was liable to him under this Act. The flagstone had broken due to a defect in manufacture.

Latimer v AEC Ltd [1953] 2 All ER 449, HL

[Discharge of duty to take reasonable care]

Statute   Factories Act 1937

Facts An exceptionally severe thunderstorm flooded the factory. The water mixed with the cooling oil used on lathes which caused the floor to become slippery. The company kept a quantity of sawdust but this was insufficient to cover all of the slippery area.

Mr Latimer hurt himself by slipping while trying to lift a 2 cwt bin. He sought damages under the Factories Act which required that floors be "properly maintained".

Decision Mr Latimer lost his case. The House of Lords held that a transient and exceptional condition of an otherwise sound floor did not cause it to be improperly maintained. The employer had taken reasonable steps to deal with the danger to his employee.

Relevance "Maintained" means maintained in an efficient state, in an efficient working order and in good repair". The term within the Act was clearly directed to the state of construction of the floor and not to a temporary and unexpected condition or obstruction on its surface.

Lister v Romford Ice and Cold Storage Co. Ltd [1957] AC 555 [Negligence of fellow employees re: vicarious liability, joint tortfeasors and subrogation]

Facts Mr Lister (junior), a lorry driver employed by Romford Ice and Cold Storage Co (RI&CS), took his father with him on a job to act as mate. While reversing the lorry, he injured his father. The father claimed damages against RI&CS.

Decision The father successfully recovered damages from RI&CS for the negligence of Lister (junior) as their employee.

The company then claimed a contribution from Lister (junior) on the basis that he had broken an implied term in his contract of employment, which was that he would use reasonable skill and care in driving.

Subrogation generally occurs when an insurance company pays damages on behalf of its insured client and then sues the party, which the claimant contends caused the injury/loss. Lister (junior) had broken an implied term in his contract of employment that he would take reasonable skill and care in driving.

Relevance The employer is vicariously liable for the negligent acts of his employees during the course of work if a third party suffers loss. RI&CS was liable for Lister's (junior) actions.

Lister (junior) had a duty of care to his employer in the performance of his duty as a driver. The employer has a right to claim damages from a negligent employee.

Note Generally, there is an agreement between insurance companies that they will not pursue claims against employees for their negligent acts except if the circumstances seem suspicious.

Machray v Stewart and Lloyds Ltd 1964 [Employers duty to provide sufficient plant].

Facts The claimant, an experienced rigger was asked to get some piping from the ground to seventy feet up on a steel structure in the course of construction. A crane that would normally be used was not available. The rigger decided he could use a chain block and tackle, but could not find one on the site. As the foreman was pressing him to do the job, he used a rope block and tackle, which was not suitable. As the pipe was being lifted, it swung out of control and hit the rigger. He claimed damages for the company's failure to provide suitable equipment.

Decision The Company was held liable. It was the company's duty to take reasonable steps to prevent injury to employees by providing equipment that was suitable for the job in hand.

The Company claimed contributory negligence in their defence, but this was completely rejected as Mr Machray had been prevented from adopting a safe system of work for the job because of the pressure put on him by the foreman.

Marshall v Gotham & Co. Ltd (1954) AC 360

[Difference between practicable and reasonably practicable]

Facts Mr Marshall was killed by a roof collapse whilst working in a gypsum mine. The roof had been tested but the roof fall had been caused by an undetectable geological fault known as "slickenside". His wife claimed compensation for breach of statutory duty.

Decision The employer was not liable as they had taken reasonable steps to secure the roof.

Relevance The term 'secure' means safe against normal or likely hazards. Thus totally unexpected or abnormal movements or falls do not prove a failure of duty. In this case the movement was caused by an unforeseeable geological fault.

In this case, a comparison between the levels of duty required by the terms "practicable" and "reasonably practicable" was made.

> "If a precaution is practicable, it must be taken unless in the whole circumstances that would be unreasonable and as men's lives may be at stake it should not lightly be held that to take a practicable precaution is unreasonable."

Figure A9-17: Practicable.   *Source: Lord Reid.*

'Practicable' denotes a stricter standard than 'reasonably practicable'. It means 'possible to be accomplished with known means or resources' or 'feasible', with cost probably not a factor.

Mersey Docks and Harbour Board V Coggins & Griffith (Liverpool) Ltd [1946] 2 ALL ER 345

[Extent to which employer may be held vicariously liable for negligence of contractor]

Facts Coggins, a firm of stevedores, hired a crane and driver (Mr Newall) from Mersey Docks and Harbour Board. Mr Newall negligently operated the crane thereby injuring a third party. The hire contract stipulated that Mr Newall was to be a temporary employee of Coggins for the duration of the agreement.

Key points
- The authority supplied the driver with the crane.
- The driver was hired, paid and liable to be dismissed by the authority.
- The contract between the authority and the stevedores stipulated that the driver supplied would be deemed to be the servant of the stevedores while carrying out the work under the contract.
- The hirers had power to control what Mr Newall lifted but not how it should be lifted.

Decision It was accepted that the driver was a servant, not a self-employed person and it was also accepted that the accident was due to his negligence. The only question was which of the two organisations should be held vicariously liable to the injured person. The House of Lords had to consider an appeal by the general employer from a decision against them by the Court of Appeal. It was not suggested that there was any personal fault on the part of either of the organisations.

It was held that control over Mr Newall's work had not passed to the hirers. Only if there is control over what work the person does and how he does it can control be held to have been transferred.

Relevance Vicarious liability cannot be easily passed to a 'quasi-employer'. There are two tests which must be passed in order for this to succeed. The new 'employer' must be in a position to dictate:

■ What work is to be done.
■ How it is to be done.

Paine v Colne Valley Electricity Supply Company [1938] 4 All ER 803

[Employer's duty to provide a safe place of work]

Facts/Decision An employer was held liable for injuries to his employee caused by the failure of contractors to install sufficient insulation in an electrical kiosk.

Relevance The employer's duty is a personal one so that he remains liable even though he has delegated the performance of the duty to a competent independent contractor.

Paris v Stepney Borough Council [1951] 1 All ER 42, HL

[Higher duty of care owed to vulnerable employees]

Facts Mr Paris worked in the Borough Council's trucks maintenance garage. He was blind in one eye, but this was not known by his employer until he was examined by a doctor for the Council's superannuation scheme. He was given two week's notice of dismissal. Two days before his leaving date, he was working underneath a truck when a piece of metal flew off into his good eye blinding him.

He claimed damages for negligence saying that he, as an individual with extra susceptibility of serious injury, should have been provided with goggles.

Decision The House of Lords upheld his claim. The duty of the employer to take reasonable steps to prevent injury to employees is owed to each employee individually. If the employer knows of a condition which makes the employee more susceptible to injury, or could make the injury more severe than usual, he must take extra precautions. The provision of goggles to Mr Paris would have been reasonable even if goggles were not provided to others doing the same job.

Qualcast v Haynes 1959 [Higher duty of care expected of an experienced employee]

Facts Mr Haynes was an experienced foundry man. He splashed molten metal on his foot while pouring from a hand-held ladle. He was not wearing foundry boots or leather spats even though they were readily available from the stores. He claimed damages for the employer's failure to urge him to wear spats.

Decision The judge found for Qualcast. The duty of care remains constant to employees, but may be discharged in varying degrees according to the gravity of risk and the experience of individual employees. In this case, the employee had sufficient experience to know the risks well and the employer's duty was discharged by making the safety equipment available and leaving it to the discretion of the experienced men to use it.

Rose v Plenty (1976) 1 AER 97 [Vicarious liability of employer for acts of employee]

Facts The defendant told all their milkman not to give rides on their milk floats to anyone. A notice was put up at the depot.

One of the milkmen paid a thirteen-year-old to help him. The thirteen-year-old was injured whilst on the milk float due to the milkman's negligence.

Decision The prohibition did not affect the nature of the job, merely the way in which it was carried out. This meant the milkman was negligent and his employers were vicariously liable for his negligence.

Rylands v Fletcher 1865 [Tort relative to escape of stored materials]

Rylands v Fletcher (1868) LR 3HL 330

Facts Mr Rylands was a mill owner who employed independent contractors to construct a reservoir on his land in order to provide water power for his mill. During the work, the contractors discovered an old mine whose shafts and passages connected with another mine on neighbouring land owned by Rylands. The contractors did not inform Fletcher and did not block up the shafts. When the reservoir was filled with water, the water seeped through some disused shafts and passages and flooded a mine belonging to Mr Fletcher. Mr Fletcher sued Mr Rylands for the resulting damages. Fletcher himself had not been negligent as he had no knowledge of the existence of the shafts. He was not vicariously liable for the actions of the contractors as they were not his employees. The key points arising in the Rylands case were that:

■ The contractor was competent.
■ There was no negligence on the part of the client.
■ There was a 'non natural' use of land.
■ There was an escape of matter.
■ The escape resulted in damage.

Decision Mr Rylands was found to be liable in tort, both by the Court of Exchequer and on appeal to the House of Lords. The Rylands v Fletcher rule of strict liability was established in this decision.

The Rylands v Fletcher rule is stated as:

> *"Where a person for his own purposes brings and keeps on land in his occupation anything likely to do mischief if it escapes, he must keep it at his peril, and if he fails to do so, he is liable for all damage which is a natural consequence of the escape."*

Figure A9-18: Strict liability - Rylands and Fletcher rule.   *Source: Rylands and Fletcher [1868].*

During the appeal Lord Cairns, in agreeing with the above statement, added the qualification that the rule only applied to a "non-natural" use of the land, and not to circumstances where a substance accumulated naturally on land. The word "natural" has since been extended to mean "ordinary". The rule has been held to apply to beasts, water, filth and stenches and fire. This 'strict liability' rule can apply to all persons (corporate or individual) and a claimant does not have to prove negligence.

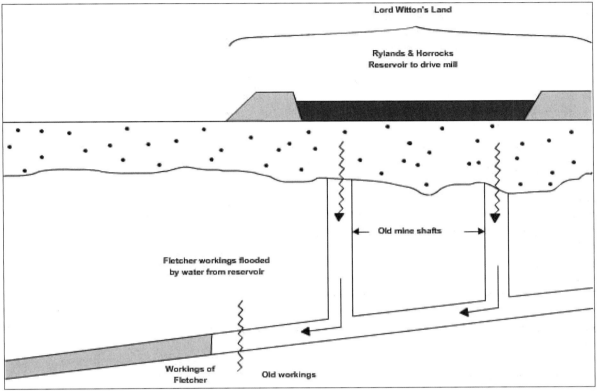

Figure A9-19: Rylands and Fletcher.   *Source: ACT.*

Smith v Crossley Brothers 1951 [Vicarious Liability relative to an extreme act of horseplay]

Circumstances   The claimant, an apprentice employed in the defendant's apprentice training school, was seriously injured by a practical joke played on him by two fellow apprentices.

Decision   The defendants were found to be not liable because the claimant's injury had occurred through an act of wilful misbehaviour, which the defendants could not have reasonably foreseen.

The employer was not liable when he did not know and had no reason to suspect that there was a risk of an apprentice being injured by being subjected to "initiation rites" by his fellows.

Speed v Swift (Thomas) & Co. Ltd (1943) [Employer duty to provide, an elements of, a safe system of work]

Facts   A hook on a winch on board a ship caught on the perimeter railing of the ship. The railing broke and fell into a barge below injuring a workman. The winch was known to be unsafe and the railing was known to be broken.

Decision   The employer was found to have failed to take reasonable steps to prevent injury to employees. As part of a safe system of work, he should have ensured that the fencing was covered or protected in some way so that hooks or other objects could not hit it or get caught up in it.

Summers (John) & Sons v Frost (1955) Ac 740 [Nature of absolute duty]

John Summers & Sons v Frost 1955 All ER 870 AC.740

F.A.1937 S14 (1) , F.A.1961 S14 (1)

Securely fenced (absolute duty)

Circumstances   Mr Frost was injured whilst using a grinding wheel. His thumb was caught between the small (1cm) gap between the guard and the grinding wheel. Although the wheel was partially guarded, s.14 of the Factories Act imposed an absolute duty to guard the dangerous parts of machinery.

Decision   The House of Lords ruled that there had been a breach of statutory duty.

Relevance The obligation to guard securely those parts of a machine which are dangerous must be fulfilled in such a manner, as to afford "complete protection" to the "careless or inattentive worker as well as the meticulous, careful one".

Moreover, the "dangerous part is securely fenced if and only if the presence of the fence makes it no longer dangerous."

The duty was to provide fencing which absolutely prevented any part of any person working on the premises from coming into contact with any dangerous part of the machine.

This illustrates the literal interpretation of statutes that the courts are required to make - if the effect of this is to make the machine unusable then so be it.

Sutherland v Hatton (2002) [reasonableness in relation to harm from stress at work]

Sutherland v Hatton and others [2002] EWCA Civ 76

Statute ref. These claims were brought in common law negligence

Facts The Court of Appeal heard four appeals by employers against compensation awards to employees who had suffered stress-induced psychiatric illness.

Decision Three of the appeals succeeded. The Court ruled that the general principle was that employers should not have to pay compensation for stress-induced illness unless such illness was reasonably foreseeable. Employers are normally entitled to assume that employees can withstand the normal pressures of a job. The Court set out a number of practical propositions for future claims concerning workplace stress. These are as follows:

- Employers do not have a duty to make searching inquiries about employees' mental health. They are entitled to take what they are told by employees at face value unless they have good reason to disbelieve the employees' statements.
- Where an employee wishes to remain in a stressful job and the only alternative is demotion or dismissal, the employer is not in breach of duty in allowing the employee to continue.
- Indications of impending harm to health at work must be clear enough to show an employer that action should be taken, in order for a duty on an employer to take action to arise.
- An employer is in breach of duty where he fails to take reasonable steps bearing in mind the following: the size of the risk; the gravity of the harm; the cost of preventing the harm; any justification for taking the risk.
- No type of work may be regarded as intrinsically dangerous to mental health.
- Employers who offer confidential counselling advice services, with access to treatment, are unlikely to be found in breach of their duty of care in relation to workplace stress.
- Employees must show that their illness has been caused by a breach of duty and not merely by occupational stress.
- The amount of compensation will be reduced to take account of pre-existing conditions or the chance that the employee would have become ill in any event.

The Court of Appeal dealt with the following cases:

1. Penelope Hatton, a schoolteacher who had been awarded £90,000 compensation for depression and debility. Her employer's appeal was allowed on the grounds that her workload was no greater than her colleagues' and her absences could be put down to reasons other than workplace stress.

2. Olwen Jones, a local authority employee, had suffered from depression and anxiety as a result of overwork. It was foreseeable that her workplace conditions would cause harm, therefore the employer's appeal against an award of £150,000 damages was dismissed.

3. Leon Barber, a teacher, developed symptoms of depression. He was awarded £100,000 compensation. The employer's appeal was allowed on the grounds that the claimant had not told the employers about his illness until he suffered a breakdown.

4. Melvyn Bishop, a factory worker awarded £7,000 compensation following a nervous breakdown and attempted suicide. The employer's appeal was allowed because the Court ruled that the demands of his work had not been excessive.

(Source: Croner's Health and Safety Case Law 2003)

Thompson & Others v Smiths Ship Repairers (N. Shields) (1984) 1 All ER 881 [employer duty to protect employees from known and reasonably foreseeable danger; date of knowledge of risk]

Facts Six cases of hearing loss from the ship repair and ship building industry, believed to be representative of the principal legal issues were consolidated into one action. This was to enable the court to establish the relevant legal guidelines.

Mr Thompson used a pneumatic scaling tool for 25% of his time, from 1936 till 1966. From 1966 he was employed as a painter, but he worked among men using chipping, scaling, riveting and caulking tools. He did not wear hearing protection until 1973, when he wore earmuffs. He suffered 50% hearing loss on the Coles-Worgan scale.

An employee is under a common law duty to take reasonable steps to protect his employees from dangers he actually knows of or can reasonably be expected to foresee. From 1963, all employers would have been expected to know about the dangers of noise when the Ministry of Labour published the booklet: "Noise and the Worker". Also at that time, earplugs, earmuffs and a sound absorbent cotton wool (Billesholm-wool) were available.

Medical opinion, at the time, was that most of the damage was already done to the employees by 1963. It was said that the greatest damage was done in the first six or seven years of exposure although the consequences of the damage did not emerge till later.

The claimants argued that, on existing precedent, an employer who contributed to any degree to an injury could be made liable for the whole injury Bonnington Castings Ltd v Wardlaw). There was also authority for the proposition that an employer whose negligence made an existing condition worse could be made liable for the whole injury (McGhee v NCB).

Decision The judge rejected these arguments. He said the employer's legal blameworthiness must be less than 100% as the greatest damage was done before knowledge and before the duty of care in respect of noise.

He did award damages for their loss of amenity, e.g. Mr Thompson was awarded £1350 because, with 50% hearing loss, he was unable to hear the doorbell, phone and television. The judge said that compensation was meant to be for physical injury, which occurred before 1963, not for the symptoms, which occurred later. That was why the damages in each case were low.

Relevance This case illustrated the date of knowledge of risk concept. Regarding noise, 1963 was the point at which the employer became liable to compensate employees for physical injury, the loss of amenity this causes and the social handicap resulting.

Where injury occurs progressively through successive employments, an apportionment of liability must be made between each employer.

Uddin v Associated Portland Cement Manufacturers Ltd. (1965) 2 All ER 213 [Contributory negligence]

F.A. s.14   Breach of Statutory Duty

Circumstances Mr Uddin went into an unauthorised part of the factory in an attempt to catch a pigeon. He climbed up onto some machinery housing. As he reached over for the pigeon, he fell onto a rotating shaft which was only accessible from above.

Decision Even though the claimant was in a part of the factory where he should not have been and not there in relation to his normal work, the injury he sustained as a result of a revolving steel shaft being left unfenced, constituted a breach of the provisions of the Factories Act. Mr Uddin was however held to be 80% responsible for his own action (contributory negligence) and was awarded 20% of damages.

Relevance It was enough to show that an employee suffered injury as a result of a breach of statutory duty for the case to succeed.

Note. It should be noted that a worker who was authorised to be in the roof space (e.g. maintenance personnel) could equally have fallen onto the unguarded shaft.

Walker v Northumberland County Council 1995 [Employers' duty of care in relation to mental ill-health arising from excessive workload]

Facts Mr Walker was employed as a social worker dealing with cases of child abuse. His workload increased steadily over the years and in 1986 he had a nervous breakdown. When he recovered and returned to work, he was promised additional resources to help him with his workload, but they failed to materialise. He had a second breakdown six months later. Mr Walker sued the council claiming they were in breach of their duty of care to provide a safe working environment.

Decision The council were not held liable for the first breakdown as they could not reasonably have foreseen Mr Walker was exposed to a significant risk of mental illness through his job. They were, however, liable for the second breakdown, given that the same circumstances were there that caused the first. The second breakdown was a reasonably foreseeable risk.

The council were found to have failed in their duty of care by not providing effective support to alleviate Mr Walker's suffering.

Wilsons and Clyde Coal Co v English [1938] 3 All ER 628 [Common law duty of care of employer and non-delegable nature of duty owed].

The nature of employers' duties at common law

Circumstances Mr English was a miner employed by Clyde Coal Company. He was crushed by haulage equipment. His employers argued that they had discharged their duty by appointing agents who managed the mine.

Decision The House of Lords held that the employer can delegate the performance of the duty but not the responsibility which attaches to it. The employer was therefore negligent and that negligence led to Mr English's injuries. The employer's duty of care to his employees was determined to extend to the provision of:

- Safe place of work including access and egress.
- Safe procedures.
- Safe plant and appliances.
- Competent fellow employees.

Relevance The duty is therefore 'personal', such that the employer must take reasonable care for the safety of his employees whether or not the employer takes any share in the conduct of the operation.

A9.3 - Occupier's liability

Main provisions of the Occupier's Liability Acts (OLA) 1957 and 1984

Under the *Occupiers' Liability Act (OLA) 1957*, an occupier owes a "common law duty of care" to all visitors, i.e. a duty to take such care as is reasonable (given the circumstances) to see that visitors will be reasonably safe in using the premises for the purposes for which they are invited or permitted to be there. The Act reminds the employer (or occupier) that they must be prepared for children to be less careful than adults. A higher duty of care exists for visitors who are children, which includes the need to foresee the attractiveness of everyday work things that may be considered to be allurements.

An occupier may expect that persons, in the exercise of their calling, will appreciate and guard against any special risks ordinarily incident to that calling, for example, the contractor electrician should be aware of electrical risks as part of his work.

An employer (or occupier) cannot be prosecuted for a breach of their duties under the OLA 1957, but if a visitor is injured, the occupier may be liable to pay compensation for the injury if it can be proved that the occupier had been negligent.

The position is slightly changed by the **Occupiers' Liability Act (OLA) 1984**. Prior to this Act, minimal duties were owed under common law by an occupier to those other than lawful visitors - for example, to trespassers. The common law duty to trespassers was considered common humanity. In other words, don't deliberately set a trap for them.

The situation was changed by the **British Railways Board v Herrington** case. A six year old boy wandered onto a railway line and was seriously injured when he came into contact with a live electrified rail. The defendants knew that the fence alongside the line was in a state of disrepair and had taken no remedial action - despite previous reports of children being seen on the line. There was clear evidence of the presence of trespassers (likely to be children) since the path was worn from the broken fencing to the railway line. The OLA 1984 followed that case and extends the rules of common law to unwelcome visitors (e.g. trespassers and ramblers), and defines under what circumstances a duty is owed. In particular, occupiers owe a duty if:

- They are aware of a danger.
- They know (or should know) that a person may put themselves at risk.
- The risk is one which the occupier might reasonably be expected to do something about.

The extent of the duty is to take such care as is reasonable in the circumstances of the case and to see that the other person does not suffer injury. The Act provides that the duty may be discharged by:

- Giving warning of the danger.
- Discouraging people from putting themselves at risk in the first place (e.g. by making it more difficult for trespassers, etc. to enter the premises).

In summary, OLA 1957 is the common law duty of care to welcome visitors and OLA 1984 the common law duty of care to unwelcome visitors.

A9.4 - Nuisance

Definitions

PRIVATE

Private nuisance is actionable under civil law. It can be considered as the interference with the claimant's enjoyment of his land and it need not be deliberate. Examples include excessive noise, fumes or smoke. The interference must be sufficiently significant and must be unreasonable. Impracticability of preventing the nuisance is taken into account.

PUBLIC

Public nuisance is a crime for which a prosecution can take place as well as being actionable at civil law. The nuisance affects the public generally rather than the individual. It affects the convenience and comfort of a class of people or their health, lives or property and includes for example, obstruction of the highway and leaving unlit scaffolding on public roads and walkways.

STATUTORY NUISANCE

Statutory nuisance legislation is enforced by the Local Authority Environmental Health Department, who will normally take action when local residents or neighbours complain. It is a defence for a business to prove that they have used "Best Practicable Means" to control any releases that may cause a statutory nuisance. The Environmental Protection Act Part III defines a number of activities that could be actionable under the statutory nuisance procedure; for example, the release of fumes, gases, dusts, steam or noise.

Measuring health and safety performance

Learning outcomes

The intended learning outcomes are that the student will be able to:

A10.1 explain the purpose of performance measurement in relation to health and safety objectives and arrangements

A10.2 explain the need for, objectives and limitations of health and safety monitoring systems

A10.3 describe the variety of monitoring and measurement techniques

A10.4 describe a range of techniques to communicate monitoring and performance data

Contents

This page is intentionally blank

A10.1 - Purpose of performance measurement

EFFECTIVENESS AND APPROPRIATENESS OF OBJECTIVES AND ARRANGEMENTS

Organisations need to monitor their health and safety performance to find out the degree to which they are being successful, just like finance, production or sales. Monitoring is an essential component of good management. An old maxim is "what gets measured tends to get done."

In modern, active and changing organisations it is essential to identify and confirm what is working and why in order to prevent these successful management actions being 'lost' at a time when resources are being reviewed.

Monitoring provides the opportunity and information to enable:

- The assessment of the effectiveness and appropriateness of health and safety objectives and arrangements, including control measures.
- The making of recommendations for review of the current management systems.
- The identification of substandard practices and or conditions.
- The identification of trends.
- Comparison of actual performance with targets.
- "Benchmarking".

RECOMMENDATIONS FOR REVIEW OF THE CURRENT MANAGEMENT SYSTEMS

It is essential for organisations to learn from their experiences and take the opportunity to decide how to improve performance. Audits by an organisation's own staff or people from outside the organisation complement other monitoring activities by looking to see if the policy, organisation and arrangements (systems) are actually achieving the right results.

The Management of Health and Safety at Work Regulations (MHSWR) 1999 (reg. 5) requires employers employing five or more employees to record their arrangements for the effective monitoring of preventive and protective measures.

A10.2 - Monitoring systems

NEED FOR A RANGE

The need for a range of both proactive (active) and reactive measures to determine whether objectives have been met. A balanced approach to monitoring seeks to learn from all available sources. Hence two forms of monitoring system are required:

- *Proactive (active) monitoring*, before the event, involves identification through regular, planned observations of workplace conditions, systems and the actions of people to ensure that standards are being implemented and management controls are working.
- *Reactive monitoring*, after the event, involves learning from mistakes, whether they result in injuries, illness, property damage or near misses.

Organisations need to ensure that information from both active and reactive monitoring is used to identify situations that create risks, and to do something about them. Priority should be given where risks are greatest. Both monitoring methods require an understanding of the immediate and the underlying causes of events.

RELIANCE ON ACCIDENT AND ILL-HEALTH DATA

Many organisations spend considerable time developing data on their health and safety performance based on the accidents they have. Whilst there is value in doing so, it has the limitation of being a little after the event. Accidents must occur to get the data, thus tending to reflect what was done to prevent them rather than what is being done. A more complete approach to monitoring will tend to include 'before the event' actions like audits and inspections to indicate what is currently being done to prevent accidents.

A low injury accident rate is not a guarantee that risks are being effectively controlled. In some cases this might be a matter of good fortune, rather than effective management.

If organisations wait till an event occurs to determine where health and safety effort is required then some sort of loss must have occurred. In order to gain sufficient management attention this could be an event resulting in personal injury to someone. Clearly this is an undesirable way of learning, particularly as, with an amount of effort, planning and thought, the event could have been foreseen and prevented. The more mature organisation seeks to learn most from activities (e.g. risk assessment) before the event or, at the very least, learn from those events that result in no personal injury, e.g. near misses.

ACTIVE MEASURES

These involve checking that workplace precautions and risk control systems remain in place and taking corrective action when they are not.

The objectives of proactive (active) monitoring are to:

- Check that health and safety plans have been implemented.
- Monitor the extent of compliance with the organisation's systems/procedures against legislative/technical standards.

Active monitoring includes the assessment of the appropriateness, implementation and effectiveness of health and safety standards (in the form of objectives and arrangements, including Risk Control Systems (RCSs)). This includes the operation of the current management systems. Organisations need to know:

- Where they are.
- Where they want to be.
- What is the difference - and why.

Active monitoring will tell the organisation about the reliability and effectiveness of its systems. This provides a good basis from which decisions and recommendations for maintenance and improvement may be made. Active monitoring also provides an opportunity for management to confirm commitment to health and safety objectives. In addition it also reinforces a positive health and safety culture; by recognising success and positive actions, instead of 'punishing' failure after an undesired event.

Organisations must see active monitoring as an integral (and normal) part of the management (work) function. As such it must take place at all levels and opportunities in the organisation. Managers should be given responsibility for the monitoring of objectives and compliance with standards for which they and their subordinates are responsible. The actual method of monitoring will depend on the situation and the position held by the person monitoring. The various forms and levels of active monitoring include (source HSG65):

- Routine procedures to monitor specific objectives, e.g. quarterly or monthly reports or returns.
- Periodic examination of documents to check that systems relating to the promotion of the health and safety culture are complied with, e.g. the way objectives for managers are established or appraised, assessment of records of training needs and delivery of training.
- Systematic inspection of premises, plant, and equipment by supervisors, maintenance staff, management, safety representatives and other employees to ensure continued effective operation of workplace precautions.
- Environmental monitoring and health surveillance to check on the effectiveness of health control measures and to detect early signs of harm to health.
- Systematic direct observation of work and behaviour by first-line supervisors to assess compliance with risk control systems (RCSs) and associated procedures and rules, particularly those concerned with risk control.
- The operation of audit systems.
- Consideration of regular reports on health and safety performance by the board of directors.

Active monitoring effort should be applied on a risk basis. Monitoring of workplace precautions would typically be more detailed and frequent than management system activities that carry a low risk if miss-applied.

REACTIVE MEASURES

Reporting, recording and analysis of loss data, including injuries and ill-health.

The primary objectives of reactive monitoring are to analyse data relating to

- Accidents.
- Ill-health.
- Other downgrading events such as property damage.

These methods are deemed to be after the event and include:

- Identification.
- Reporting.
- Investigation.
- Collation.
- Analysis of data and statistics on the events.

The events monitored include those resulting in:

- Injuries.
- Cases of illness (including sickness absence).
- Property damage / environmental damage.
- Near misses.

It is important to identify, in each case, why performance was sub-standard. Trends and common features may be identified, such as when, where and how these events occur. This provides an opportunity to learn and put into place improvements to the overall management system and to specific risk controls.

In order to carry out reactive monitoring effectively systems must be in place to identify the event for what it is, record it and report it. Without this nothing may be learnt. Indeed, what little data that is communicated might serve to reinforce that there is no need to put in a great deal of health and safety effort. If reporting etc. is planned and encouraged it is not uncommon to find a large increase in recorded events. This does not necessarily mean an increase in events, merely an increase in reporting.

Events contribute to the 'corporate memory', helping to prevent a repeat in another part of the organisation or at a later time. Though it should be remembered that the 'corporate memory' is said to be short, in the average organisation (one undergoing some change) it is said to be 4 years. Data may be gained from other organisations to re-enforce or extend experience of events and the hazards involved.

A10.3 - Monitoring and measurement techniques

Methods

DEFINITIONS

Health and safety audits

An in-depth examination of systems and procedures to check their compliance with known standards.

Workplace inspections

A safety inspection is a scheduled inspection of premises usually carried out by a safety specialist.

Safety tours

An unscheduled examination of a work area, carried out by a manager, sometimes accompanied by health and safety committee members; usually to ensure that conditions such as housekeeping are up to standards.

Safety sampling

Samples may be taken of similar topics as in inspections, the basis of the sample being to take an appropriate small portion to represent the whole of the topic being sampled.

Safety surveys

Surveys of the workplace, systems or people to determine facts about their health and safety status.

KEY ELEMENTS AND FEATURES

Health and safety audits

A systematic, critical examination of an organisation's systems to determine the extent to which there is compliance with a set of agreed standards.

The entire health and safety management system should be subjected to a comprehensive audit from time to time. Individual elements of the health and safety programme can, of course, be subjected to individual audits: e.g.

- Evaluation of compliance with health and safety programme procedures.
- Evaluation of compliance with set occupational health standards.
- Evaluation of compliance with physical safeguards (health and safety hardware).
- Evaluation of compliance with fire prevention/control standards.

Audits can be carried out by the management of the organisation, provided that the managers do not audit their own efforts directly (bias must be eliminated) and that the managers concerned have been trained in audit technique. Often a small team will be commissioned to conduct the exercise, in order to widen the experience base and establish some degree of independence. A team may comprise three key groups of people:

- A manager.
- A representative from the workforce.
- A health and safety professional.

Extra individuals may be co-opted to the team when specific topics are under assessment. A more independent approach would be to conduct an audit using auditors from outside the organisation or location.

The audit must be structured and co-ordinated in its assessment of the systems. This is best achieved by utilising audit checklists, developed or obtained before the audit. The audit involves assessment of documents, interviews of people and observations in the workplace. The outcome from an audit should be a detailed report of findings and recommendations to improve or maintain the health and safety management system.

Workplace inspections

Inspections involve examination of the workplace or items of equipment in order to identify hazards and determine if they are effectively controlled. Four different types of inspections are common:

- General workplace inspections - carried out by local first-line managers and employee representatives.
- Statutory inspections (thorough examination) of equipment, e.g. boilers, lifting equipment - carried out by specialist Competent Persons.
- Preventive maintenance inspections of specific (critical) items - carried out by maintenance staff.
- Pre use 'checks' of equipment, e.g. vehicles, forklift trucks, access equipment - carried out by the user.

An important aid used by anyone carrying out an inspection is a checklist, i.e. a list of "the way things ought to be". When a work area or item of equipment fails this test it is considered substandard and represents a hazard. Each substandard condition should be assessed and corrective action carried out and details recorded.

Safety tours

These present an opportunity for management to explore the effectiveness of risk control measures through planned visits to the workplace to observe and discuss the controls in use.

It is important, when developing a positive health and safety culture that management commitment be visible. The conducting of planned tours to workplaces to meet work groups is one effective way of achieving this. As such it is a monitoring method that senior and middle managers would find useful. It has the advantage of enabling direct contact and communication between employees and senior management. This gives an accurate picture of work conditions and the understanding of employees. It can indicate deficiencies or success in managers carrying the organisation's objectives through to action. It also provides a forum for gaining the viewpoint of employees directly, without the translation that takes place through formal management channels.

In order to be planned there must be an intended outcome e.g. to communicate or review a topic, even if this includes some free time for other comment. Details of the tour and outcomes, including improvement actions, must be recorded to be effective.

Safety sampling

Sampling is where only a partial amount of a potential group/area is examined to establish facts that can indicate the standard of compliance of the whole. A very small sample, such as the examination of three pieces of lifting tackle, may only give a rough, but acceptable, indication of the situation relating to lifting tackle as a whole.

When a representative sample is taken this may be considered to reasonably represent the situation for the whole group.

Sampling is conducted relating to the following:

- *Specific hazards* - such as noise or dust - typically conducted by staff trained in appropriate hygiene techniques.
- *Good practice* - such as the wearing of personal protective equipment - typically conducted by first- line managers.
- *General workplace hazards* - such as those identified during a defined walk through a work area - typically conducted by first-line managers, employee representatives and employees.

Safety surveys

It may be described as an examination of a narrow field of the health and safety programme on an exploratory basis, with no fixed expectation of findings. The term survey is usually applied to an exercise, which involves a limited number of critical aspects, for example:

- Noise survey - usually with the aid of noise measuring equipment.
- Lighting survey - usually with the aid of a light meter.
- Temperature survey (to measure both high & low temperature levels) - usually with the aid of a thermometer.
- Personal protective equipment needs survey - usually involving review of standards and workplace conditions/activities.

The term survey is also used to define an exercise in which managers/employees are interviewed in order to identify knowledge, understanding, and details of specific needs within the working environment. Examples of these might be:

- Training needs usually involving written questionnaires to managers and employees.
- Attitudes to health and safety usually involving written questionnaires to managers and employees.
- The need for specific health and safety rules for specific tasks - usually involving review of standards and workplace conditions/activities.

Should these exercises seek to identify details from only a small number of people within a subject group or small geographical area it would cease to be a survey and would become a sample.

In-house and proprietary audit systems

In-house audits can be developed by an organisation for its own use. This has the advantage of being closely tailored to the needs of the organisation. In developing the audit system a number of key points need to be considered including:

- The purpose and objective of the audit.
- Which standards will be used.
- The need for trained auditors.
- Management, financial and budgetary provision.
- The audit programme.
- How the planning, performance of the audit will be measured and the system for monitoring will be implemented.
- How the auditing policy together with its implementation will be reviewed.
- The revision of the auditing system based on the above review.

This can however be a time consuming process involving, as a minimum, the compilation of appropriate checklists and detailed guidance to the auditors. An alternative course of action would be to use a proprietary audit system which has been developed by a specialist organisation.

There are a number of commercially available "off the shelf" systems available to the organisation in order to enable them to develop a proactive approach to health and safety management. Some notable systems include ones developed by the British Safety Council, DuPont, ISRS and ROSPA.

In general these early systems have been structured in question format, with particular emphasis being given to objective yes / no type questions. The purpose was to "ensure consistency between auditors in interpretation of data". Typically the majority of the questions were so designed to ensure credit could only be given for each question when the requirement was fully met. This consequently led to low scores and a feeling of low achievement by those audited.

More modern systems, such as ACT's "Audit 123" have been developed to allow a much more positive approach to auditing. *See also - diagram, 'Extract from Audit 123, Level 3' - on next page.*

Many audit systems, including Audit 123, have both paper and software-based versions. The use of software allows for a more flexible approach with a number of advantages. These include the ability to:

- Tailor the package to more closely reflect company procedures and standards.
- Add new, and change existing, audit questions as risks are identified and legislation/standards are introduced.
- Change auditors' guidance.
- Automatically summarise results.
- Analyse data more easily in order to allow comparisons to be made.
- Automatically produce reports.
- Track outstanding actions.
- Generate graphical information such as charts.

Performance measures

ACTIVE/REACTIVE

Continuous performance measurement will ensure that trends and common features (such as when, where and how these events have occurred) are identified. This provides an opportunity to learn and put into place improvements to the overall management system and to specific risk controls.

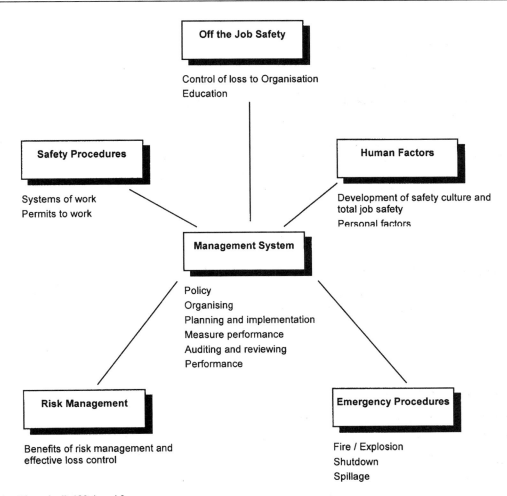

Figure A10-1: Extract from Audit 123, Level 3. *Source: ACT.*

Examples of active monitoring data

The range of active measures include:

- The extent to which plans and objectives have been set and achieved.
- Staff perceptions of management commitment to OH&S.
- Whether a director for OH&S has been appointed.
- Whether OH&S specialist staff have been appointed.
- The extent of the influence of OH&S specialists.
- Whether a safety policy has been published.
- Whether a safety policy has been adequately communicated.
- The numbers trained in OH&S.
- Effectiveness of OH&S training.
- Number of risk assessments completed as a proportion of those required.
- Extent of compliance with risk controls.
- Extent of compliance with statutory requirements.
- Number and effectiveness of senior managers' OH&S tours.
- Number of staff suggestions for OH&S improvements.
- Staff attitudes to risks and risk controls.
- Staff understanding of risks and risk controls.
- Frequency of OH&S audits.
- Time to implement OH&S audit recommendations.
- Frequency and effectiveness of OH&S committee meetings.
- Frequency and effectiveness of staff OH&S briefings.
- OH&S specialist reports.
- Time to implement action on complaints or suggestions.
- Health surveillance reports.
- Personal exposure sampling reports.
- Workplace exposure levels (e.g. noise, dust, fumes).
- Personal protective equipment use.

Examples of reactive monitoring data

Examples of reactive monitoring data include:

- Unsafe acts.
- Unsafe conditions.

- Near misses.
- Damage only accidents.
- Reportable dangerous occurrences.
- Lost-time accidents - when at least one work shift (or other time period) is lost by a person as a result of an accident injury.
- Reportable accidents involving absence from work for more than three days.
- Reportable major injuries.
- Sickness absences - employee absences due to illness (occupationally-related or non-occupationally-related).
- Complaints made, e.g. by members of the public.
- Criticisms made by regulatory agency staff.
- Regulatory enforcement action.

Organisations should adopt a well-formulated combination of all four types of measure in an occupational health and safety programme. This allows a much better overall assessment of occupational health and safety performance than reliance on any single measure. Attention should be given to the level of competence required of those responsible for devising, carrying out and analysing data from all performance measures.

OBJECTIVE/SUBJECTIVE

Objective measures that are detached from an assessor's personal judgement (e.g. reading a calibrated noise meter; number of personnel using hearing protection; whether an occupational health and safety specialist is in post). However, they may not be the most important things to measure.

Subjective measures that may be influenced by those doing the measuring. Examples are measures of adequacy of housekeeping or a safe system of work where no defined standard has been laid down. These measures can be very useful but need to be treated with caution (e.g. two people may report different findings about the adequacy of the workplace controls).

QUALITATIVE/QUANTITATIVE

Qualitative measures that are descriptions of conditions or situations that cannot be recorded numerically (e.g. a commentary on the deliberations of occupational health and safety committee). While qualitative indicators may be very important they may be difficult to relate to other performance measures.

Quantitative measures that can be described in terms of numbers and recorded on a scale. Where possible, it is desirable to quantify performance measures so that comparisons can be made over time. However, such measures may give an unjustified impression of precision.

COMBINED ASPECTS OF PERFORMANCE MEASURES

Objective measures that are detached from an assessor's personal judgement. This compares with subjective measures relied on, and is influenced by, the judgement of the auditor. Quantitative measures are those that can be described in terms of numbers and recorded on a scale whereas qualitative measures are descriptions of conditions or situations that cannot be recorded numerically.

Good auditing packages/aids will simplify the analysis of data, and, in some cases it may be helpful to score audit findings to allow an audit-to-audit comparison. Implicit in any safety audit is some form of quantitative and qualitative measuring/evaluation process, usually in the form of a scoring system. This allows the organisation to see how it is performing in comparison to an absolute standard, and indeed compared to other organisations (assuming that they are using the same measures). There are many types of scoring system available to the organisation. These can be qualitative or quantitative. The examples below illustrate the principles involved.

Sampling based scoring system - (quantitative)

In this process an appropriate sample size is selected which relates to the number of items to be audited and a risk factor. The risk factor is determined by the auditor and can be based on consequence, likelihood and number of people exposed. For example:

400 items with a risk factor of 15%

Total affected x $\dfrac{15}{100}$ = sample quantity, therefore: 400 x $\dfrac{15}{100}$ = 60 items to be sampled

22 items of the 60 sampled conform to requirements, therefore: $\dfrac{22}{60}$ x 100 = 36.7%

All or nothing points scoring system

Some items to be audited can best be assessed by awarding all the points - 100%, or no points at all - 0%. In some instances a number of detailed sub-questions combine to give a maximum of 100%.

Judgmental scoring system (subjective)

Some questions can only be effectively assessed by the auditor making a judgement of the level of compliance based on auditor's guidance. This is fundamentally a qualitative measure which can be made semi-quantitative by, for example, selecting a figure between 0% and 100%.

The value of an audit is dependent upon the experience, training and knowledge of the auditors and their ability to interpret and use the findings. It is also dependent on the integrity of all the parties involved. A system of checks and balances should be built into the system in order to avoid misrepresentation.

PERFORMANCE INDICES

Many organisations use standard indices to enable comparison of accident and ill-health statistics over given periods. Examples of performance measures and how they can be utilised to review the effectiveness of the safety management system are shown below:

Incidence rate = accidents compared with number of people and takes into account the varying size of the workforce.

$$\frac{\text{Number of accidents in the period}}{\text{Average number employed during the period}} \times 1\,000$$

Prevalence rate = similar to incidence rate but is an index of ill health rather than accidents.

$$\frac{\text{Number of ill - health conditions observed over the period}}{\text{Number of people in the population exposed to agent over period}} \times 1\,000$$

Frequency rate = accidents compared with time. Takes account of changes in work patterns and includes part time workers.

$$\frac{\text{Number of accidents in the period}}{\text{Total hours worked during the period}} \times 1\,000\,000$$

Other useful indices

Severity rate

(Average number of days lost compared with hours worked.)

$$\frac{\text{Total no. of days lost}}{\text{Total no. of man hours worked}} \times 1\,000$$

Mean duration rate

(Average number of days lost per accident.)

$$\frac{\text{Total no. of days lost}}{\text{Total number of accidents}}$$

Duration rate

(Average number of work hours between accidents.)

$$\frac{\text{No. of hours worked}}{\text{Total no. of accidents}}$$

As with all statistical calculations, the accuracy of the outcome is entirely dependent on the quality of the input. However, judicious use of these indices will enable trend analyses to be carried out when organisational changes (that can affect health and safety) are being made. This can produce useful feedback on the effectiveness of the safety management system.

PERFORMANCE DATA COMPARISON

For statistics derived to be of value their limitations have to be understood. Variables in work methods, hours of work, hazard controls and management system effort make it fundamentally difficult to make comparisons outside the organisation deriving the data. Indices, such as these, are best suited to comparison of performance of the same organisation over similar periods of time, for example, yearly. In this way trends may be observed and conclusions drawn. If comparisons are to be made outside the organisation it should be remembered that other organisations may have a different understanding of:

- Definition of an accident (lost time or reportable).
- Hours worked may not be actual (contracted minimum hours - easier to work out).
- Who is included (are contractors included or excluded?).
- What multiplier is used (ILO and HSE use 1,000,000 for the frequency rate, USA use 200,000).

A10.4 - Presenting and communicating findings

Reporting techniques

TEXTUAL

For many, the most important aspect of an audit is the report arising from it. This will provide confirmation of the correctness of features of the programme and its implementation, and identify specific opportunities for improvement that may be translated into objectives for a given period. The recommendations arising from an audit should be accurate and confidential. This should be in three stages:

1. Initial feedback.
2. Draft report.
3. Final report.

Initial feedback

The purpose of the initial feedback meeting is to allow the auditor to share his findings and observations with the appropriate management, so that:

- The manager hears the complete story before anyone more senior in the organisation.
- The auditor can make sure that he has explained the results to the audit unit management.
- It allows an opportunity to correct any misunderstandings by the auditor.

Before discussing any details of the auditor's findings, time should be taken to explain to the audit unit personnel why the meeting is taking place and what you hope to accomplish. The good auditor will not only report the problems that exist but also the positive aspects found.

Draft report

The factual accuracy of the report should be checked by local management in order to confirm factual accuracy and to confirm understanding.

Final report

The final report should give a clear assessment of the overall performance of the organisation. It should identify inadequacies and make recommendations for improvement. It should also identify the observed strengths and weaknesses and suggest how they can be built upon. Responsibility for carrying out action plans should then be assigned together with target completion dates. Progress should be monitored. It is essential that management take ownership both of the audit and the subsequent action plans. In any event reports need to be accurately and clearly communicated.

Record retention

All the papers gathered during the audit and working papers need to be kept. This is to allow the next auditor to refer back to them before the next audit, and will also allow other personnel to review them.

GRAPHICAL

The benefits of graphics fall into three basic categories:

- Making it easier for the audience to follow and remember your presentation.
- Illustrating complex concepts with images.
- And providing you with aids for organisation and pacing.

To make good information graphics is not an easy process. It is fundamental to know what purpose the graph is to serve and to whom it is addressed, but it's also convenient to follow a coherent process in order to correctly make it. The process is divided into three parts:

1. Establish why graphical representation will be used. This determines the type of data to gather (quantitative, sequential categorical ...) and more importantly determine whether they are relevant to that which is required.

2. Determine how the data is to be represented. A fundamental aspect of this section is that information graphics are interesting because they reveal differences. For this reason refining them and representing the data derived from their statistical treatment often reveals aspects that which otherwise would be confusing. Sometimes, for a little data, a table or even a sentence can be clearer than a chart. On certain occasions changing the colour palette or the type of chart can clarify the situation enormously.

3. Review; does it deliver that which is required. An elegant chart can be developed but, if it doesn't fit the goal defined in the first step, it will have failed. The key resides in revising and experimenting with what has been done until an improvement is found. Varying the colours, reducing the saturation of what is less important and increasing it for the most relevant data, modifying the typography, the size of fonts, eliminating everything that doesn't contribute to showing and clarifying the data (irrelevant grids, redundant data, unnecessary labels) without losing relevant information, sometimes provides surprisingly improved results. In the end, making good information graphics consists of facilitating the understanding of complexity, instead of complicating what is simple. This cannot be achieved without clear understanding of what goal is being pursued, who the audience is, and a good deal of work and reflection.

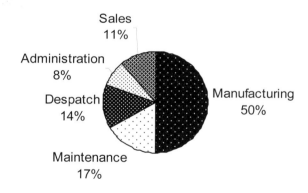
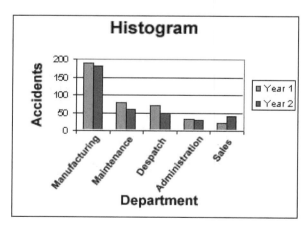

Figure A10-2: Examples of graphical data.

Source: ACT.

See also - 'How to present and interpret loss event data' - Element A2.

CONTENT AND STYLE OF RECOMMENDATIONS

These should flow logically from the main body of the report. Recommendations should consist of a plain statement of action without repeating the arguments of the preceding section.

The recommendations should be clearly connected to the results of the rest of the report. You may need to make those connections explicit at this point -the reader should be clear in their understanding of what has been written. This section may also include plans for how further work should proceed.

Include justification for the recommendation by referring to information summarised. A recommendation's justification is usually based on a reference to material already provided in the summary.

See also - 'Written communications' - Element CS1.

Communication skills

Learning outcomes

The intended learning outcomes are that the student will be able to:

CS1.1 identify the phases in the communication cycle and demonstrate effective verbal communication in one to one and in group situations

CS1.2 demonstrate effective listening skills and techniques and use different questioning techniques in order to gain information and understanding

CS1.3 identify the elements of a written report and the formal presentation of references and supplementary information

CS1.4 explain the use of information technology for the effective search and presentation of information

CS1.5 outline the skills needed to effectively organise, run and control both formal and informal meetings

CS1.6 discuss how style of leadership, management and can influence individuals and can help to resolve conflict

Contents

This page is intentionally blank

CS1.1 - Verbal communication

The communication cycle

Communication is a skill that we take for granted. Like any other skill some people are better at it than others. The purpose of this document is to provide the reader with some of the basic principles.

Communication is a two-way process where the needs of the receiver are equally as important as the needs of the speaker. Because it is a two-way process, both participants must be sure they are using the same language (e.g. British Rail's previous use of the term 'wait *whilst* red light shows' at a rail crossing compared with the Yorkshire use of the term whilst, meaning until... the red light shows). Assumptions that the receiver of a communication understands the speaker should not be made. To ensure the success of a communication:

- Use clear and unambiguous terms.
- Have an open mind.
- Consider the views of the other person.
- Be assertive but not aggressive.
- Use open ended questions and avoid questions which yield yes/no answers.
- Avoid entering communication with a view to apportioning blame.
- Do not assume receivers will understand.
- Use the 'why' question to investigate.
- Check to ensure you have been understood.

SIX SIMPLE RULES OF COMMUNICATION

1. Direct yourself towards and reach the intended recipient.
2. Communicate in a form capable of being understood by the recipient.
3. Ensure the recipient understands.
4. Be as concise as the content requires.
5. Budget time to encourage feedback.
6. Evoke and monitor the desired response.

PERSONAL INFLUENCE (INTERPERSONAL SKILLS)

The medium by which people influence each other is called 'communication' and, when a person influences the behaviour of another, they are communicating - even if no words are spoken. In the theory of communication two people talking to each other are referred to as the 'transmitter' (A) and the 'receiver' (B). Diagrammatically it can look like this:

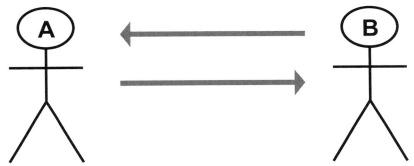

Figure CS1-1: Communication.

Source: ACT.

The two arrows emphasise the point that communication only takes place when '*B*' gives *feedback* to '*A*'. This feedback can, of course be in the form of total silence or even withdrawal, and this is the basis for the first 'law' of communication:

"It is not what 'A' says which is true, but what 'B' understands"

We all process the information we receive, and what we understand to be real is simply our perception of the truth. Recognising this, '*A*' needs to make sure that his/her communication is as clear as possible. In other words, whoever communicates information to another must make sure that the receiver has picked up the information correctly. It is the transmitter's responsibility to elicit feedback. This leads to Communication Law 2:

"If 'B' misinterprets the information 'A' gives him/her, it is 'A's' fault."

Communication involves more than the words spoken and even if it is only cold silence or withdrawal, it is impossible not to communicate. The very presence of another person is enough to make us change our behaviour. Thus, Communication Law 3 is:

"It is impossible not to communicate."

How we are influenced is affected not only by what is said (*content*), but how it is said (the *relationship* it implies).

All communication has two aspects:

> **Content** - We can be influenced by the facts, opinions, suggestions put forward. We are influenced by the additional *content*.

> **Relationship** - We are also influenced by the 'way' the content is presented and the relationship it suggests between the speaker and us.

This leads to Communication Law 4:

"Every type of communication has both a content aspect and a relationship aspect."

Take, for example, the responses:

"We are unable to accept your findings as they do not take into account the rate of inflation," and,

"This is abysmal, we can't accept this!"

Both have approximately the same content but define very different relationships. This relationship aspect, which is part of all communication, establishes the way in which the content is to be received. When communication is assertive, the relationship is established as honest, direct and fair. Thus more detailed attention can be directed toward the content. Where it is aggressive, passive or devious, the relationship itself limits the content and the information that can be discussed.

Barriers

TO RECEPTION

There are a number of reasons why the message communicated is not being received. The person on the receiving end of the information may have sensory problems (deafness, partial deafness, ear infection) or they may be wearing hearing protection, which may prevent the message being received. The communication may also be taking place in a noisy environment or where there are many distractions.

TO UNDERSTANDING

The lack of understanding of the message could be a language problem: different first languages, with either the speaker or recipient having to cope with the other's partial understanding of the language used; different accents, i.e. the way the words are pronounced; different dialects, i.e. different words being used for the same thing, e.g. snap, piece, bait, sandwiches, packed lunch, all refer to the same thing.

The language used may contain technical terms or jargon which the recipient does not understand. Health and safety is full of jargon that the experts forget is not part of everyone's vocabulary, for example, referring to "Regs" or "COSHH".

The speaker could be trying to pass on information that he himself does not quite understand. It is difficult to explain something clearly if you only partially understand it yourself.

TO ACCEPTANCE

The acceptance of the information may be affected by the relationship between the speaker and recipient. The recipient may not want to accept information from someone he sees as not as experienced as himself, "What does he know, straight out of college." There may also be dislike between them, so although the recipient looks as though he is listening, he is in fact ignoring the message.

The recipient might be in awe of or frightened of the speaker and this could cause a lack of real attention to the actual words spoken.

Features of communications

NON-VERBAL INFORMATION

We convey as much, if not more information through non-verbal ways as we do through the spoken word. It is far easier to tell lies on the phone than in a face-to-face situation because the recipient does not see the facial expressions, body language or gestures.

FACIAL EXPRESSION

Facial expressions are a large part of the message being communicated. It would be incongruous to communicate bad news with a smile on your face. Along with the words spoken, facial expressions can convey sympathy, friendliness, anger, fear, etc. The expression can belie the words spoken, as most of us are not capable of a "poker" face. For people with hearing difficulties, facial expressions are more important than they realise. For example, many people swear that they can hear better with their glasses on. Part of the glasses aiding hearing is lip-reading along with facial expression.

GESTURES

Many people are said to "talk with their hands". Hand gestures are very common in communication and it is difficult to talk without using your hands. "Over there", usually involves a pointing gesture and talking about movement usually involves the hands rotating. Most cultures have gestures that convey a message where no words are necessary. These may be positive or negative messages.

POSTURE

Posture conveys messages that could make the speaker more believable. For example, with an upright stance, the speaker seems to have confidence and therefore whatever he says must be accurate. A slumped posture does not convey confidence and may convey a lack of conviction.

EXPECTATIONS

We often hear what we want or expect to hear rather than what is said. Someone may appear to listen, but they are not hearing the words because they expect a certain message to be conveyed. For example, someone being told how to carry out a certain task may think they already know what is going to be said and not actually hear the instructions.

CONTEXT

We find it easier to understand a message that is conveyed in context; demonstrating a task while talking through it is more effective than explaining the task in a classroom setting.

VOICE QUALITIES

Voice has a variety of qualities that can relay information and we tend to vary our voice without really thinking about it. The voice pitch rising denotes frustration, anger or excitement; rising at the end of the speech denotes a question; low pitch can show calmness, enforced calmness or menace.

We expect certain messages according to voice pitch, e.g. we do not expect to be told off if the speaker has laughter in his voice. A soft voice quality can denote kindliness, concern or discretion.

LINGUISTIC FEATURES

Linguistic features, such as vocal sounds that are not words, but have some meaning can communicate many meanings. For example, when listening, the recipient will often make "mm" noises to show he is listening or "uhuh" or "yeah" to show agreement. This is more encouraging for the speaker than being met with silence.

Some sounds can convey a lot of information, such as a short throat-clearing noise may mean, "I don't believe that", or "I am being ironic". The meaning will be clear in context and we grow up understanding what these linguistic features mean.

Presentation skills

EFFECTIVE USE OF VISUAL AIDS

Visual aids are something that visually increase teaching effectiveness. Not only do they add interest to a presentation but by engaging more than one of the senses they also facilitate listening and remembering. It is said that people remember 20% of what is heard, 30% of what is seen and 50% of what is seen and heard at the same time.

A certain willingness to experiment and the ability to improvise are especially important where aids must be hand-made on a limited budget and with a restricted set of materials.

Visual aids may be PowerPoint presentations, flipcharts, videos/DVDs, examples of inspection reports, examples of personal protective equipment, etc. Seeing a filled-in permit to work may be more useful than explaining all day how a permit to work is utilised.

DEALING WITH QUESTIONS

The presenter needs to be confident in the subject matter and convey enthusiasm. Being competent in the subject is not about knowing everything, but being confident enough to say that you do not know the answer to a particular question, but you will find out. Pretending to know the answer and making something up will destroy your credibility when the answer is found to be wrong. In fact, it is a criminal offence to give false information and cause another individual to be in breach of the law. *(See also - 'Enforcement of health and safety law, HASAWA section 36' - in Element A7).*

Questions may be dealt with throughout the presentation, as they arise, or they may be dealt with at the end. The questions can be "parked" on the flipchart as a reminder. Questions throughout can be disruptive and spoil the flow of the presentation. On the other hand, the questioner's understanding of what follows might depend on the question being dealt with.

The presenter should never suggest that a question is silly. If the recipient does not understand something, then the presenter may not be effectively communicating the message and it is up to him to find another way to explain it.

SECURING AUDIENCE PARTICIPATION

Audience participation can vary from listening to taking part in discussions. A certain enthusiasm is required of the presenter, which will let the audience know that this is a topic that is worthy of communication. Many experienced presenters will say that the audience will participate if they are happy with the answer they get when they ask, "What's in it for me".

The presenter should be confident, change his voice pitch so it is not monotone, occasionally bring up some controversial topics for discussion, bring some humour into it where appropriate and be wary of using stereotypical language and ideas. For example, referring to the "ladies" in the audience does not go down well with women, nor does suggesting that they do not understand technical matters.

CS1.2 - Effective listening

POSITIVE LISTENING TECHNIQUES

In any significant and meaningful human interaction the listener needs to listen to what is said and listen for what is not said. He also has to show that he is listening and interested in the outcome. In other words, how he listens is as important as the fact that he is listening.

There are two basic types of listening; listening with the mind and listening with the body.

Listening with the mind (active listening) - this is nothing more than applying as much thought and concentration to listening as to any other mental activity which one takes seriously - writing a report, playing a game of chess, reading a poem.

Listening with the mind consists of:

- *Concentration.* Shutting out all physical distractions like the phone and interruptions; and also mental distractions - daydreaming, showing off, and pursuing irrelevancies.
- *Evaluating what is said.* We speak much more slowly than we think, so that the active listener has plenty of time to think about what is said. Why did he say that? What does it mean exactly? Does that make sense? Is there any evidence for that statement? Why did he use that form of words?
- *Evaluating what is not said.* The unspoken agenda is as important as the words themselves - perhaps more important. The active listener attends to the spaces between words - hesitation, confusion, embarrassment and to non-verbal communication or body language.

■ **Neutrality.** The active listener does not impose his views and comments. He attends to what the speaker is saying. The cardinal sin is 'yes butting'. 'Yes butting' is a sign that you're more interested in what you're thinking than what the other person is saying.

Listening with the body - how do we know that someone is listening to us? More than anything by physical signs. If they are leaning forward, seem eager to hear what we have to say, watch the speaker closely, are alert and attentive, nod occasionally, we feel we are on the same wavelength. If they lean back, look out of the window, yawn and seem physically disengaged, we feel we are not being listened to.

Summary

There is a difference between hearing and listening.

The impact of good listening skills on the customer is important (if it's a telephone conversation explain that you are taking notes, it shows that you are taking it seriously and really listening)

■ The verbal give away of when someone is not listening: "Yes, but …"
■ The physical signs of not listening are leaning back, yawning, etc.

The development and application of good listening skills can often enable a customer contact person to 'sense' and pre-empt complaints and criticism. They are valuable skills in this context since some customers don't complain, they simply take their business elsewhere.

QUESTIONING TECHNIQUES

Types of questions:

Open	'How', 'What', 'Tell me about', 'What makes it enjoyable', i.e. you cannot give yes/no answers.
Probing Questions	'How have you done…?', 'What effect did it have?', 'Why do you think that is?', etc.
Closed Questions	Short direct answers required or even a yes/no response, not allowing further clarification.
Restating	Repeating what someone else has said in your own words to check understanding is a type of questioning.

Open questions

Who

■ **Who** presented the proposal?

Where

■ **Where** did all this take place?
■ **Where** are the faulty batches/units now?

What

■ **What** exactly is your position at the moment?
■ **What** makes you think that this is a problem?

How

■ **How** did you reach this conclusion?
■ **How** does this problem affect your work?

When

■ **When** does this problem occur?
■ **When** will you know that this problem has been solved?

Which

■ **Which** people are involved in this problem?
■ **Which** issue would you like to examine first?

Use of open questions

The open question allows the recipient to talk rather than just answer. The "Can you tell me in your own words what happened" question will get much more information than the "Did he fall over" question, making the open question a useful tool in accident investigation interviewing techniques.

The open question is also beneficial in job interviews, allowing the interviewer to sit back and listen and the interviewee to open up and make the best of his application or eventually talk himself out of the job.

Closed questions

Those questions that produce a **yes/no** answer, e.g.:

■ Did the sales meeting go well?
■ Will you increase the distribution network?
■ Do you like being a manager?
■ Did you get that order?
■ Will you sort the problem out?
■ Are you happy in your job?

DISCUSSION OF CLARIFICATION VERSUS JUSTIFICATION

In communication, the recipient may occasionally need to ask the speaker for clarification, for example, "Did you mean finish the report by lunchtime or by the close of the day?" This allows the speaker to clarify the message, "Lunchtime would be preferable".

Justification is used if the recipient asks, "Why?" "Why must I finish the report by lunchtime?" The speaker will then be expected to justify what he has stated, "Because …".

Asking for clarification is an important part of communication so misunderstandings don't arise. However, misunderstandings can occur when clarification is asked for and the speaker believes that he is being asked to justify what he said, "Did you mean finish by lunchtime?" "Of course I mean lunchtime. If it's not finished by then, we'll never get the job". This altercation can escalate and leave both parties feeling aggrieved.

CS1.3 - Written communications

Formal report writing

The effective communication of the safety message is an important element of managing safety. How we communicate will depend on the target audience and the desired effect.

GENERAL FORMAT

Layout of document to enhance clarity and visual impact

One simple structure is as follows:

- Introduction and background.
- Main body of the report.
- Recommendations.
- Conclusions.

Introduction and background: This section includes the title page that should clearly identify the writer and the document. It should contain a brief explanation of the subject described in the document title and the reason for the document. Consider the aim of the report and inform the reader of the problems it intends to address.

Main body of the report: This section deals with details, facts and findings. Keep the style simple and to the point. Avoid the use of jargon or embellishment. Inaccuracy, inadequate and sloppy presentation can distract the reader and lessen the impact.

Recommendations: These should flow logically from the main body of the report. Recommendations should consist of a plain statement of action without repeating the arguments of the preceding section.

Conclusions: This section should contain a summary of the main findings and inferences. Ideally, the writer should end on a positive note.

If the report is also for the senior manager, then it is useful to have an "executive summary" just behind the title page so the manager can get the gist of the findings without reading it all. The details of the report can be dealt with by the delegated person.

A report that is just a block of text will not encourage anyone to read it. The use of sub-headings, white space and a largish size font will make it easier to read. Also, the inclusion of photographs, sketches and diagrams can enhance clarity and visual impact.

WRITING STYLES

Plain English is generally considered the best for report writing. It is a formal way to write, allowing the majority of English speakers, whether as a first or second language to understand it. It consists of Standard English, i.e. no geographical dialect words (Black Country "doobin" for wheelbarrow), no slang words ("gaffer" for boss) and no colloquial expressions (If the HSE come in we'll be "up the creek without a paddle").

Plain English is also meant to be free of jargon, acronyms and abbreviations. Health and safety, along with other specialised subjects has many examples of these, e.g. COSHH, NEBOSH, MIOSH, RIDDOR and EMAS, which have a different meaning dependent on the writer/reader being involved with health and safety or the environment. Jargon, which is technical terms used by a group of people from a particular profession or similar, is acceptable if the report has a small, in-house readership. If the report has to be read by people outside the company and outside the industry, then jargon can be impenetrable.

The use of technical terms may be necessary in a report; therefore a glossary of terms should be included.

THE USE OF APPENDICES AND ABSTRACTS

Reports often need to make reference to other documents, which, if included in the main text, would complicate the issues. These documents can be included at the end of the report as appendices and referred to in the report. The reader can then turn to the relevant appendix and consider it in whatever depth required. For example, a report with a reference to risk assessments could have a sample risk assessment as an appendix.

An abstract is a statement summarising the important points of a text. The abstract is usually placed at the beginning and allows the reader get a feel for the report before he begins. It may often be fore grounded by placing it in a text box.

CRITICAL ANALYSIS AND ITS USE AND APPLICATION IN ASSIGNMENT REPORTS

Critical analysis is stating the strengths and weaknesses of an issue. For example, a critical analysis of an organisation's welfare facilities may show there to be an adequate number of sanitary conveniences, but they are not kept clean. The critical analysis is used to show which areas need to be improved and which just need to be maintained. It can also be used to justify recommendations.

LITERATURE SEARCH TECHNIQUES

Books and papers necessary for research can be found by author's name, title, topic, year of publication or the International Standard Book Number (ISBN). Libraries have facilities for finding publications by any of these methods. The books in the libraries are shelved by subject, in alphabetical order and numbered according to the Dewey system.

The Internet can also be used to find publications by typing any of the above into the search engine. This type of search can also be used to find the source of chunks of text, which allows the source document to be read and referenced as necessary. The latter method can be used by examiners/markers to check that an assignment report is the candidate's own work if no reference to other authors is made.

METHODS FOR REFERRING TO PRIMARY SOURCES

Primary sources are "first-hand" sources, such as interviews, case studies, conference papers, and raw data.

Précis

A précis of the whole report should be complete and intelligible by itself. For reports to business managers this is often called an executive summary which is often a critical portion of the report as they will delve no further unless the executive summary interests them.

The précis is a highly structured four sentence paragraph that records the essential elements of a unit of spoken or written discourse, including the name of the speaker/writer, the context of the delivery, the major assertion, the mode of development and/or support, the stated and/or apparent purpose, and the relationship established between the speaker/writer and the audience (the last element is intended to identify the tone of the work). Each of the four sentences requires specific information; you are also encouraged to integrate brief quotations to convey the author's sense of style and tone.

Direct quote and paraphrasing

If you have included the exact words of an author, you are using a ***direct quotation***. These directly taken words must have quotation marks placed around them, and you must also provide attribution: the author's name and the year of publication. If you have used the idea of an author but have communicated that idea in your own words, you are employing a ***paraphrase***, which does not receive quotation marks, but does-and this is very important to follow-receive the same attribution as a direct quotation. Always provide an attribution to someone else's writing or ideas-whether the words come from your professor, a text, a film, an interview, or online.

METHODS AND NOTATION FOR REFERENCING RESEARCHED SOURCES

In-text citation

It is important to acknowledge the sources that are used so the writer is not accused of plagiarism. Plagiarism is using the words or ideas of another and passing them off as one's own.

Citation and reference are synonymous terms. There are many variations on reference styles and whichever is chosen, it is important that it remains consistent and is the style recommended by the tutor.

Two styles for citing are the Harvard and Vancouver: for example, in the ***Harvard*** style the reference can be immediately acknowledged by giving (in parentheses) the author's surname and the year of publication, e.g. (Darwell 2001). Page numbers may also be included: p. for one page and pp. for a range of pages, for example, (Darwell 2001, p. 4).

Alternatively, the author's name may be left out of the parentheses, e.g.

According to Darwell (2001, p. 7), several types of cutting edges are used.

Using the ***Vancouver*** style, references are numbered in the order that they appear in the text. For example,

…as one author states, "pre-HSWA, accidents were of greater severity" [1]

The author's name can also be part of the text, e.g.

Darwell [2] has argued that …

The brackets can be square or curved, but should be consistent. Superscripts can be used instead of brackets, e.g.

…as was stated.[1]

End reference lists

The end reference list in the ***Harvard*** style is in alphabetical order by author name or title when there is no author. If there is more than one work by an author, they should be listed in publication date order starting with the earliest, e.g.:

1. Adamson, J. 1999, *Engineering Methods*, Longman, UK.
2. Adamson, J. 2002, *Engineering and Design*, Longman, UK.
3. Bateman, D. 1998, *Ergonomics in Practice*, Oxford Press, UK.

In the ***Vancouver*** style, references are listed at the end of the paper in numerical order, e.g.:

1. Smith AB. Health and Safety for Professionals 2001; 140-5.
2. Brown FB. Starting Out 1999; 23-8.

Bibliography

A bibliography is a list of every item that was read in the preparation of the assignment whether referred to in the work or not. It goes at the end and is in alphabetical order, just the same as the Harvard method of referencing.

Footnote systems

There are two kinds of notes: reference notes, which cite authority for a statement or cross reference a source, and content notes, which contain acknowledgments or make incidental comments that would otherwise interrupt the flow of the paper. Whether you are making a reference or content note, the place in the text where the note is introduced is indicated by a superscript (an Arabic numeral raised slightly above the line). The note number follows all punctuation except a dash and ideally comes at the end of a sentence. Do not follow the superscript with a period.

Footnotes are placed in numerical order at the bottom of the page on which the reference occurs just below a separator, which is a short line of twelve spaces. The first line of each note is indented five spaces and indicated by an Arabic numeral (not a superscript) followed by a period and a space. Notes may be single spaced with a blank space between. The following are sample *footnote* examples.

Book footnote

1.   William Faulkner, *The Unvanquished* (New York: Vintage, 1991). 27.

Anthology footnote

2.   Plato, Republic, in Classics of Moral and Political Theory, 2nd ed., ed. Michael Morgan,

     (Indianapolis: Hackett Publishing, 1992). 63.

Journal article footnote

3.   Bernard Williams, "Pagan Justice and Christian Love," *Apeiron* 26, no. 3-4 (Sept.-Dec. 1993): 196.

Citing electronic sources

There are two basic types of electronic sources: physical entities such as CD-ROMs and online sources such as networks and bulletin boards. *Online!* makes the following recommendation for documenting a file available from the World Wide Web:

- Author's name (if known).
- Title of document (in quotation marks).
- Title of complete work (in italics or underlined).
- Date of publication or last revision (if known).
- URL, in angle brackets.
- Date of access in parentheses.

Your citation would then look like this (from *Online!*):

1.   Leslie R. Shade, "Gender Issues in Computer Networking," 14 February 1994,

     <http://liquid2-sun.mit.edu/fells.short.html> (26 November 2004).

Subsequent footnote references to a source

After the first full citation of a work, an abbreviated citation is used for all subsequent references. This includes the author's name followed by the page number of the reference and looks like this:

2.   Mason, 18.

If you are using more than one text by the same author, an abbreviated title is also given. (In one method of the Chicago system, an abbreviated title is always given, but we will use the simpler method.)

When references to the same work follow one another with no intervening references, then ibid. may be used. The reference would look like this:

3.   Ibid.

or, if page numbers are different, like this:

4.   Ibid., 17.

CS1.4 - Information technology

THE USE OF INFORMATION TECHNOLOGY

Bullet-pointing

A bullet point is not a sentence. Too many times an author puts an entire sentence as a bullet point. This defeats the entire purpose of the bullet point, which is to convey the key point only.

Reveal the key idea only. A bullet point is supposed to be a short summation of the key point that you want to make. It should not reveal all you know about the idea, or there is nothing left for you to say. For each idea you want to convey, consider what the key point is and put that as a bullet point. Then add to the bullet point by the words that you speak during the presentation.

When using bullet points, make sure that they have a consistent style. This means that:

- Each bullet point starts with either a verb or a noun - a verb is more action oriented and is usually preferred.
- If using verbs they are all in the same tense - the most common is the present tense with the past tense being the next most common.
- The use of capitalisation is the same in each bullet point - usually the first letter of the first word is capitalised and the rest of the words are in lower case unless it is a proper name.

Use of graphics

Purpose

Both quality and number of visual aids should enhance, not distract from message - display or distribute an outline to help audience follow long or group presentations - use variety to increase interest; remember the value of pictures, graphs, symbols and objects.

Appearance

Use a plain font (e.g. Swiss or Helvetica) of substantial size (18 point or more) - if you use colour, don't use more than three colours - ask yourself - Can the audience quickly and easily grasp what they see? - Are they spending time reading and not listening?

Text

Make only one key point per visual unless the audience is very familiar with the subject - organise material into natural categories and contrasts before vs. after, problem and solution, advantages vs. disadvantages, beginning to end; costs vs. benefits - include no more than three or four points under one heading - don't use whole sentences or paragraphs - use bulleted words or short phrases only, except for quotes.

Graphs

No more than three curves on a line chart or graph - don't use a page full of numbers - translate complex numbers into representative pie charts or bar graphs - use diagrams or models to present complex concepts; use multiple charts illustrating different stages or parts of the full model; start with simple framework and build components successively into the full model or process.

Typefaces

Type is important. The right typeface can encourage people to read your message. The wrong typeface or bad typography can make your message go unread. The two most important things to remember...

1. Type is on the page to serve the text. It should make the words easy to read and provide a suitable background. Type should not overpower the text.

2. There are no good and bad typefaces; there are appropriate and inappropriate typefaces. Think about your reader and the feeling you want to convey, and then choose a typeface that fits.

INTERNET SEARCH ENGINES AND THE SCOPE AND LIMITATIONS OF INTERNET INFORMATION SOURCES

Uses and limitations

Advantages	Limitations
Data - and information-rich, including a range of media	Knowledge-poor; information overload
Anyone can publish online	No librarians for quality control
Learners can become researchers because of easier access to data	Need for quality control in the data that students find and use
Search engines that are fast and powerful	Search engines that show results based on who pays the most
Easy to use	Not enough training for effective use
Smaller, faster, cheaper all the time	Push to upgrade constantly
Ability to link to people and places immediately	Speed takes precedence over quality
Global dissemination of information	Risk of a growing information gap between haves and have-nots
Motivation for students in sharing their work online with the world	Copyright issues - it's easy to get caught, so teachers need to make sure their students follow the rules

Figure CS1-2: Advantages and limitations of internet information sources.   *Source: ACT.*

Evaluating websites

Evaluation of web documents:	How to interpret the basics:
Accuracy of web documents ■ Who wrote the page and can you contact him or her? ■ What is the purpose of the document and why was it produced? ■ Is this person qualified to write this document?	**Accuracy** ■ Make sure author provides e-mail or a contact address/phone number. ■ Know the distinction between author and Webmaster.
Authority of web documents ■ Who published the document and is it separate from the "Webmaster?" ■ Check the domain of the document, what institution publishes this document? ■ Does the publisher list his or her qualifications?	**Authority** ■ What credentials are listed for the authors)? ■ Where is the document published? Check URL domain.
Objectivity of web documents ■ What goals/objectives does this page meet? ■ How detailed is the communication? ■ What opinions (if any) are expressed by the author?	**Objectivity** ■ Determine if page is a mask for advertising; if so information might be biased. ■ View any Web page as you would an infomercial on television. Ask yourself why was this written and for whom?

Currency of web documents	Currency
■ When was it produced? ■ When was it updated? ■ How up-to-date are the links (if any)?	■ How many dead links are on the page? ■ Are the links current or updated regularly? ■ Is the information on the page outdated?
Coverage of the web documents	**Coverage**
■ Are the links (if any) evaluated and do they complement the documents' theme? ■ Is it all images or a balance of text and images? ■ Is the information presented cited correctly?	■ If page requires special software to view the information, how much are you missing if you don't have the software? ■ Is it free or is there a fee, to obtain the information? ■ Is there an option for text only, or frames, or a suggested browser for better viewing?

Figure CS1-3: Evaluating websites.   *Source: ACT.*

Putting it all together
- ***Accuracy.*** If your page lists the author and institution that published the page and provides a way of contacting him/her and.
- ***Authority.*** If your page lists the author credentials and its domain is preferred (.edu, .gov, .org, or .net), and…
- ***Objectivity.*** If your page provides accurate information with limited advertising and it is objective in presenting the information, and . . .
- ***Currency.*** If your page is current and updated regularly (as stated on the page) and the links (if any) are also up-to-date, and
- ***Coverage.*** If you can view the information properly-not limited to fees, browser technology, or software requirement, then . . .
- You may have a Web page that could be of value to your research.

GENERATION OF VISUAL AIDS

A good presentation with visuals is much more effective than a good presentation without them! Visual aids are used to enhance a presentation and can include a whole range of still or moving images: video or film, whiteboards or flipcharts, PowerPoint slides or overhead transparencies, 35mm slides, models or handouts. A picture is worth a thousand words… try to be creative. The visual aids will help the listener to retain the information better than by just hearing the words spoken. They should:

- Explain, simplify, clarify or highlight points.
- Hold the attention and help concentration.
- Add interest and variety.

If the design and use of visual aids is not planned and relevant, it will detract from the presentation and confuse rather than help the audience.

1. ***Draw out the key points.*** What are the key points you want to make? Are you trying to put across too much information in one go? Does each key point need to be reinforced by one or more visual aid? Are there secondary points that would benefit from the use of visual aids? Remember, too many secondary points will be likely to distract your audience from your key points.

2. ***Think about your audience.*** You should have a good picture of your likely audience. Think about their level of knowledge because this will affect the level of detail you can communicate to them successfully and perhaps give you some pointers about the sort of visual aids which might help get your message across.

3. ***Think about the content, format and style.*** Now you can consider what will be best in helping you get across your key points. Text may be suitable for most occasions, either as bullet points or short individual sentences, but remember, a word only slide isn't really a true visual aid. Graphical displays can be computer generated and include drawings, graphs, diagrams or charts, or photographs. Make sure all the visual aids you intend to use are clearly legible from the back of the room you will be using and, if they're not, change them! How often have you heard presenters say "You won't be able to read all this, but I'll put the slide up all the same"? Whatever the presentation, remember that:

- Visual aids can be used in combination and are often much more effective because of the different formats.
- Colour should be used sparingly for maximum impact and minimum confusion; the eye is drawn to the brightest spot so choose your colours for the best effect.
- Dark backgrounds work best for slides; light backgrounds can be a nightmare, showing every speck of dust or fingerprint, and the glare from the screen can be unpleasant for the audience.
- Excessive detail will only cause confusion.
- You may need to break down complex points into several visual aids, but you should try to show how they all fit together.
- The best slides should need the presenter's words to complete them; they are not supposed to be able to stand alone and they are not supposed to be your script.

4. ***What equipment are you going to use?*** Find out what equipment is available and, if you need to book it for your presentation, make sure you do so well in advance.

Make sure the equipment can be used successfully at your venue. For example, if you are using a PowerPoint presentation, overhead transparencies or slides, can you black out the room enough for them to be visible? Will you need some extra help to pull blinds or curtains or to dim lights so that you minimise any disruption to your presentation? Will the size of the room and audience mean that you need extra screens or monitors, or audio speakers?

Can you operate the equipment, to enlarge, reduce or focus images? If you don't know how, make sure you have someone who can at hand to help you.

1. ***Prepare your visual aids.*** Are there some already prepared and available in-house? Who should prepare them: you, someone in your team, or is there an in-house department to help you? Allow plenty of time for the production of your visual aids, including any corrections and amendments. Do make sure they are worded properly, that spelling and figures are accurate and that the slides are numbered in sequence. Is there a house style to follow? Even if there isn't, make sure you use a uniform

layout for all your visual aids and avoid distracting leaps from one style to another. Visual aids should be cost-effective so bear in mind not just the costs involved in preparing them, but also hiring in any equipment.

2. ***Plan your use of the visual aids and rehearse your presentation using them.*** Carefully plan when you will introduce your visual aids during your presentation. A visual aid will focus attention away from you and that might not be what you want, especially at the beginning of your talk. You may want to vary the timing so consider the pros and cons of each approach. For example, you might decide to introduce one point before showing the accompanying visual aid, but to display another one "cold" and wait a few seconds for your audience to take it in before you start to speak. Make a note on your prompt cards so you know when to introduce each visual aid.

Handouts can be given out at the end as a summary. If you decide to hand them out at the beginning, remember there is always the danger that your audience will end up reading your handout rather than listening to you.

Keep any visual aid concealed from your audience until you are ready to use it and, after it has served its purpose, remove it so that it won't distract attention. You should allow enough time for people to take notes if they want, but generally 40 seconds should be enough.

Have at least one full rehearsal, using all your visual aids, to ensure a smooth transition between your speaking and the visual aids. Ask a colleague to sit in and give you some feedback on how well it is working. Make sure you don't end up standing with your back to the audience, talking at the screen or flipchart.

3. ***Make a final check.*** Get to the venue early enough to make sure that all your equipment has arrived and is working properly. Run through your slides and make sure they are in the correct order. Check right down to last detail. You might not have thought about the flipchart pens, but are they still usable? Any mishap of this kind when you are giving your presentation will undermine your confidence, look unprofessional to the audience and detract from the overall impact you make.

4. ***Have an alternative plan!*** If, in spite of your best efforts, the equipment does break down, have an alternative plan prepared as back up so you can still carry on with your presentation. This may mean having a second projector available, or an alternative way of making your presentation (e.g. on OHP instead of PowerPoint).

Do's and don'ts for the effective use of visual aids

Do:

- Make sure each visual aid, or combination of visual aids, is the best for the job.
- Ask yourself, can I manage just as well without it? If the answer is yes, get rid of it.
- Ask yourself, is it really a visual or is it just a visible verbal prompt to me?
- Try to find out as much as possible about your audience.
- Make sure you know how to operate the equipment you are going to use.

Don't:

- Display a visual aid for too long because it will only distract your audience.
- Put too much detail into any one visual aid - if every detail is essential, provide it as a handout to be taken away instead.
- Forget to rehearse your complete presentation, with visual aids, at least once.

SEARCHING LITERATURE SOURCES

Effective searching of the literature primarily needs a methodical approach and some advanced planning. Journal articles provide the most up-to-date source of published research and often cover subjects not readily to be found in book format. Some articles, known as review articles, provide overviews of a subject often with extensive reference lists and they can make excellent starting places for research. The principles of searching for articles can also be usefully applied to searching for other types of literature.

It is worth bearing in mind that you will frequently have to search beyond the confines of your subject area to find relevant literature so you may need to look in journals in related subject areas such as psychology, sociology, education etc to locate relevant material.

CS1.5 - Meeting skills

DESIGNING MEETINGS

Meetings can range from short informal "chats" between two people to formal presentations with dozens of participants. They can be scheduled regularly, like a weekly production meeting for example, or ad-hoc, "something needs to be fixed."

The selection of members

It's often obvious who should attend; sometimes it isn't. Consider inviting representatives from other departments to your own department meetings - they will appreciate being asked, and it will help their understanding of your issues. Having outside guests from internal and external suppliers helps build relationships and strengthen the chain of supply, and they can often also shed new light on difficult issues too. Use your discretion though - certain sensitive issues should obviously not be aired with 'outsiders' present. Avoid and resist senior managers and directors attending your meetings unless you can be sure that their presence will not be intimidating. Senior people are often quick to criticise and pressurise without knowing the facts, which can damage team relationships, morale, motivation and trust.

The request/control of their input

The key to success is keeping control. You do this by sticking to the agenda, managing the relationships and personalities, and concentrating on outcomes. Meetings must have a purpose. Every item must have a purpose. Remind yourself and the group of the required outcomes and steer the proceedings towards making progress, not hot air. Politely suppress the over-zealous, and encourage the nervous.

THE PREPARATION OF THE AGENDA

Produce the meeting agenda. This is the tool with which you control the meeting. Include all the relevant information and circulate it in advance. If you want to avoid having the ubiquitous and time-wasting 'Any Other Business' on your agenda, circulate the agenda well in advance and ask for additional items to be submitted for consideration.

Formal agendas for board meetings and committees will normally have an established fixed format, which applies for every meeting. This type of formal agenda normally begins with:

- Apologies for absence.
- Approval of previous meeting's minutes (notes).
- Matters arising (from last meeting).
- And then the main agenda, finishing with 'any other business'.

MEETING SKILLS

Formal

Before any meeting, try to plan as thoroughly as possible. The last thing you want is to be surprised at the meeting, whether you are in charge of it, or simply attending.

For each item, explain the purpose, and if a decision is required, say so. If it's a creative item, say so. If it's for information, say so. Insert timings, or time-per-item, or both (having both is helpful for you as the chairman). If you have guest speakers or presenters for items, name them. Plan coffee breaks and a lunch break if relevant, and ensure the caterers are informed. Aside from these formal breaks you should allow natural 'comfort' breaks every 45-60 minutes, or people lose concentration and the meeting becomes less productive.

Informal

For more common, informal meetings, try to avoid the formality and concentrate on practicality. The important thing to keep in mind is not the quantity (length or frequency) of a meeting but the quality of a meeting. A well-planned and executed meeting always bears more fruit than something thrown together at the last minute with no clear purpose.

PREPARATION FOR A MEETING

The environment

Venue choice is critical for certain sensitive meetings, but far less so for routine, in-house gatherings. Whatever, there are certain preparations that are essential, and never leave it all to the hotel conference organiser or your own facilities department. They do their best but they're not you, and they can't know exactly what you want. You must ensure the room is right - mainly big enough with all relevant equipment and services. It's too late to start hunting for a 20 ft power extension lead five minutes before the meeting starts. Other aspects that you need to check or even set up personally are:

- Table and seating layout.
- Top-table (if relevant) position.
- Tables for demonstration items, paperwork, hand-outs, etc.
- Electricity power points and extensions.
- Heating and lighting controls.
- Projection and flip chart equipment positioning and correct operation.
- Whereabouts of toilets and emergency exits - fire drill.
- Confirm reception and catering arrangements.
- Back-up equipment contingency.

All of the above can and will go wrong unless you check and confirm - when you book the venue and then again a few days before the meeting. For a big important meeting, you should also arrive an hour early to check everything is as you want it. Some meetings are difficult enough without having to deal with domestic or logistics emergencies; and remember if anything goes wrong it reflects on you - you lose credibility, reputation and control.

Support materials

Positioning of seating and tables is crucial. Ensure the layout is appropriate for the occasion:

- Presentations to large groups - theatre-style - the audience in rows, preferably with tables, facing the chairman.
- Medium-sized participative meetings - horse-shoe (U) table layout with the open part of the U facing the chairman's table.
- Small meetings for debate and discussion - board-room style - one rectangular table with chairman at one end.

Your own positioning in relation to the group is important. If you are confident and comfortable and your authority is in no doubt you should sit close to the others, and can even sit among people. If you expect challenge or need to control the group strongly set yourself further away and clearly central, behind a top-table at the head of things.

Ensure everyone can see screens and flip charts properly - actually sit in the chairs to check - you'll be surprised how poor the view is from certain positions. You don't need an acetate to check the focus of an overhead projector - laying a pen on the glass works just as well.

Set up of projectors and screens is important - strive for the perfect square image, as this gives a professional, controlled impression as soon as you start. Experiment with the adjustment of projector and screen until it's how you want it. If you are using LCD projector and overhead projector you may need two screens. A plain white wall is often better than a poor screen.

People from the western world read from left to right, so if you want to present anything in order using different media, set it up so that people can follow it naturally from left to right. For instance show introductory bullet points (say on a flip chart on the left - as the audience sees it) and the detail for each point (say on projector and screen on the right).

Position screens and flip chart where you can use them comfortably without obscuring the view.

Ensure extension leads and loose wiring is taped to the floor or otherwise covered and protected.

Supply additional flip chart easels and paper, or write-on acetates and pens, for syndicate work if applicable. You can also ask people to bring laptops for exercises and presentation to the group, assuming you have LCD projector available and compatible.

CHAIRMANSHIP SKILLS

Opening

- Be sure meeting input materials are prepared and brought to the meeting.
- Introduce any guests or new members to the group.
- Verify that a quorum exists.
- Review the group's goals and progress on the goals.
- Agree on the meeting's desired outcomes.
- Finalise the meeting agenda, including asking for any new agenda items.
- Prioritise the agenda items with items requiring the most participation coming first; estimate times for each agenda item.

Concluding meetings

- Summarise all action items and decisions.
- Plan next meeting; desired outcomes, agenda items, and any meeting inputs.
- Identify roles and responsibilities for next meeting; meeting leader, recorder, etc.
- Critique the meeting and overall teamwork.
- Prepare and distribute minutes of the meeting.

Encouraging participants and controlling meetings

The key to success is keeping control. You do this by sticking to the agenda, managing the relationships and personalities, and concentrating on outcomes. Meetings must have a purpose. Every item must have a purpose. Remind yourself and the group of the required outcomes and steer the proceedings towards making progress, not hot air.

Dealing with disagreement and conflict

Keep insisting that each side really tries to learn and understand the other side's aims, objectives, feelings, background etc. Understanding is different to agreeing - very important to keep explaining this - by understanding each other there can be constructive debate towards agreement; without understanding, any agreement is impossible, so too is sensible adult discussion.

Gaining commitment

What is the meeting's purpose? Always have one; otherwise don't have a meeting. Decide the issues for inclusion in the meeting and their relative priority: importance and urgency.

Controlling time

If someone persistently complains unreasonably about a specific issue that is not on the agenda, quickly translate it into a simple exploratory or investigative project, and bounce it back to them, with a deadline to report back their findings and recommendations to you.

- Use the rules on delegation to help you manage people and tasks and outcomes through meetings.
- Always look at how people are behaving in meetings - look for signs of tiredness, exasperation, and confusion, and take necessary action.
- As a general rule, don't deviate from the agenda, but if things get very heavy, and the next item is very heavy too, swap it around for something participative coming later on the agenda - a syndicate exercise, or a team game, a quiz, etc.

CS1.6 - Interpersonal skills

THE INTERRELATIONSHIP BETWEEN INDIVIDUALS AND THE INFLUENCE OF INDIVIDUAL DIFFERENCES ON RELATIONSHIPS

The consultative process depends on both personal relationships and the culture of the organisation. Conflict will exist if managers view consultation on health and safety matters as a burden which interferes with production. It is management's responsibility to take executive action and to have adequate arrangements for regular and effective checking for health and safety precautions and for ensuring that the declared health and safety policy is being fulfilled. The work of consultative mechanisms such as safety committees should supplement these arrangements: it cannot be a substitute for them. Alternatively, employees can have a negative effect on the process if they view consultation as a way of getting back at managers without having to go through any grievance procedures.

In essence the attitudes towards safety representatives and committees on both sides of the management 'divide' say a great deal about the culture of the organisation. The general attitudes of groups of employees can play either a positive or negative role in the consultative process. The social need of most individuals to both belong to, and be accepted by, a group is a powerful motivating factor. The need to belong to a group provides our need for friendship and affiliation and supports both self esteem and identity. The attitudes of the peer group can play a powerful role in either helping or hindering the consultation and thus the safety effort. Those who manage organisations are well advised to influence both organisational and individual performance by working with and through groups.

An essential condition to effective consultation is good communications between all parties. It should be recognised that there is a genuine desire on the part of management to use the knowledge and experience of its employees and an equally genuine desire on the part of the employees to improve the standards of health and safety at the work place.

ASSESSING AND CONTROLLING CONFLICT

Common sources of conflict

- *Unclear definition of responsibility:* there will be numerous occasions for conflict to arise over decisions made or actions taken in disputed territory.
- *Limited resources:* time, money, space, materials, supplies, and equipment are all valuable resources. Competition for any of these resources will inevitably lead to interpersonal and interdepartmental conflict.
- *Conflict of interest:* individuals may fight for their personal goals and lose sight of organisational goals. Each individual needs to know how his or her personal goals and efforts fit within the organisational goals and efforts.

What to do:	How to do it:
Talk with the other person.	■ Ask the other person to name a time when it would be convenient to meet. ■ Arrange to meet in a place where you won't be interrupted.
Focus on behaviour and events, not on personalities.	■ Say "When this happens …" instead of "When you do …" ■ Describe a specific instance or event instead of generalising.
Listen carefully.	■ Listen to what the other person is saying instead of getting ready to react. ■ Avoid interrupting the other person. ■ After the other person finishes speaking, rephrase what was said to make sure you understand it. ■ Ask questions to clarify your understanding.
Identify points of agreement and disagreement.	■ Summarise the areas of agreement and disagreement. ■ Ask the other person if he or she agrees with your assessment. ■ Modify your assessment until both of you agree on the areas of conflict.
Prioritise the areas of conflict.	■ Discuss which areas of conflict are most important to each of you to resolve.
Develop a plan to work on each conflict.	■ Start with the most important conflict. ■ Focus on the future. ■ Set up future meeting times to continue your discussions.
Follow through on your plan.	■ Stick with the discussions until you've worked through each area of conflict. ■ Maintain a collaborative, "let's-work-out-a-solution" attitude.
Build on your success.	■ Look for opportunities to point out progress. ■ Compliment the other person's insights and achievements. ■ Congratulate each other when you make progress, even if it's just a small step. Your hard work will pay off when scheduled discussions eventually give way to ongoing, friendly communication.

STYLES OF MANAGEMENT AND LEADERSHIP

Their influence on the individual

Managers have to perform many roles in an organisation and how they handle various situations will depend on their style of management. A management style is an overall method of leadership used by a manager. There are two sharply contrasting styles that will be broken down into smaller subsets later:

- Autocratic.
- Permissive.

Each style has its own characteristics:

Autocratic: Leader makes all decisions unilaterally.

Permissive: Leader permits subordinates to take part in decision making and also gives them a considerable degree of autonomy in completing routine work activities.

Combining these categories with democratic (subordinates are allowed to participate in decision making) and directive (subordinates are told exactly how to do their jobs) styles give us four distinct ways to manage:

1. *Directive democrat:* Makes decisions participatively; closely supervises subordinates.
2. *Directive autocrat:* Makes decisions unilaterally; closely supervises subordinates.
3. *Permissive democrat:* Makes decisions participatively; gives subordinates latitude in carrying out their work.
4. *Permissive autocrat:* Makes decisions unilaterally; gives subordinates latitude in carrying out their work.

Situational leadership

Managers must also adjust their styles according to the situation that they are presented with. Below are four quadrants of situational leadership that depend on the amount of support and guidance needed:

1. *Telling:* Works best when employees are neither willing nor able to do the job (high need of support and high need of guidance).
2. *Delegating:* Works best when the employees are willing to do the job and know how to go about it (low need of support and low need of guidance).
3. *Participating:* Works best when employees have the ability to do the job, but need a high amount of support (low need of guidance but high need of support).

4. ***Selling:*** Works best when employees are willing to do the job, but don't know how to do it (low need of support but high need of guidance).

The different styles depend on the situation and the relationship behaviour (amount of support required) and task behaviour (amount of guidance required).

Training skills

Learning outcomes

The intended learning outcomes are that the student will be able to:

CS2.1 identify the principles of systematic training and the sequence of its application from needs identification to evaluation

CS2.2 design and present a training programme

CS2.3 describe the effective planning, design and running of presentations

Contents

This page is intentionally blank

CS2.1 - Training principles

THE PRINCIPLES OF SYSTEMATIC TRAINING

Training is defined by the Department of Employment as the "systematic development of attitude, knowledge and skill patterns required by an individual to perform adequately a given task of job". Given the enormous range, number and level of jobs in industry and commerce, it is easy to see how complex "training" can be and how it overlaps with "education".

THE STAGES IN SYSTEMATIC TRAINING

The term "systematic" immediately distinguishes such training from the traditional apprenticeship consisting of "sitting by Nellie", i.e. learning through listening and observation. Systematic training makes full use of skills available in training staff. It attracts recruits, achieves the target of an experienced operator's skill in one half to one third of the traditional time, and creates confidence in the minds of trainees. It guarantees better safety performance and morale, and results in greater earnings and productivity, ease of mind, a sense of security and contentment at work. Furthermore, it excludes misfits and diminishes unrest, whilst facilitating the understanding and acceptance of change.

Systematic training implies the following:

- The presence of a trained and competent instructor working with suitable trainees.
- Defined training objectives.
- A content of knowledge broken down into sequential units which can be readily assimilated.
- A content of skill analysed by elements.
- A clear and orderly training programme.
- An appropriate place in which to learn.
- Suitable equipment and visual aids.
- Sufficient time to attain a desired standard of knowledge and competence, with frequent testing to ensure trainees understand and know what has to be learned.

Any process of systematic training must take place in a number of clearly defined stages. These stages are:

- Identification of training needs.
- Development of the training plan and programme.
- Implementation of the training programme.
- Evaluation of the results.

Identifying training needs

The analysis of training needs, particularly in relation to health and safety, is an important task in any organisation.

A list of the employees at all levels needs to be made and their roles and responsibilities written alongside. The training requirements to allow each person to work safely and to fulfil their responsibilities should be devised and added to the document. This can then have priorities and timescales attached.

Employees can also highlight their own training needs according to their self-development objectives. For example, someone moving more into a health and safety advisory role may feel they need to move from Level 3 to Level 4 and ask for that to be planned in for the coming year.

Examples of training needs:

- Newly appointed fire marshals will need training on their responsibilities, which could include the use of fire extinguishers.
- Newly appointed first aiders will need first aid training at an approved centre.
- The directors of the company may attend "Safety for Senior Executives" or "Directing Safely".
- Operatives will need to be trained on the "Permit to Work" system.
- Managers could attend "Managing Safely".

Designing training

Defining learning objectives in terms of levels of skill and knowledge required

When designing training courses, the objectives, which are the levels of skill and knowledge required, should be kept in mind. For example, the fire marshals need to be able to:

- Understand their role.
- Understand the principles of combustion.
- Know how smoke inhalation and flames and heat affect the human body.
- Use fire extinguishers, etc.

Referring to the different levels of training is useful, e.g. Levels 2, 3 and 4, where the standards to be achieved can be clearly seen. People in the organisation can attain the level suitable for their role.

Carrying out training

The training should be devised according to the subject matter, the training objectives and the trainees' existing skills and knowledge. The type of training can vary according to needs; for example, classroom based "chalk and talk", demonstrations, role-play, the use of videos and DVDs.

Demonstration and practice are probably the best methods to teach the skills in the use of fire extinguishers, while a talk followed by discussion may be best for training people in their legal duties.

The person carrying out the training must be competent in the subject matter and be able to get the subject across in an interesting way. The training venue should be comfortable, not too warm, well ventilated, have good acoustics, with the seating arranged so everyone has a good view of the trainer and no-one can "hide".

Evaluating training

An evaluation form should be used at the end of the course for the trainees to fill in. The feedback can be analysed in order to improve the training course.

Further evaluation can be carried out at a later date by observing working patterns to see if the training has had the desired effect. Accident rates can also be used to evaluate training. If the training was on reporting accidents, the rates may go up if the training was good, and if the training was on working safely, the rates may go down if the training was good.

Where the training programme does not meet the desired objectives, it can be adjusted accordingly and further evaluated.

Evaluation can also take the form of assessment, where the newly acquired skills and knowledge can be tested to see if the training has achieved the objectives.

CS2.2 - Presentation skills

HOW TO PLAN A PRESENTATION

Planning a presentation requires the following issues to be considered:

- Objectives.
- Timescales: number of days, hours of training, breaks.
- Method of presentation: lecture, demonstration, practical, etc.
- Handouts, including pen and paper.
- Suitable training room.
- Necessary equipment: PowerPoint presentation, flipchart, other visual aids and demonstration kit.
- Competent trainer(s).
- Means of evaluating the training.

The first consideration is what the objectives of the training are. Everything else follows from this.

It is useful for the trainer to have the programme prepared for each trainee and to have a lesson plan so he can see exactly what he has to do at each stage of the day. A little bit of time built in for flexibility is always useful in case there are a few problems and parts of the training have to be reiterated.

THE DESIGN OF AN EFFECTIVE PROGRAMME

An effective programme will have enough time to achieve the objectives and have regular breaks built in, as people find it difficult to concentrate for long periods. The learning objectives should be clearly set out.

It is also effective to have a variety of teaching methods within the programme, e.g. some talk, some discussion, group work, use of visual aids, demonstration, group or individual presentations and question and answer sessions. The variety will encourage participation and help prevent boredom. Bored trainees switch off and do not learn.

An effective programme will follow through in a logical way and build up on the knowledge and skills. It is also useful to have an assessment or exam at the end to see if the trainees can demonstrate the skills and knowledge that were set out in the learning objectives.

EFFECTIVE COMMUNICATION

Use of voice

The presenter's voice needs to be projected according to the number of trainees and the size of the room. In some cases this may require a microphone. For the most part, the trainer raising or lowering his voice according to the situation is sufficient. Quietly spoken trainers or those who always shout will have difficulty holding the attention of the group.

A monotone voice becomes boring after a short while no matter how interesting the topic. The presenter should vary the pitch of his voice and bring some enthusiasm into it. Changes of accent are often used for comic effect, but care should be taken so as not to offend the trainees.

Hesitant speech and speech filled with linguistic tics (umm, eh) can be very distracting. These usually occur when the presenter is nervous or is unsure of the subject matter.

The most effective communication is when the voice is the right loudness, rises and falls as appropriate and sounds enthusiastic and confident.

Use of body language

Body language can assist communication or cause a distraction. Normally, we are not aware of our body language, but the presenter needs to be aware that he does not communicate aggression, boredom or arrogance to the trainees. The presenter turning his back on the trainees to read something creates a distance between them as it breaks the continuity.

Walking up and down while talking is also very distracting.

A relaxed but confident stance is best; and the presenter should be aware that a difficult trainee or a difficult question could show its effect on his body language.

EFFECTIVE USE OF VISUAL AIDS

Visual aids are something that will visually increase teaching effectiveness. Not only do they add interest to a presentation but by engaging more than one of the senses they also facilitate listening and remembering. It is said that people remember 20% of what is heard, 30% of what is seen and 50% of what is seen and heard at the same time.

A certain willingness to experiment and ability to improvise are especially important where aids must be hand-made on a limited budget and with a restricted set of materials.

The most commonly available and more frequently used visual aids are: the flipchart and the overhead projector or a laptop and projector.

Flipchart

Advantages

- Can be used as a write-on board.
- Sheets can be prepared in advance.
- It is cheap.
- It is quick.
- No time required to erase information.
- If sheets are flipped over and not torn off, they are available for recapitulation and review.
- Also the flipchart is quite easily portable.

Disadvantages

- Pages have limited space.
- They can present a transport problem.
- Dramatic effects are greatly limited.
- Prepared drawings must be stored flat, otherwise they will curl.

Laptop and projector

Advantages

- Colourful visual aids may be prepared before session and a planned order created for presentation.
- Power Point presentations look professional.
- Slides can be animated.
- Easy to move backwards and forwards within the presentation.
- Amendments can be made quickly.
- Equipment is quite portable.
- Easy on the eye.

Disadvantages

- Equipment can be heavy to carry about.
- A screen on which to project is normally required.
- Electric power is needed.
- Light from the projector can be hard on the speaker's eyes.

Tips

- Rehearse in advance so that you know it works.
- Check the focus and clarity of the projector in advance.
- Switch off the projector when not in use, otherwise it will act as a distraction.

To summarise:

1. Keep visual aids **simple**

   - Use key words and phrases.
   - Do not crowd the layout.
   - Keep shapes and lines simple.
   - Use a few well chosen colours.

2. Make visual aids **bold**

   - They must be large enough to be seen easily by everyone.
   - And have a strong impact.

3. Ensure they are **clear**

   - Easy to understand.
   - Say the message you want.
   - Logical.
   - The main points stand out.

METHODS

Dealing with questions

The presenter needs to be confident in the subject matter and convey enthusiasm. Being competent in the subject is not about knowing everything, but being confident enough to say that you do not know the answer to a particular question, but you will find out. Pretending to know the answer and making something up will destroy your credibility when the answer is found to be wrong. In fact, it is a criminal offence to give false information and cause another individual to be in breach of the law. *(See also - 'Enforcement of health and safety law, HASAWA 1974 section 36' - in Element A7).*

Questions may be dealt with throughout the presentation, as they arise, or they may be dealt with at the end. The questions can be "parked" on the flipchart as a reminder. Questions throughout can be disruptive and spoil the flow of the presentation. On the other hand, the questioner's understanding of what follows might depend on the question being dealt with.

The presenter should never suggest that a question is silly. If the recipient does not understand something, then the presenter may not be effectively communicating the message and it is up to him to find another way to explain it.

Securing audience participation

Audience participation can vary from listening to taking part in discussions. A certain enthusiasm is required of the presenter, which will let the audience know that this is a topic that is worthy of communication. Many experienced presenters will say that the audience will participate if they are happy with the answer they get when they ask, "What's in it for me"?

The presenter should be confident, change his voice pitch so it is not monotone, occasionally bring up some controversial topics for discussion, bring some humour into it where appropriate and be wary of using stereotypical language and ideas. For example, referring to the "ladies" in the audience does not go down well with women, nor does suggesting that they do not understand technical matters.

It is important that the presenter does not mock any ideas or statements put forward by a member of the audience. Ideas may be challenged, but the person offering those ideas should be respected.

Checking understanding of principles presented

A question and answer slot is a useful way to check understanding on what has been presented, and it is good practice to allow time for this in the training programme. Asking the audience if they have any questions or asking questions of the audience are both viable methods.

Checking understanding can also be done by written questions with a written response. The response required can vary from a tick box for multi-choice to essay-style discussion answers.

The trainee doing a demonstration of carrying out the task can also check understanding. This is a useful method for training such as manual handling methods, forklift truck driving and setting up the workstation and display screen equipment.

Relevant Statutory Provisions

Content

Construction (Design and Management) Regulations (CDM) 2007

Revisions to the Construction (Design and Management) (CDM) Regulations (1994) (CDM 94) came into force on 6th April 2007.

Construction remains a disproportionately dangerous industry where improvements in health and safety are urgently needed. The improvements require significant and permanent changes in duty holder attitudes and behaviour. Since CDM 94 was introduced in 1995, concerns have been raised that their complexity, and the bureaucratic approach of many duty holders, frustrate the Regulations' underlying health and safety objectives. These views were supported by an industry-wide consultation in 2002, resulting in the Health and Safety Commission's (HSC) decision to revise the Regulations.

The new, simplified CDM Regulations revise and bring together the existing CDM 1994 and the Construction (Health Safety and Welfare) (CHSWR) Regulations 1996 into a single regulatory package. They are supported by an Approved Code of Practice (ACoP) and industry-approved guidance.

To give construction and design professionals time to plan and prepare for the regulatory changes, the ACoP was made available in February 2007, two months before the regulations came into force.

The new CDM regulations offer an opportunity for a step change in health and safety performance and will be used to re-emphasise the health, safety and broader business benefits of a well-managed and co-ordinated approach to the management of health and safety in construction.

Arrangement of regulations

Part 1 - Introduction

1.   Citation and commencement.
2.   Interpretation.
3.   Application.

Part 2 - General management duties applying to construction projects

4.   Competence.
5.   Co-operation.
6.   Co-ordination.
7.   General principles of prevention.
8.   Election by clients.
9.   The client's duty in relation to arrangements for managing projects.
10.   Client's duty in relation to information.
11.   Duties of designers.
12.   Designs prepared or modified outside Great Britain.
13   Duties of contractors.

Part 3 - Additional duties where project is notifiable

14.   Appointments by the client.
15.   Client's duty in relation to information.
16.   The client's duty in relation to the start of construction phase.
17.   The client's duty in relation to the health and safety file.
18.   Additional duties of designers.
19.   Additional duties of contractors.
20.   General duties of CDM co-ordinators.
21.   Notification of project by CDM co-ordinator.
22.   Duties of the principal contractor.
23.   Principal contractor's duties in relation to the construction phase plan.
24.   Principal contractor's duties in relation to co-operation and consultation with workers.

Part 4 - Duties relating to health and safety on construction sites

25.   Application of regulations 26-44.
26.   Safe places of work.
27.   Good order and site security.
28.   Stability of structures.
29.   Demolition or dismantling.
30.   Explosives.
31.   Excavations.
32.   Cofferdams and caissons.

33.   Reports of inspections.

34.   Energy distribution installations.

35.   Prevention of drowning.

36.   Traffic routes.

37.   Vehicles.

38.   Prevention of risk from fire etc.

39.   Emergency procedures.

40.   Emergency routes and exits.

41.   Fire detection and fire-fighting.

42.   Fresh air.

43.   Temperature and weather protection.

44.   Lighting.

Part 5 - General

45.   Civil liability.

46.   Enforcement in respect of fire.

47.   Transitional provision.

48.   Revocation and amendments.

SCHEDULES

Schedule 1 (regulation 21(1), (2) and (4)) - Particulars to be notified to the Executive

Schedule 2 (regulation 11, 16(l)(b)and 19(4)) - Welfare facilities

1.   Sanitary conveniences.

2.   Washing facilities.

3.   Drinking water.

4.   Changing rooms and lockers.

5.   Facilities for rest.

Schedule 3 (regulation 33(1)(b)) - Particulars to be included in a report of inspection

Schedule 4 (regulation 48(1)) - Revocation of instruments

Schedule 5 (regulation 48(2)) - Amendments

OUTLINE OF KEY POINTS - PART 2 - GENERAL MANAGEMENT DUTIES

Competence

4(1)   No person on whom these regulations place a duty shall:

    (a)   Appoint or engage a co-ordinator, designer, principal contractor or contractor unless he has taken reasonable steps to ensure that he is competent.

    (b)   Accept such appointment or engagement unless he is competent.

    (c)   Arrange for or instruct a worker to carry out or manage design or construction work unless he is -

        (i) Competent.

        (ii) Under the supervision of a competent person.

Co-operation

5(1)   Every person concerned in a project on whom a duty is placed by these regulations, including paragraph (2), shall:

    (a)   Co-operate with any other person concerned in any project involving construction work at the same or an adjoining site so far as is necessary to enable the latter to perform any duty or function under these regulations.

    (b)   Seek the co-operation of any other person concerned in any project involving construction work at the same or an adjoining site so far as is necessary to enable the former to perform any duty or function under these regulations.

(2)   Every person concerned in a project who is working under the control of another person shall report to him anything which he is aware is likely to endanger the health or safety of himself or others.

Co-ordination

6   All persons shall coordinate their activities with one another in a manner which ensures, so far as is reasonably practicable, the health and safety of persons affected by the work.

General principles of prevention

7   Every person on whom a duty is placed by these regulations in relation to the design, planning and preparation of a project shall take account of the general principles of prevention in the performance of those duties during all the stages of the project.

Election by clients

8.   If, in relation to a project, one or more clients elect in writing to be treated for the purposes of these regulations as the only clients, other clients who have agreed in writing to such election shall not be subject to any duty owed by a client under these regulations after such election and consent, save the duties in regulations 5(1)(a), 10(1) so far as it relates to information in his possession, and 12(1).

The client's arrangements for managing projects

9(1)   The client shall take reasonable steps to ensure that arrangements are made, and maintained throughout the project, for managing it which are suitable to ensure:

   (a)   That -

      (i) The construction work can be carried out; and

      (ii) Any structure to which the construction work relates, and which is designed for use as a place of work, can be
         used,

   Without risk to health or safety; and

   (b)   The welfare of the persons carrying out the construction work.

(2)   The arrangements referred to in paragraph (1) shall include:

   (a) The allocation of resources (including time) to:

      (i) The design of a structure;

      (ii) Planning and preparation for construction work; and

      (iii) The construction work itself,

   Which are, so far as the client in question can reasonably determine, adequate; and

(b)   Arrangements for:

   (i) Review and revision of the arrangements;

   (ii) Review of the suitability and compatibility of designs and for any modification;

   (iii) Ensuring that persons arc appointed under regulation 8 or engaged as designers or contractors in a suitable sequence
      and in good time;

   (iv)The planning for and monitoring of construction work; (v) ensuring that the duties in regulations 5 and 16 are performed;
      and

   (vi) Communication.

Client's duty in relation to information

10(1)   The client shall ensure that the persons specified in regulation 13(l)(f)(i) to (iii) are promptly provided by the co-ordinator with all the information in the client's possession, or prepared by the co-ordinator, or which is reasonably obtainable (or with such of the information as is relevant to the person to whom the co-ordinator provides it), including:

   (a)   Any such information in a health and safety file;

   (b)   Any such further information about or affecting the site or the construction work;

   (c)   Information provided by a designer under regulation 14(5);

   (d)   The minimum notice which will be allowed to the principal contractor, and the contractors directly appointed by the client, for planning and preparation for construction work, which is relevant to the purposes specified in paragraph (2).

(2)   The purposes referred to in paragraph (1) are:

   (a)   To secure so far as is reasonably practicable the health, safety of persons engaged in the construction work and the health and safety of persons liable to be affected by the way in which it is carried out;

   (b)   Without prejudice to sub-paragraph (a), to assist the persons to whom information is provided under this regulation

      (i) To perform their duties and functions under these regulations; and

      (ii) To determine the adequacy of the resources referred to in regulation 7(2) to be allocated by them.

Duties of designers

11 No designer shall commence work in relation to a project unless any client for the project is aware of his duties under these regulations.

Every designer shall in preparing or modifying a design which may be used in construction work in Great Britain avoid foreseeable risks to the health and safety of any person liable to be affected by such construction work;

In discharging these duties, the designer shall -

■ Eliminate hazards which may give rise to risks.
■ Reduce risks from any remaining hazards, and in so doing shall give collective measures priority over individual measures.

In designing any structure for use as a workplace the designer shall take account of the provisions of the Workplace (Health, Safety and Welfare) Regulations 1992 which relate to the design of, and materials used in, the structure.

The designer shall take all reasonable steps to provide with his design sufficient information about aspects of the design of the structure or its construction or maintenance as will adequately assist -

■ Clients.
■ Other designers.
■ Contractors.

to comply with their duties under these Regulations.

Designs prepared or modified outside Great Britain

12. Where a design is prepared or modified outside Great Britain for use in construction work to which these Regulations apply:

(a) The person who commissions it, if he is established within Great Britain; or

(b) If that person is not so established, the client, shall ensure that Regulation 14 is complied with.

Duties of contractors

13 No contractor shall carry out construction work in relation to a project unless any client for the project is aware of his duties under these Regulations.

Every contractor shall ensure that any contractor whom he appoints or engages in his turn in connection with a project is informed of the minimum amount of time which will be allowed to him for planning and preparation before he begins construction work

Every contractor shall provide every worker carrying out the construction work under his control with any information and training which he needs for the particular work to be carried out safely and without risk to health.

No contractor shall begin work on a construction site unless reasonable steps have been taken to prevent access by unauthorised persons to that site.

OUTLINE OF KEY POINTS - PART 3 - ADDITIONAL DUTIES FOR NOTIFIABLE PROJECTS

Appointments by the client

14(1) The client shall:

(a) Appoint a person ("the co-ordinator"), before design work, or planning or other preparation for construction work is begun, to perform the functions specified in regulation 13(1); and

(b) Ensure so far as is reasonably practicable that the functions are performed.

(2) The client shall appoint one person (in these Regulations called "the principal contractor") as soon as is practicable after the client knows enough about the project to be able to select a suitable person for such appointment, to perform the functions specified in regulations 16 to 18.

(3) The client shall ensure that appointments under paragraphs (1) and (2) are changed or renewed as necessary to ensure that there are at all times until the end of the construction phase -

(a) A co-ordinator; and

(b) A principal contractor, filling them.

(4) The client shall:

(a) Be deemed for the purposes of these Regulations, save paragraphs (1) and (2) and regulations 14(l)(b) and 19(1)(b), to have been appointed as the co-ordinator or principal contractor for any period for which no person (including himself) has been so appointed; and

(b) Accordingly be subject to the duty imposed by regulation 13(2) on a co-ordinator or, as the case may be, the duties imposed by regulations 16 to 18 on a principal contractor.

(5) Any reference in this regulation to appointment is to appointment in writing.

Client's duty in relation to information where a project is notifiable

15.   Where the project is notifiable, the client shall provide the CDM co-ordinator with pre-construction information consisting of -

- Any information about or affecting the site or the construction work.
- Any information concerning the proposed use of the structure as a workplace.
- The minimum amount of time before the construction phase which will be allowed to the contractors appointed by the client for planning and preparation for construction work.
- Any information in any existing health and safety file.

The client's duty in relation to the start of construction phase

16.   The client shall ensure that the construction phase does not start unless:

(a)   The principal contractor has prepared a construction phase plan which is sufficient to enable the construction work to start without undue risk to health or safety; and

(b)   The requirements of Schedule 2 are complied with.

The client's duty in relation to the health and safety file

17(1)   The client shall ensure that the co-ordinator is provided with all the health and safety information likely to be needed during any subsequent works for inclusion in a record ("the health and safety file").

(1)   Where a single health and safety file relates to more than one project, site or structure, or where it includes other related information the client shall ensure that the information relating to each site or structure can be easily identified.

(2)   The client shall take reasonable steps to ensure that after the construction phase the information in the health and safety file:

(a)   Is kept available for inspection by any person who may need it to comply with the relevant statutory provisions; and

(b)   Is revised as often as may be appropriate to incorporate any relevant new information, including information specified in regulation 4(9)(c) of the Control of Asbestos at Work Regulations 2002(d) *(see S.I. 2002/2675.)*

(3)   It shall be sufficient compliance with paragraph (3)(a) by a client who disposes of his entire interest in the site if he delivers the health and safety file to the person who acquires his interest in it and ensures that he is aware of the nature and purpose of the file.

Additional duties of designers

18(1)   No designer shall commence work in relation to a project unless:

(a)   The client is aware of his duties under these Regulations;

(b)   A co-ordinator has been appointed for the project; and

(c)   Notice of the project has been given to the Executive under regulation 9.

(2)   The duties in paragraphs (3) and (4) shall be performed so far as is reasonably practicable, taking due account of other relevant design considerations.

(3)   Every designer shall in preparing or modifying a design which may be used in construction work in the United Kingdom avoid risks to the health and safety of any person:

(a)   Carrying out construction work;

(b)   Cleaning or maintaining the permanent fixtures and fittings of a structure;

(c)   Using a structure designed as a place of work; or

(d)   Liable to be affected by such construction work.

(4)   In discharging the duty in paragraph (3), the designer shall:

(a)   Eliminate hazards which may give rise to risks; and

(b)   Reduce risks from any remaining hazards, and in doing so shall give collective measures priority over individual measures.

(5)   The designer shall provide with the design sufficient information about aspects of the design of a structure or its construction or maintenance as will adequately assist:

(a)   Other designers to comply with their duties under this regulation;

(b)   Contractors to comply with their duties under regulation 19.

Additional duties of contractors

19   *Where a project is notifiable,* no contractor shall carry out construction work in relation to the project unless -

- He has been provided with the names of the CDM co-ordinator and principal contractor.
- He has been given access to such part of the construction phase plan as is relevant to the work to be performed by him, containing sufficient detail in relation to such work.
- Notice of the project has been given to the Executive.

Every contractor shall -

- Provide the principal contractor with any information (including any relevant part of any risk assessment in his possession or control) which -
- Might affect the health or safety of any person carrying out the construction work or of any person who may be affected by it.
- Might justify a review of the construction phase plan.
- Which has been identified for inclusion in the health and safety file in pursuance of regulation 22(1)(j).
- Identify any contractor whom he appoints or engages in his turn in connection with the project to the principal contractor.
- Comply with -
- Any directions of the principal contractor given to him under regulation 22(1)(e).
- Any site rules.
- Provide the principal contractor with the information in relation to any death, injury, condition or dangerous occurrence which the contractor is required to notify or report under the Reporting of Injuries, Diseases and Dangerous Occurrences Regulations 1995.

Every contractor shall -

- Take all reasonable steps to ensure that the construction work is carried out in accordance with the construction phase plan.
- Notify the principal contractor of any significant finding which requires the construction phase plan to be altered or added to.

General duties of CDM co-ordinators

20(1) The functions of a co-ordinator, referred to in regulation 8(I)(a), are to:

(a) Advise and assist the client in undertaking the measures he needs to take to comply with these Regulations (including in particular, in assisting the client in complying with regulations 9 and 16);

(b) Identify and extract the information specified in regulation 10;

(c) Advise on the suitability and compatibility of designs and on any need for modification;

(d) Co-ordinate design work, planning and other preparation;

(e) Liaise with the principal contractor in relation to any design or change to a design requiring a review of the construction phase plan, during the construction phase;

(f) Promptly provide, in a convenient form, to:

(i) Every person designing the structure;

(ii) The principal contractor; and

(iii) Every contractor who has been or is likely to be appointed by the client, the information specified in regulation 10 (or such of it as is relevant to him);

(g) Prepare, where none exists, and otherwise review and update the health and safety file;

(h) At the end of the construction phase, pass the health and safety file to the client.

(2) A co-ordinator shall so far as is reasonably practicable perform any function specified in paragraph (1) for which he is appointed.

Notification of the project by the CDM co-ordinator

21 The CDM co-ordinator shall as soon as is practicable after his appointment ensure that notice is given to the Executive containing such of the particulars specified in Schedule 1 as are available.

Duties of the principal contractor

22 The principal contractor for a project shall -

- Plan, manage and monitor the construction phase in a way which ensures that, so far as is reasonably practicable, it is carried out without risks to health or safety, including facilitating -
- (i) Co-operation and co-ordination between persons concerned in the project in pursuance of regulations 5 and 6; and
- (ii) The application of the general principles of prevention in pursuance of regulation 7.
- Liaise with the CDM co-ordinator in performing his duties in regulation 20(2)(d) during the construction phase in relation to any design or change to a design.
- Ensure that sufficient welfare facilities are provided.
- Draw up rules which are appropriate to the construction site and the activities on it.
- Give reasonable directions to any contractor.
- Ensure that every contractor is informed of the minimum amount of time which will be allowed to him.
- Consult a contractor before finalising such part of the construction phase plan as is relevant to the work to be performed by him.
- Ensure that every contractor is given, access to such part of the construction phase plan as is relevant to the work to be performed by him.
- Ensure that every contractor is given, such further information as he needs to carry out the work to be performed by him without risk.

- Identify to each contractor the information relating to the contractor's activity which is likely to be required by the CDM co-ordinator for inclusion in the health and safety file.
- Ensure that the particulars required to be in the notice are displayed in a readable condition in a position where they can be read by any worker.
- Take reasonable steps to prevent access by unauthorised persons to the construction site.

The principal contractor shall take all reasonable steps to ensure that every worker carrying out the construction work is provided with -

- A suitable site induction.
- Any further information and training which he needs for the particular work to be carried out without undue risk to health or safety.

The principal contractor's duty in relation to the construction phase plan

The principal contractor shall -

- Prepare a construction phase plan.
- Update, review, revise and refine the construction phase plan.
- Arrange for the construction phase plan to be implemented in a way which will ensure so far as is reasonably practicable the health and safety of all persons carrying out construction work and all persons who may be affected by the work.

The principal contractor's duty in relation to co-operation and consultation with workers

The principal contractor shall -

- Consult those workers or their representatives on matters connected with the project which may affect their health, safety or welfare.
- Ensure that such workers or their representatives can inspect and take copies of any information except any information
    - The disclosure of which would be against the interests of national security.
    - Which he could not disclose without contravening a prohibition imposed by or under an enactment.
    - Relating specifically to an individual, unless he has consented to its being disclosed.
    - The disclosure of which would, for reasons other than its effect on health, safety or welfare at work, cause substantial injury to his undertaking or, where the information was supplied to him by some other person, to the undertaking of that other person.
    - Obtained by him for the purpose of bringing, prosecuting or defending any legal proceedings.

Principal contractor's duties in relation to the construction phase plan

23(1)   The principal contractor shall

(a)   Before the start of the construction phase, prepare a sufficient health and safety plan to allow the construction phase to start, so far as is reasonably practicable, without risk to health and safety

(b)   Review, update, revise and refine the plan as necessary

(c)   Arrange for the construction phase to be implemented in such a way as to ensure, so far as is reasonably practicable, the health and safety of people carrying out the construction work

(2)   Take reasonable steps to ensure that the construction phase plan identifies all the risks arising from the construction phase.

Principal contractor's duties in relation to co-operation and consultation with workers

24   The principal contractor shall

(a)   Make and maintain arrangements to ensure that workers co-operate in promoting and developing measures to ensure the health, safety and welfare of workers.

(b)   Consult with workers or their representatives in good time on matters that may affect their health, safety or welfare.

(c)   Ensure that relevant information is available to workers except any information which is specified in the Health and Safety (Consultation with Employees) Regulations 1996.

OUTLINE OF KEY POINTS - PART 4 - DUTIES RELATING TO HEALTH AND SAFETY ON CONSTRUCTION SITES

A general duty to ensure a safe place of work and safe means of access to and from that place of work, this Regulation sets out a general requirement which applies to all construction work. It applies equally to places of work in the ground, at ground level and at height. In essence it requires that 'reasonably practicable' steps should be taken to provide for safety and to ensure risks to health are minimised. This means that action to be taken should be proportionate to the risk involved.

Work on structures (regulations 28, 29 and 30)

- Prevent accidental collapse of new or existing structures or those under construction.
- Make sure any dismantling or demolition of any structure is planned and carried out in a safe manner under the supervision of a competent person.
- Only fire explosive charges after steps have been taken to ensure that no one is exposed to risk or injury from the explosion.

Every year there are structural collapses which have the potential to cause serious accidents. The CHSW 1996 set a high standard to prevent collapses which involves taking into account the hazard during the planning stage. Demolition or dismantling are recognised as high risk activities. In any cases where this work presents a risk of danger to anyone, it should be planned and carried out under the direct supervision of a competent person.

Excavations, cofferdams and caissons (regulations 31 and 32)

■ Prevent collapse of ground both in and above excavations.
■ Identify and prevent risk from underground cables and other services.
■ Ensure cofferdams and caissons are properly designed, constructed and maintained.

From the outset, and as work progresses, any excavation which has the potential to collapse unless supported, should have suitable equipment immediately available to provide such support. Underground cables and services can also be a source of danger. These should be identified before work starts and positive action taken to prevent injury.

Energy distribution installations (regulation 34)

■ Where necessary to prevent danger, energy distribution installations shall be suitably located, checked and clearly indicated.
■ Where there is a risk from electric power cables: they shall be directed away from the area of risk; or the power shall be cut off; or if it is not reasonably practicable to comply with these requirements:
  • Suitable warning notices.
  • Barriers suitable for excluding work equipment which is not needed.
  • Where vehicles need to pass beneath the cables, suspended protections.
  • In either case, measures providing an equivalent level of safety, shall be provided or (in the case of measures) taken.
■ No construction work which is liable to create a risk to health or safety from an underground service, or from damage to or disturbance of it, shall be carried out unless suitable and sufficient steps (including any steps required by this regulation) have been taken to prevent such risk, so far as is reasonably practicable.

Prevention or avoidance of drowning (regulation 35)

■ Take steps to prevent people from falling into water or other liquid so far as is reasonably practicable.
■ Ensure that personal protective and rescue equipment is immediately available for use and maintained, in the event of a fall.
■ Make sure safe transport by water is under the control of a competent person.

Traffic routes and vehicles (regulations 36 and 37)

■ Ensure construction sites are organised so that pedestrians and vehicles can both move safely and without risks to health.
■ Make sure routes are suitable and sufficient for the people or vehicles using them.
■ Prevent or control the unintended movement of any vehicle.
■ Make arrangements for giving a warning of any possible dangerous movement, e.g. reversing vehicles.
■ Ensure safe operation of vehicles including prohibition of riding or remaining in unsafe positions.
■ Make sure doors and gates which could present danger, e.g. trapping risk of powered doors, have suitable safeguards.

Prevention and control of emergencies (regulations 38, 39, 40 and 41)

■ Prevent risk from fire, explosion, flooding and asphyxiation.
■ Provide emergency routes and exits.
■ Make arrangements for dealing with emergencies, including procedures for evacuating the site.
■ Where necessary, provide fire-fighting equipment, fire detectors and alarm systems.

These Regulations require the prevention of risk as far as it is reasonably practicable to achieve. However, there are times when emergencies do arise and planning is needed to ensure, for example, that emergency routes are provided and evacuation procedures are in place. These particular Regulations (as well as those on traffic routes, welfare, cleanliness and signing of sites) apply to construction work which is carried out on construction sites. However, the rest of the Regulations apply to all construction work.

The HSE continues to be responsible for inspection of means of escape and fire-fighting for most sites. However, fire authorities have enforcement responsibility in many premises which remain in normal use during construction work. This continues the sensible arrangement which ensures that the most appropriate advice is given.

Site-wide issues (regulations 27, 42, 43, and 44)

■ Ensure sufficient fresh or purified air is available at every workplace, and associated plant is capable of giving visible or audible warning of failure.
■ Make sure a reasonable working temperature is maintained at indoor work places during working hours.
■ Provide facilities for protection against adverse weather conditions.
■ Make sure suitable and sufficient emergency lighting is available.
■ Make sure suitable and sufficient lighting is available, including providing secondary lighting where there would be a risk to health or safety if primary or artificial lighting failed.
■ Keep construction sites in good order and in a reasonable state of cleanliness.
■ Ensure the perimeter of a construction site to which people, other than those working on the site could gain access, is marked by suitable signs so that its extent can be easily identified.

Reports of inspections (regulation 33)

■ The person who carries out an inspection under regulations 31 or 32 must:
  • Inform the person for whom the inspection was carried out if he is not satisfied that the construction work can be carried out safely at the place inspected.
  • Prepare a report which includes the particulars set out in Schedule 3 and within 24 hours of completion of the inspection, to which the report relates, provide a copy to the person for whom the inspection was carried out.
■ The inspector's employer, or the person under whose control he works, shall ensure that the inspector performs his duty.

- The person for whom the inspection was carried out must keep the report or a copy of it available for inspection at the site of the place of work until that work is completed, and after that for 3 months, and send out extracts from or copies of it as required by an inspector appointed under section 19 of The Health and Safety at Work etc. Act 1974.
- No further inspection reports required within a 7 day period.

OUTLINE OF KEY POINTS - SCHEDULE 2 (REGULATIONS 9(1)(B), 13(7) AND 22(1)(C)) WELFARE FACILITIES

SANITARY CONVENIENCES

1. Suitable and sufficient sanitary conveniences shall be provided or made available at readily accessible places. So far as is reasonably practicable, rooms containing sanitary conveniences shall be adequately ventilated and lit.

2. So far as is reasonably practicable, sanitary conveniences and the rooms containing them shall be kept in a clean and orderly condition.

3. Separate rooms containing sanitary conveniences shall be provided for men and women, except where and so far as each convenience is in a separate room the door of which is capable of being secured from the inside.

Washing facilities

4. Suitable and sufficient washing facilities, including showers if required by the nature of the work or for health reasons, shall so far as is reasonably practicable be provided or made available at readily accessible places.

5. Washing facilities shall be provided:

   (a) In the immediate vicinity of every sanitary convenience, whether or not provided elsewhere; and

   (b) In the vicinity of any changing rooms required by paragraph 15 whether or not provided elsewhere.

6. Washing facilities shall include:

   (a) A supply of clean hot and cold, or warm, water (which shall be running water so far as is reasonably practicable); and

   (b) Soap or other suitable means of cleaning; and

   (c) Towels or other suitable means of drying.

7. Rooms containing washing facilities shall be sufficiently ventilated and lit.

8. Washing facilities and the rooms containing them shall be kept in a clean and orderly condition.

9. Subject to paragraph 10 below, separate washing facilities shall be provided for men and women, except where and so far as they are provided in a room the door of which is capable of being secured from inside and the facilities in each such room arc intended to be used by only one person at a time.

10. Paragraph 9 above shall not apply to facilities which are provided for washing hands, forearms and face only.

Drinking water

11. An adequate supply of wholesome drinking water shall be provided or made available at readily accessible and suitable places.

12. Every supply of drinking water shall be conspicuously marked by an appropriate sign where necessary for reasons of health and safety.

13. Where a supply of drinking water is provided, there shall also be provided a sufficient number of suitable cups or other drinking vessels unless the supply of drinking water is in a jet from which persons can drink easily.

Changing rooms and lockers

14(1) Suitable and sufficient changing rooms shall be provided or made available at readily accessible places if:

   (a) A worker has to wear special clothing for the purposes of his work; and

   (b) He cannot, for reasons of health or propriety, be expected to change elsewhere, being separate rooms for, or separate use of rooms by, men and women where necessary for reasons of propriety.

(2) Changing rooms shall:

   (a) Be provided with seating;

   (b) Include, where necessary, facilities to enable a person to dry any such special clothing and his own clothing and personal effects.

(3) Suitable and sufficient facilities shall, where necessary, be provided or made available at readily accessible places to enable persons to lock away:

   (a) Any such special clothing which is not taken home;

   (b) Their own clothing which is not worn during working hours; and

(c)   Their personal effects.

Facilities for rest

15(1)   Suitable and sufficient rest rooms or rest areas shall be provided or made available at readily accessible places.

(1)   Rest rooms and rest areas shall:

     (a)   Include suitable arrangements to protect non-smokers from discomfort caused by tobacco smoke;

     (b)   Be equipped with an adequate number of tables and adequate seating with backs for the number of persons at work likely to use them at any one time;

     (c)   Where necessary, include suitable facilities for any person at work who is a pregnant woman or nursing mother to rest lying down;

     (d)   Include suitable arrangements to ensure that meals can be prepared and eaten; and

     (e)   Include the means for boiling water.

Control of Major Accident Hazard Regulations (COMAH) 1999

Law considered in context in Element A4.

Arrangement of Regulations

PART 1 - INTRODUCTION

1)   Citation and commencement.
2)   Interpretation.
3)   Application.

PART 2 - GENERAL

4)   General duty.
5)   Major accident prevention policy.
6)   Notifications.

PART 3 - SAFETY REPORTS

7)   Safety report.
8)   Review and revision of safety report.

PART 4 - EMERGENCY PLANS

9)   On-site emergency plan.
10)   Off-site emergency plan.
11)   Review and testing of emergency plans.
12)   Implementing emergency plans.
13)   Charge for preparation, review and testing of off-site emergency plan.

PART 5 - PROVISION OF INFORMATION BY OPERATOR

14)   Provision of information to the public.
15)   Provision of information to the competent authority.
16)   Provision of information to other establishments.

PART 6 - FUNCTIONS OF COMPETENT AUTHORITY

17)   Functions of competent authority in relation to the safety report.
18)   Prohibition of use.
19)   Inspections and investigations.
20)   Enforcement.
21)   Provision of information by competent authority.
22)   Fee payable by operator.

PART 7 - AMENDMENTS, REVOCATIONS, SAVINGS AND TRANSITIONAL PROVISIONS

23)   Amendments.
24)   Revocations and savings.
25)   Transitional provisions.

SCHEDULES

Schedule 1   Dangerous substances to which the regulations apply.

Schedule 2   Principles to be taken into account when preparing major accident prevention policy document.

Schedule 3   Information to be included in a notification.

Schedule 4   Purpose and Contents of Safety Reports.

Schedule 5   Emergency Plans.

Schedule 6   Information to be supplied to the public.

Schedule 7   Criteria for notification of a major accident to the European Commission and information to be notified.

Schedule 8   Provision of information by competent authority.

Outline of key points

The Control of Major Accident Hazards Regulations 1999 (COMAH) came into force on 1 April 1999. These Regulations implemented the Seveso II Directive (except for the land use planning requirements), and replaced the Control of Industrial Major Accident Hazards Regulations 1984 (CIMAH).

An Amendment Directive broadening Seveso II is planned for implementation by July 2005.

COMAH applies mainly to the chemical industry, but also to some storage activities, explosives and nuclear sites, and other industries where threshold quantities of dangerous substances identified in the Regulations are kept or used.

Their main aim of COMAH is to prevent and mitigate the effects of a major accident involving dangerous substances, such as chlorine, LPG, explosives and arsenic pentoxide which can cause serious damage/harm to people and/or the environment. COMAH treats risks to environment as seriously as those to people.

The main duty is to prepare a safety report which will include:

- A policy on how to prevent and mitigate major accidents.
- A management system for implementing that policy.
- An effective method for identifying any Major Accidents that may occur.
- Measures (safe plant and procedures) to prevent and mitigate major accidents.
- Information on safety precautions built into the plant when designed and constructed.
- Details of measures(fire fighting, relief systems, filters, etc) to limit the consequences of any accident.
- Information about the emergency plan for the site, this is used by the Local Authority for their off site plan.

Control of Major Accident Hazard Regulations 1999 (Amendment) Regulations 2005

Law considered in context in Element A4.

Arrangement of Regulations

1)   Citation and commencement.

2-19)   Amendment of the Control of Major Accident Hazards Regulations 1999.

Outline of key points

AMENDMENT OF THE CONTROL OF MAJOR ACCIDENT HAZARDS REGULATIONS 1999

1)   These Regulations may be cited as the Control of Major Accident Hazards (Amendment) Regulations 2005 and shall come into force on 30th June 2005.

2)   The Control of Major Accident Hazards Regulations 1999[4] shall be amended in accordance with the following provisions of these Regulations.

3)   In regulation 2(1) -

(a)   there shall be added to the definition of "the Directive" the words "as amended by Directive 2003/105/EC of the European Parliament and of the Council of 16 December 2003[5]";

(b)   for the definition of "notify" there shall be substituted -

"'notify' means notify -

(a) In writing, including in an email; or

(b) By such other means as the recipient may allow, and "notification" shall be construed accordingly.".

4)   (1) In regulation 3(3), for sub-paragraphs (c) and (d) there shall be substituted -

"(c) the exploration, extraction and processing of minerals in mines, quarries or by means of boreholes, except -

(i) Chemical and thermal processing operations; and

(ii) Storage relating to those operations, which involve dangerous substances; and

(d) Waste land-fill sites, except tailing ponds or dams and other operational tailings disposal facilities containing dangerous substances, in particular when any such facilities are used in connection with the chemical and thermal processing of minerals.".

(2) Regulation 3(4) shall be revoked.

5)   For paragraph (1) of regulation 5, there shall be substituted -

(1) Every operator shall without delay but at all events within 3 months after the establishment becomes subject to this regulation prepare, and thereafter keep, a document setting out his policy with respect to the prevention of major accidents (in these Regulations referred to as a "major accident prevention policy document").".

6)   (1) After paragraph (3) of regulation 6 there shall be inserted -

"(3A) Where paragraphs (1) to (3) do not apply, the operator of the establishment shall send to the competent authority a notification containing the information specified in Schedule 3 within 3 months after the establishment becomes subject to this regulation".

(2) In regulation 6(4)(b)(iii), after "authority", there shall be inserted "under this regulation".

(3) After regulation 6(4)(b) there shall be inserted -

"(ba) modification of the establishment or an installation which could have significant repercussions with respect to the prevention of major accidents;".

7)   After paragraph (10) of regulation 7 there shall be inserted -

" (10A) Where paragraphs (1) to (10) do not apply, the operator shall, subject to paragraph (12), without delay, but at all events within 1 year after the establishment becomes subject to this regulation, send to the competent authority a report which is sufficient for the purpose specified in Part 1 of Schedule 4 and comprising at least the information specified in Part 2 of that Schedule.".

8)   (1) For regulation 8(1) there shall be substituted -

" 8. - (1) Where a safety report has been sent to the competent authority the operator shall, subject to paragraph (3), review it -

(a) Whenever the operator makes a change to the safety management system (referred to in paragraph 1 of Part 1 of Schedule 4) which could have significant repercussions with respect to the prevention of major accidents or the limitation of consequences of major accidents to persons and the environment;

(b) Whenever such a review is necessary because of new facts or to take account of new technical knowledge about safety matters; and

(c) Fully at least every 5 years,

and where in consequence of that review it is necessary to revise the report, the operator shall do so forthwith and notify the competent authority of the details of such revision.".

(2) In regulation 8(2) -

(a) For "inform" there shall be substituted "notify";

(b) For "(1)(a)" there shall be substituted "(1)(c)".

(3) In regulation 8(3), for "(1)(a)" there shall be substituted "(1)(c)".

(4) In regulation 8(4)(b), for "inform" there shall be substituted "notify".

9)   In regulation 9(2), for sub-paragraph (c) there shall be substituted -

"(c) In the case of an establishment which has not started to operate, before it starts to operate;

(d) In any other case, without delay but at all events within 1 year after the establishment becomes subject to this regulation.".

10)   In regulation 9(3)(a), for "employed" there shall be substituted "working".

11)   In regulation 10(6), after "competent authority," there shall be inserted "the Agency,".

12)   There shall be added to regulation 11(1) "and, in the case of a review of an off-site emergency plan, shall involve consultation by the local authority of such members of the public as it considers appropriate".

13)   For paragraph (1) of regulation 14 there shall be substituted -

" 14. - (1) The operator of an establishment shall -

(a) Ensure that -

(i) Every person who is likely to be in an area referred to in paragraph (2); and

(ii) Every school, hospital or other establishment serving the public which is situated in such area, is supplied regularly and in the most appropriate form, without their having to request it, with information on safety measures at the establishment and on the requisite behaviour in the event of a major accident at the establishment; and

(b) Make that information permanently available to the public.".

14)   For Schedule 1 there shall be substituted the schedule in the Schedule to these Regulations.

15)   (1) In paragraph 4(a) of Schedule 2, for "The involvement of employees and, where appropriate, sub-contractors", there shall be substituted "The involvement of persons working in the establishment".

(2) For paragraph 4(e) of Schedule 2 there shall be substituted -

"(e) Planning for emergencies - adoption and implementation of procedures to -

(i) Identify foreseeable emergencies by systematic analysis;

(ii) Prepare, test and review emergency plans to respond to such emergencies; and

(iii) Provide specific training for all persons working in the establishment.".

16)   There shall be added to paragraph 5 of Schedule 3 "including, in relation to petroleum products listed in Part 2 of Schedule 1, the quantity falling within each of classes (a) to (c)".

17)   (1) Paragraph 2(a) of Part 2 of Schedule 4 shall be amended -

(a) By substituting for "meterological" the word "meteorological";

(b) By substituting for "geographical", where it secondly occurs, the word "geological".

(2) The following sub-paragraph shall be substituted for paragraph 4(b) of that Part -

"(b) Assessment of the extent and severity of the consequences of identified major accidents including maps, images or, as appropriate, equivalent descriptions, showing areas which are liable to be affected by such accidents arising from the establishment;".

(3) The following paragraph shall be added to that Part -

"6. The names of the relevant organisations involved in the drawing up of the report.".

18)   After paragraph 1(b) of Schedule 8 there shall be inserted -

"(ba) Notifications under regulation 8(2);".

19)   After paragraph 13 of Schedule 8 there shall be inserted -

"(13A) Where information in a safety report is excluded from the register, the operator shall within 3 months after being notified of its exclusion, or such longer period as the competent authority may allow, send to the competent authority a safety report which omits that information.".

Health and Safety (Consultation with Employees) Regulations (HSCER) 1996

Law considered in context in Element A5.

Arrangement of Regulations

1)   Citation, extent and commencement.

2)   Interpretation.

3)   Duty of employer to consult.

4)   Persons to be consulted.

5)   Duty of employer to provide information.

6)   Functions of representatives of employee safety.

7)   Training, time off and facilities for representatives of employee safety and time off for candidates.

8)   Amendment of the Employment Rights Act 1996.

9)   Exclusion of civil liability.

10)   Application of health and safety legislation.

11)   Application to the Crown and armed forces.

12)   Disapplication to sea-going ships.

13)   Amendment of the 1977 Regulations.

Outline of key points

1)   The HSCER come into force on 1 October 1996 and are made under the European Communities Act 1972.

2)   "Employees" do not include persons employed in domestic service in private households. Workplaces are defined as "any place where the employee is likely to work, or which he is likely to frequent in the course of his employment or incidentally to it."

3)   Where there are employees not represented by the Safety Representatives and Safety Committee Regulations (SRSCR), the employer shall consult those employees in good time on matters relating to their health & safety at work. In particular they must be consulted on:

■   The introduction of any new measures which may affect their safety and health.

■   Arrangements made by the employer for appointing or nominating competent persons in accordance with regs. 6(1) and 7(1) of the Management of Health and Safety at Work Regs 1999 (MHSWR).

■   Any safety information the employer is legally obliged to provide to workers.

■   The planning and organisation of any health and safety training required under particular health and safety laws.

■   The health and safety consequences for employees of the introduction of new technologies into the workplace.

4)   Employers can consult either directly with employees or, in respect of any group of employees, one or more elected representatives of that group. These are referred to as "representatives of employee safety" (RES). If the latter option is chosen, then employers must tell the employees the name of the representative and the group he/she represents. An employer which has been consulting a representative may choose to consult the whole workforce. However, the employer must inform the employees and the representatives of that fact.

5)   If the employer consults employees directly then it must make available such information, within the employers' knowledge, as is necessary to enable them to participate fully and effectively in the consultation. If a representative is consulted, then the employer must make available all necessary information to enable them to carry out their functions, and of any record made under the Reporting of Injuries, Diseases and Dangerous Occurrences Regs 1995 which relates to the represented group of employees.

6)   Representatives of employee safety have the following functions:

■   To make representations to the employer on potential hazards and dangerous occurrences at the workplace which affect, or could affect the represented employees.

■   Make representations to the employer on general matters of health and safety.

- To represent the employees in workplace consultations with HSE or local authority inspectors.

7) Representatives of employee safety must be given reasonable training in order to carry out their duties. Employers must meet the costs of the training and any travel and subsistence. They must also permit the representatives to take time off with pay during working hours in order for them to carry out their functions. Time off shall also be given, with pay, where this is required for any person standing as a candidate for election as a representative. Employers must also provide suitable facilities for the representatives to carry out their duties.

8) The Employment Rights Act 1996, which gives protection against unfair dismissal or discrimination on grounds of health and safety, is amended to protect representatives of employee safety and candidates for their election.

9) A breach of the HSCER does not confer any right of action in any civil proceedings.

10) Ensures that certain provisions of health and safety legislation (including enforcement provisions) operate in respect of the HSCER. The Regulations are made under the European Communities Act 1972. Enforcement is by the enforcing authorities appointed under the Health & Safety at Work Act 1974.

11) The HSCER will apply in respect of the armed forces. However, the representatives of employee safety will be appointed by the employer, rather than elected. Furthermore, representatives in the armed forces will not be entitled to time off with pay under reg.7.

12) The HSCER do not apply to the master or crew of a seagoing ship.

13) The SRSCR are amended so that they now include employees of coal mines.

Health and Safety at Work etc. Act (HASAWA) 1974

Law considered in context in:
Element A1 (for Section 2); and
Element A5 (for Sections 2, 3 and 4).

Arrangement of Regulations

PRELIMINARY

1) Preliminary.

GENERAL DUTIES

2) General duties of employers to the employees.

3) General duties of employers and self-employed to persons other than their employees.

4) General duties of persons concerned with premises to persons other than their employees.

5) [Repealed].

6) General duties of manufacturers etc. as regards articles and substances for use at work.

7) General duties of employees at work.

8) Duty not to interfere with or misuse things provided pursuant to certain provisions.

9) Duty not to charge employees for things done or provided pursuant to certain specific requirements.

THE HEALTH AND SAFETY COMMISSION AND THE HEALTH AND SAFETY EXECUTIVE

10) Establishment of the Commission and the Executive.

11) General functions of the Commission and the Executive.

12) Control of the Commission by the Secretary of State.

13) Other powers of the Commission.

14) Power of the Commission to direct investigations and Inquiries.

HEALTH AND SAFETY REGULATIONS AND APPROVED CODES OF PRACTICE

15) Health and safety regulations.

16) Approval of codes of practice by the Commission.

17) Use of approved codes of practice in criminal proceedings.

ENFORCEMENT

18) Authorities responsible for enforcement of the relevant statutory provisions.

19) Appointment of inspectors.

20) Powers of inspectors.

21) Improvement notices.

22) Prohibition notices.

23) Provisions supplementary toss. 21 and 22.

24) Appeal against improvement or prohibition notice.

25) Power to deal with cause of imminent danger.

26) Power of enforcing authorities to indemnify their inspectors.

OBTAINING AND DISCLOSURE OF INFORMATION

27) Obtaining of information by the Commission, the Executive, enforcing authorities etc.
28) Restrictions on disclosure of information.

SPECIAL PROVISIONS RELATING TO AGRICULTURE

29-32) [repealed].

PROVISIONS AS TO OFFENCES

33) Offences.
34) Extension of time for bringing summary proceedings.
35) Venue.
36) Offences due to fault of other person.
37) Offences by bodies corporate.
38) Restriction on institution of proceedings in England and Wales.
39) Prosecutions by inspectors.
40) Onus of proving limits of what is practicable etc.
41) Evidence.
42) Power of court to order cause of offence to be remedied or, in certain cases, forfeiture.

FINANCIAL PROVISION

43) Financial provisions.

MISCELLANEOUS AND SUPPLEMENTARY

44) Appeals in connection with licensing provisions in the relevant statutory provisions.
45) Default powers.
46) Service of notices.
47) Civil liability.
48) Application to Crown.
49) Adaptation of enactments to metric units or appropriate metric units.
50) Regulations under the relevant statutory provisions.
51) Exclusion of application to domestic employment.
52) Meaning of work and at work.
53) General interpretation of Part I.
54) Application of Part I to Isles of Scilly.

Outline of key points

AIMS

1) To protect people.
2) To protect the public from risks which may arise from work activities.

THE MAIN PROVISIONS - SECTION 1

a) Securing the health, safety and welfare of people at work.
b) Protecting others against risks arising from workplace activities.
c) Controlling the obtaining, keeping, and use of explosive and highly flammable substances.
d) Controlling emissions into the atmosphere of noxious or offensive substances.

Duties imposed on:

a) The employer.
b) The self employed.
c) Employees.
d) Contractors and subcontractors.
e) Designers, manufacturers, suppliers, importers and installers.
f) Specialists - architects, surveyors, engineers, personnel managers, health and safety specialists, and many more.

EMPLOYER'S DUTIES - [TO EMPLOYEES]

Section 2(1)

To ensure, so far as *reasonably practicable*, the health, safety and welfare at work of employees.

Section 2(2)

Ensuring health, safety and welfare at work through:

a)   Safe plant and systems of work e.g. provision of guards on machines.

b)   Safe use, handling, storage and transport of goods and materials e.g. good manual handling of boxes.

c)   Provision of information, instruction, training and supervision e.g. provision of induction training.

d)   Safe place of work including means of access and egress e.g. aisles kept clear.

e)   Safe and healthy working environment e.g. good lighting.

Further duties are placed on the employer by:

Section 2(3)

Prepare and keep up to date a written safety policy supported by information on the organisation and arrangements for carrying out the policy. The safety policy has to be brought to the notice of employees. If there are fewer than five employees, this section does not apply.

Section 2(4)

Recognised Trade Unions have the right to appoint safety representatives to represent the employees in consultations with the employer about health and safety matters.

Section 2(6)

Employers must consult with any safety representatives appointed by recognised Trade Unions.

Section 2(7)

To establish a safety committee if requested in writing by two or more safety representatives.

EMPLOYER'S DUTIES - [TO PERSONS NOT HIS EMPLOYEES]

Section 3

a)   Not to expose them to risk to their heath and safety e.g. contractor work barriered off.

b)   To give information about risks which may affect them e.g. location induction for contractors.

SELF EMPLOYED DUTIES

Section 3

a)   Not to expose themselves to risks to their health and safety e.g. wear personal protection.

b)   Not to expose other persons to risks to their health and safety e.g. keep shared work area tidy.

Some of the practical steps that an organisation might take in order to ensure the safety of visitors to its premises are:

- Identify visitors by signing in, badges etc.
- Provide information regarding the risks present and the site rules and procedures to be followed, particularly in emergencies.
- Provide escorts to supervise visitors throughout the site.
- Restrict access to certain areas.

PEOPLE IN CONTROL OF PREMISES

Section 4

This section places duties on anyone who has control to any extent of non-domestic premises used by people who are not their employees. The duty extends to the provision of safe premises, plant and substances, e.g. maintenance of a boiler in rented out property.

MANUFACTURERS, DESIGNERS, SUPPLIERS, IMPORTERS, INSTALLERS

Section 6

This section places specific duties on those who can ensure that articles and substances are as safe and without risks as is reasonably practicable. The section covers:

- Safe design, installation and testing of equipment (including fairground equipment).
- Safe substances tested for risks.
- Provision of information on safe use and conditions essential to health and safety.
- Research to minimise risks.

EMPLOYEES' DUTIES

Section 7

a)   To take reasonable care for themselves and others that may be affected by their acts / omissions e.g. wear eye protection, not obstruct a fire exit.

b)   To co-operate with the employer or other to enable them to carry out their duty and/or statutory requirements e.g. report hazards or defects in controls, attend training, provide medical samples.

Additional duties created by the Management of Health and Safety at Work

Regulations employees' duties:

- Every employee shall use any equipment, material or substance provided to them in accordance with any training and instruction.

- Every employee shall inform (via supervisory staff) their employer of any (a) risk situation or (b) shortcoming in the employer's protection arrangements.

OTHER DUTIES

Section 8

No person to interfere with or misuse anything provided to secure health and safety - e.g. wedge fire door open, remove first aid equipment without authority, breach lock off systems.

Section 9

Employees cannot be charged for anything done or provided to comply with a specific legal obligation e.g. personal protective equipment, health surveillance or welfare facilities.

OFFENCES COMMITTED BY OTHER PERSONS

Section 36

- Where the commission by any person of the breach of legislation is due to the act or default of some other person, that other person shall be guilty of the offence and may be charged with and convicted of the offence whether or not proceedings are taken against the first mentioned person.
- Case law indicates that 'other person' refers to persons lower down the corporate tree than mentioned in section 37, e.g. middle managers, safety advisors, training officers; and may extend to people working on contract e.g. architects, consultants or a planning supervisor.

OFFENCES COMMITTED BY THE BODY CORPORATE

Section 37

- Where there has been a breach of legislation on the part of a body corporate (limited company or local authority) and the offence can be proved to have been committed with the consent or connivance of or to be attributable to any neglect on the part of any director, manager, secretary or similar officer of the body corporate, he, as well as the body corporate, can be found guilty and punished accordingly.

ONUS OF PROOF

Section 40

In any proceedings for an offence under any of the relevant statutory involving a failure to comply with a duty or requirement:

- To do something so far as is practicable.
- To do something so far as is reasonably practicable.

it shall be for the accused to prove that the requirements were met rather than for the prosecution to prove that the requirements were not met.

Health and Safety Information for Employees Regulations (IER) 1989

Law considered in context in Element A5.

Arrangement of Regulations

1) Citation and commencement.
2) Interpretation and application.
3) Meaning of and revisions to the approved poster and leaflet.
4) Provision of poster or leaflet.
5) Provision of further information.
6) Exemption certificates.
7) Defence.
8) Repeals, revocations and modifications.

The Schedule   Repeals, revocations and modifications.

Part I - Repeals.

Part II - Revocations.

Part III - Modifications.

Outline of key points

The Health And Safety (Information for Employees) Regulations 1989 require that information relating to health and safety at work to be furnished to all employees by means of posters or leaflets in a form approved by the Health and Safety Executive.

The approved poster *"Health and Safety Law - what you should know"* should be placed in a prominent position and should contain details of the names and addresses of the enforcing authority and employment medical advisory service (EMAS). Since the modification to these Regulations *(see below)*, the name(s) of the competent person(s) and the names and locations of trade union or other safety reps and the groups they represent must also be included. Any change of name or address should be shown within 6 months of the alteration.

The Health and Safety Executive (HSE) may approve a particular form of poster or leaflet for use in relation to a particular industry or employment and, where any such form has been approved, the HSE shall publish it. If a poster is used, the information must be legible and up to date. The poster must be prominently located in an area which all employees have access. If a leaflet is used, revised leaflets must be issued to employees when any similar changes occur.

MODIFICATION TO THE REGULATIONS

The Health and Safety Information for Employees (Modifications and Repeals) Regulations 1995 amended these regulations, this allows the HSE to approve an alternative poster to the basic 'Health and Safety Law' poster. The basic poster required updating in order to take account of European directives and recent legal developments.

The updated poster includes two new sections which allow employers to personalise information. There is now a box for the names and location of safety representatives, and a similar one for details of competent people appointed by the employer and their health and safety responsibilities.

The earlier version of the poster could have been used until the end of June 2000. After that, the new version of the poster must be displayed and the new leaflet used.

Management of Health and Safety at Work Regulations (MHSWR) 1999

Law considered in context in:
Element A1 (for Regulations 3, 4, 5 and 7);
Element A3 (for Regulation 3);
Element A4 (for Regulation 4 and Schedule 1 plus Regulations 5, 7, 8 and 9); and
Element A5 (for Regulations 7, 10, 11 and 12).

Arrangement of Regulations

1) Citation, commencement and interpretation.
2) Disapplication of these Regulations.
3) Risk assessment.
4) Principles of prevention to be applied.
5) Health and safety arrangements.
6) Health surveillance.
7) Health and safety assistance.
8) Procedures for serious and imminent danger and for danger areas.
9) Contacts with external services.
10) Information for employees.
11) Co-operation and co-ordination.
12) Persons working in host employers' or self-employed persons' undertakings.
13) Capabilities and training.
14) Employees' duties.
15) Temporary workers.
16) Risk assessment in respect of new or expectant mothers.
17) Certificate from a registered medical practitioner in respect of new or expectant mothers.
18) Notification by new or expectant mothers.
19) Protection of young persons.
20) Exemption certificates.
21) Provisions as to liability.
22) Exclusion of civil liability.
23) Extension outside Great Britain.
24) Amendment of the Health and Safety (First-Aid) Regulations 1981.
25) Amendment of the Offshore Installations and Pipeline Works (First-Aid) Regulations 1989.
26) Amendment of the Mines Miscellaneous Health and Safety Provisions Regulations 1995.
27) Amendment of the Construction (Health, Safety and Welfare) Regulations 1996.
28) Regulations to have effect as health and safety regulations.
29) Revocations and consequential amendments.
30) Transitional provision.

SCHEDULES

Schedule 1.   General principles of prevention.

Schedule 2.   Consequential amendments.

Outline of key points

Management of Health and Safety at Work Regulations (MHSWR) 1999 set out some broad general duties which apply to almost all kinds of work. They are aimed mainly at improving health and safety management. You may already be familiar with broad health and safety law of this kind - as it is the form taken by the Health and Safety at Work Act (HASAWA) 1974. The Regulations work in a similar way, and in fact they can be seen as a way of fleshing out what is already in the HASAWA. The 1999 Regulations replace the Management of Health and Safety at Work Regulations 1992, the Management of Health and Safety at Work (Amendment) Regulations 1994, the Health and Safety (Young Persons) Regulations 1997 and Part III of the Fire Precautions (Workplace) Regulations 1997. *The Principal Regulations are discussed below.*

RISK ASSESSMENT (REGULATION 3)

The regulations require employers (and the self-employed) to assess the risk to the health and safety of their employees and to anyone else who may be affected by their work activity. This is necessary to ensure that the preventive and protective steps can be identified to control hazards in the workplace.

A *hazard* is defined as something with the potential to cause harm and may include machinery, substances or a work practice.

A *risk* is defined as the likelihood that a particular hazard will cause harm. Consideration must be given to the population, i.e. the number of persons who might be exposed to harm and the consequence of such exposure.

Where an employer is employing or about to employ young persons (under 18 years of age) he must carry out a risk assessment which takes particular account of:

- The inexperience, lack of awareness of risks and immaturity of young persons.
- The layout of the workplace and workstations.
- Exposure to physical, biological and chemical agents.
- Work equipment and the way in which it is handled.
- The extent of health and safety training to be provided.
- Risks from agents, processes and work listed in the Annex to Council Directive 94/33/EC on the protection of young people at work.

Where 5 or more employees are employed, the significant findings of risk assessments must be recorded in writing (the same threshold that is used in respect of having a written safety policy). This record must include details of any employees being identified as being especially at risk.

PRINCIPLES OF PREVENTION TO BE APPLIED (REGULATION 4)

Regulation 4 requires an employer to implement preventive and protective measures on the basis of general principles of prevention specified in Schedule 1 to the Regulations. These are:

1) Avoiding risks.
2) Evaluating the risks which cannot be avoided.
3) Combating the risks at source.
4) Adapting the work to the individual, especially as regards the design of workplaces, the choice of work equipment and the choice of working and production methods, with a view, in particular, to alleviating monotonous work and work at a predetermined work-rate and to reducing their effect on health.
5) Adapting to technical progress.
6) Replacing the dangerous by the non-dangerous or the less dangerous.
7) Developing a coherent overall prevention policy which covers technology, organisation of work, working conditions, social relationships and the influence of factors relating to the working environment.
8) Giving collective protective measures priority over individual protective measures.
9) Giving appropriate instructions to employees.

HEALTH AND SAFETY ARRANGEMENTS (REGULATION 5)

Appropriate arrangements must be made for the effective planning, organisation, control, monitoring and review of preventative and protective measures (in other words, for the management of health and safety). Again, employers with five or more employees must have their arrangements in writing.

HEALTH SURVEILLANCE (REGULATION 6)

In addition to the requirements of specific regulations such as Control of Substances Hazardous to Health (COSHH) and Asbestos regulations, consideration must be given to carry out health surveillance of employees where there is a disease or adverse health condition identified in risk assessments.

HEALTH AND SAFETY ASSISTANCE (REGULATION 7)

The employer must appoint one or more competent persons to assist him in complying with the legal obligations imposed on the undertaking (including Part II of the Fire Precautions (Workplace) Regulations (FPWR) 1997). The number of persons appointed should reflect the number of employees and the type of hazards in the workplace.

If more than one competent person is appointed, then arrangements must be made for ensuring adequate co-operation between them. The Competent person(s) must be given the necessary time and resources to fulfil their functions. This will depend on the size the undertaking, the risks to which employees are exposed and the distribution of those risks throughout the undertaking.

The employer must ensure that competent person(s) who are not employees are informed of the factors known (or suspected) to affect the health and safety of anyone affected by business activities.

Competent people are defined as those who have sufficient training and experience or knowledge and other qualities to enable them to perform their functions.

Persons may be selected from among existing employees or from outside. Where there is a suitable person in the employer's employment, that person shall be appointed as the 'competent person' in preference to a non-employee.

PROCEDURES FOR SERIOUS AND IMMINENT DANGER AND FOR DANGER AREAS (REGULATION 8)

Employers are required to set up emergency procedures and appoint **competent persons** to ensure compliance with identified arrangements, to devise control strategies as appropriate and to limit access to areas of risk to ensure that only those persons with adequate health and safety knowledge and instruction are admitted.

The factors to be considered when preparing a procedure to deal with workplace emergencies such as fire, explosion, bomb scare, chemical leakage or other dangerous occurrence should include:

- The identification and training requirements of persons with specific responsibilities.
- The layout of the premises in relation to escape routes etc.
- The number of persons affected.
- Assessment of special needs (disabled persons, children etc.).
- Warning systems.
- Emergency lighting.
- Location of shut-off valves, isolation switches, hydrants etc.
- Equipment required to deal with the emergency.
- Location of assembly points.
- Communication with emergency services.
- Training and/or information to be given to employees, visitors, local residents and anyone else who might be affected.

CONTACTS WITH EXTERNAL SERVICES (REGULATION 9)

Employers must ensure that, where necessary, contacts are made with external services. This particularly applies with regard to first-aid, emergency medical care and rescue work.

INFORMATION FOR EMPLOYEES (REGULATION 10)

Employees must be provided with relevant information about hazards to their health and safety arising from risks identified by the assessments. Clear instruction must be provided concerning any preventative or protective control measures including those relating to serious and imminent danger and fire assessments. Details of any competent persons nominated to discharge specific duties in accordance with the regulations must also be communicated as should risks arising from contact with other employer's activities **(see Regulation 11).**

Before employing a child (a person who is not over compulsory school age) the employer must provide those with parental responsibility for the child with information on the risks that have been identified and preventative and protective measures to be taken.

CO-OPERATION AND CO-ORDINATION (REGULATION 11)

Employers who work together in a common workplace have a duty to co-operate to discharge their duties under relevant statutory provisions. They must also take all reasonable steps to inform their respective employees of risks to their health or safety which may arise out of their work. Specific arrangements must be made to ensure compliance with fire legislation (i.e. the Fire Precautions (Workplace) Regulations (FPWR) 1997).

PERSONS WORKING IN HOST EMPLOYERS' OR SELF EMPLOYED PERSONS' UNDERTAKINGS (REGULATION 12)

This regulation extends the requirements of regulation 11 to include employees working as sole occupiers of a workplace under the control of another employer. Such employees would include those working under a service of contract and employees in temporary employment businesses under the control of the first employer.

CAPABILITIES AND TRAINING (REGULATION 13)

Employers need to take into account the capabilities of their employees before entrusting tasks. This is necessary to ensure that they have adequate health and safety training and are capable enough at their jobs to avoid risk. To this end consideration must be given to recruitment including job orientation when transferring between jobs and work departments. Training must also be provided when other factors such as the introduction of new technology and new systems of work or work equipment arise.

Training must :

- Be repeated periodically where appropriate.
- Be adapted to take account of any new or changed risks to the health and safety of the employees concerned.
- Take place during working hours.

EMPLOYEES' DUTIES (REGULATION 14)

Employees are required to follow health and safety instructions by using machinery, substances, transport etc. in accordance with the instructions and training that they have received.

They must also inform their employer (and other employers) of any dangers or shortcoming in the health and safety arrangements, even if there is no risk of imminent danger.

TEMPORARY WORKERS (REGULATION 15)

Consideration is given to the special needs of temporary workers. In particular to the provision of particular health and safety information such as qualifications required to perform the task safely or any special arrangements such as the need to provide health screening.

RISKS ASSESSMENT IN RESPECT OF NEW OR EXPECTANT MOTHERS (REGULATION 16)

Where the work is of a kind which would involve risk to a new or expectant mother or her baby, then the assessment required by regulation 3 should take this into account.

If the risk cannot be avoided, then the employer should take reasonable steps to:

- Adjust the hours worked, or
- Offer alternative work, or
- Give paid leave for as long as is necessary.

CERTIFICATE FROM A REGISTERED MEDICAL PRACTITIONER IN RESPECT OF NEW OR EXPECTANT MOTHERS (REGULATION 17)

Where the woman is a night shift worker and has a medical certificate identifying night shift work as a risk then the employer must put her on day shift or give paid leave for as long as is necessary.

NOTIFICATION BY NEW OR EXPECTANT MOTHERS (REGULATION 18)

The employer need take no action until he is notified in writing by the woman that she is pregnant, has given birth in the last six months, or is breastfeeding.

PROTECTION OF YOUNG PERSONS (REGULATION 19)

Employers of young persons shall ensure that they are not exposed to risk as a consequence of their lack of experience, lack of awareness or lack of maturity.

No employer shall employ young people for work which:

- Is beyond his physical or psychological capacity.
- Involves exposure to agents which chronically affect human health.
- Involves harmful exposure to radiation.
- Involves a risk to health from extremes of temperature, noise or vibration.
- Involves risks which could not be reasonably foreseen by young persons.

This regulation does not prevent the employment of a young person who is no longer a child for work:

- Where it is necessary for his training.
- Where the young person will be supervised by a competent person.
- Where any risk will be reduced to the lowest level that is reasonably practicable.

(Note: Two HSE publications give guidance on the changes. HSG122 - New and expectant mothers at work: a guide for employers and HSG165 - Young people at work: a guide for employers.)

EXEMPTION CERTIFICATES (REGULATION 20)

The Secretary of State for Defence may, in the interests of national security, by a certificate in writing exempt the armed forces, any visiting force or any headquarters from certain obligations imposed by the Regulations.

PROVISIONS AS TO LIABILITY (REGULATION 21)

Employers cannot submit a defence in criminal proceedings that contravention was caused by the act or default either of an employee or the competent person appointed under Regulation 7.

EXCLUSION OF CIVIL LIABILITY (REGULATION 22)

Breach of a duty imposed by these Regulations shall not confer a right of action in any civil proceedings for those other than employees.

REVOCATIONS AND AMENDMENTS (REGULATIONS 24-29)

The Regulations:

- Revoke regulation 6 of the Health and Safety (First-Aid) Regulations (FAR) 1981 which confers power on the Health and Safety Executive to grant exemptions from those Regulations.
- Amend the Offshore Installations and Pipeline Works (First-Aid) Regulations 1989.
- Amend the Mines Miscellaneous Health and Safety Provisions Regulations 1995.
- Amend the Construction (Health, Safety and Welfare) Regulations 1996.

The Regulations provide that, with some exceptions, the Fire Precautions (Workplace) Regulations (FPWR) 1997 are to be considered as health and safety regulations within the meaning of the Health and Safety at Work etc Act (HASAWA) 1974. The Regulations also make amendments to the statutory instruments as specified in Schedule 2.

TRANSITIONAL PROVISION (REGULATION 30)

The Regulations contain a transitional provision (regulation 30). The substitution of provisions in the 1999 Regulations for provisions of the Management of Health and Safety at Work Regulations (MHSWR) 1992 shall not affect the continuity of the law; and accordingly anything done under or for the purposes of such provision of the 1992 Regulations shall have effect as if done under or for the purposes of any corresponding provision of these Regulations.

Management of Health and Safety at Work and Fire Precautions (Workplace) (Amendment) Regulations 2003

Arrangement of Regulations

1)   Citation and commencement.

2-6)   Amendments to the Management of Health and Safety at Work Regulations 1999.

7-13)   Amendments to the Fire Precautions (Workplace) Regulations 1997.

Outline of key points

AMENDMENTS TO MANAGEMENT OF HEALTH AND SAFETY AT WORK REGULATIONS 1999

2.   The Management of Health and Safety at Work Regulations 1999[5] shall be amended in accordance with regulations 3 to 6 of these Regulations and any reference in those provisions to any specified provision shall, unless the context requires otherwise, be taken to be a reference to the provision so specified of the Management of Health and Safety at Work Regulations 1999.

3.   For regulation 2 there shall be substituted the following regulation -

" Disapplication of these Regulations 2. -

(1) These Regulations shall not apply to or in relation to the master or crew of a ship, or to the employer of such persons, in respect of the normal ship-board activities of a ship's crew which are carried out solely by the crew under the direction of the master.

(2) Regulations 3(4), (5), 10(2) and 19 shall not apply to occasional work or short-term work involving work regarded as not being harmful, damaging or dangerous to young people in a family undertaking.

(3) In this regulation -

"normal ship-board activities" include -

(a)   The construction, reconstruction or conversion of a ship outside, but not inside, Great Britain; and

(b)   The repair of a ship save repair when carried out in dry dock; "ship" includes every description of vessel used in navigation, other than a ship belonging to Her Majesty which forms part of Her Majesty's Navy.".

4.   In regulation 3(3) the words "and where" to the end shall follow and not appear in sub-paragraph (b).

5.   Regulation 19(4) shall be omitted.

6.   For regulation 22 there shall be substituted the following regulation - " Restriction of civil liability for breach of statutory duty 22. Breach of a duty imposed on an employer by these Regulations shall not confer a right of action in any civil proceedings insofar as that duty applies for the protection of persons not in his employment."

AMENDMENTS TO FIRE PRECAUTIONS (WORKPLACE) REGULATIONS 1997

7.   The Fire Precautions (Workplace) Regulations 1997[6] shall be amended in accordance with regulations 8 to 13 of these Regulations and any reference in those provisions to any specified provision shall, unless the context requires otherwise, be taken to be a reference to the provision so specified of the Fire Precautions (Workplace) Regulations 1997.

8.   In regulation 9(1) there shall be omitted the words "provisions of health and safety regulations or".

9.   In regulation 9(2) (a) (ii), for the words "premises to which" there shall be substituted the words "premises of a description specified in Part I of Schedule 1 to" and the word "apply" shall be omitted.

10.   For paragraph (ii) of regulation 9(2) (b) there shall be substituted the following paragraph -

"(ii) have effect in relation to a workplace in Great Britain other than -

(a)   An excepted workplace, or

(b)   Any workplace referred to in paragraphs (i) and (ii) of paragraph (2) (a), other than a building on the surface at a mine,".

11.   After regulation 9(2) there shall be inserted the following paragraph -

" (2A) Not withstanding that the provisions of Part II of these Regulations are not provisions forming part of the relevant statutory provisions, the provisions of Part II shall, in so far as they apply to any workplace referred to in paragraphs (i) and (ii) of paragraph (2)(a) other than a building on the surface at a mine, be deemed to be health and safety regulations for the purposes of sections 16 to 24, 26, 28, 33 to 40, 42, 46 and 47 of the 1974 Act.".

12.   At the end of regulation 9 there shall be inserted the following regulation -

"Civil liability for breach of statutory duty 9A. - (1) Subject to paragraph (2), and notwithstanding section 86 of the Fires Prevention (Metropolis) Act 1774[7], breach of a duty imposed on an employer by the workplace fire precautions legislation shall, so far as it causes damage, confer a right of action in civil proceedings.

(2) Breach of a duty imposed on an employer by the workplace fire precautions legislation shall not confer a right of action in civil proceedings insofar as that duty applies for the protection of persons not in his employment".

13.   In regulation 17 -

   (a)   In paragraph (2), the words "27A (civil and other liability)" shall be omitted;

   (b)   At the end of paragraph (5) there shall be inserted the following paragraph -

   "(6)   Insofar as Part II of these Regulations contains any provision which is made under the 1971 Act, section 27A (a) of the 1971 Act shall not apply in respect of any contravention of such provision."

Occupiers' Liability Acts (OLA) 1957 and 1984

Law considered in context in Element A5.

Outline of key points

The Acts make it obligatory for the occupier (not specifically the landlord) 'to provide safe premises (including land, buildings and any fixed or moveable structure, including any vessel, vehicle or aircraft)'. It includes dangers arising from acts or omissions relating to things to be done on the premises, and covers damage to both personal injury and property. Liability is not strict, but the difference between this and negligence is minimal.

Under the Act, the occupier owes all lawful visitors the 'common law duty of care'. The Act does not specify responsibility to trespassers, who are dealt with under the Occupiers' Liability Act 1984, which basically applies a reasonable duty of care of the occupier. Defences under the Act are:

■   Warnings to those using the premises, but subject of the Unfair Contract Terms Act [UCTA] 1977.
■   Knowing acceptance of the risk by the visitor.
■   Employing a competent contractor.

An occupier is a person or other entity who has control of the premises. This includes an occupational tenant and could include a landlord. The Act does not apply to builders or others who install or maintain the premises or equipment (unless in occupation of the property).

A warning does not absolve the occupier of liability unless it enables the visitor to be reasonably safe, and is subject to UCTA 1977. It will not protect an occupier where death or personal injury is caused by the occupier's negligence.

Note: There is a more onerous duty of care in respect of children or specialist visitors, e.g. zoos and theme parks must take precautions based on the assumption that a significant proportion of their visitors will be children.

Reporting of Injuries, Diseases and Dangerous Occurrences Regulations (RIDDOR) 1995

Law considered in context in Element A2.

Arrangement of Regulations

1)   Citation and commencement.

2)   Interpretation.

3)   Notification and reporting of injuries and dangerous occurrences.

4)   Reporting of the death of an employee.

5)   Reporting of cases of disease.

6)   Reporting of gas incidents.

7)   Records.

8)   Additional provisions relating to mines and quarries.

9)   Additional provisions relating to offshore workplaces.

10)   Restrictions on the application of regulations 3, 4 and 5.

11)   Defence in proceedings for an offence contravening these Regulations.

12)   Extension outside Great Britain.

13)   Certificates of exemption.

14)   Repeal and amendment of provisions in the Regulation of Railways Act 1871, the Railway Employment (Prevention of Accidents) Act 1900 and the Transport and Works Act 1992.

15)   Revocations, amendments and savings.

SCHEDULES

Schedule 1   Major Injuries.

Schedule 2   Dangerous Occurrences.

Schedule 3   Reportable Diseases.

Schedule 4   Records.

Schedule 5   Additional provisions relating to mines and quarries.

Schedule 6   Additional provisions relating to offshore workplaces.

Schedule 7   Enactments or instruments requiring the notification of events which are not required to be notified or reported under these Regulations.

Schedule 8   Revocations and amendments.

Outline of key points

The Reporting of Injuries, Diseases and Dangerous Occurrences Regulations (RIDDOR) 1995 covers the requirement to report certain categories of injury and disease sustained at work, along with specified dangerous occurrences and gas incidents, to the relevant enforcing authority. These reports are used to compile statistics to show trends and to highlight problem areas, in particular industries or companies.

THE MAIN POINTS OF RIDDOR

Reporting

1) When a person *dies or suffers any major injury* specified in Schedule 1 *(Reporting of Injuries)* and Schedule 2 *(Reporting of Dangerous Occurrences)* a responsible person is to notify by the quickest possible means (usually by telephone) the enforcing authorities and must send them a written report within 10 days (F2508).

2) In cases of diseases which are linked to work activities listed in Schedule 3 *(Reporting of Diseases)* a responsible person must notify by the quickest possible means (usually by telephone) the enforcing authorities and must send them a written report forthwith (F2508A).

3) If personal injury results in *more than 3 days incapacity* from work which they might reasonably be expected to do in the normal course of their work, but does not fall in the category of "major injury", the written report alone is required. The day of the accident is not counted, but any days which would not have been working days are included.

4) The enforcing authority is either the Health and Safety Executive or the Local Authority. The approved form for reporting is F2508 for injuries and dangerous occurrences and F2508A for diseases.

Accident

"Accident" includes:

- An act of non-consensual physical violence done to a person at work.
- An act of suicide which occurs on or in the course of the operation of a relevant transport system.

Responsible person

Reportable event	To	Responsible person
Death, Major injury, over 3 day injury, disease	Employee	Employer
	Self-employed person working in someone else's premises	Person in control of the premises: At the time of the event and In connection trade, business or undertaking
Major injury, over 3 day injury, disease	Self-employed in own premises	Self-employed person or someone acting for them
Dangerous occurrences - general		Person in control of the premises where, or in connection with the work going on at which, the dangerous occurrence happened: At the time of the event and In connection trade, business or undertaking

Road traffic accidents

Road traffic accidents only have to be reported if:

- Death or injury results from exposure to a substance being conveyed by a vehicle.
- Death or injury results from the activities of another person engaged in the loading or unloading of an article or substance.
- Death or injury results from the activities of another person involving work on or alongside a road.
- Death or injury results from an accident involving a train.

Non employee

The responsible person must not only report non-employee deaths, but also cases that involve major injury or hospitalisation.

Employee death

Where an employee dies as a result of a reportable injury, within one year of the date of the accident, as soon as the employer knows the employer must inform the enforcing authority in writing of the death.

Gas incidents

Specified gas incidents are notified 'forthwith' and reported within 14 days to the Health and Safety Executive.

Injury under medical supervision

If a person is injured as a result of an accident arising directly from the conduct of an operation, examination or other medical treatment whilst under the supervision of a registered medical practitioner or dentist the injury does not need to be reported.

Self-employed people

If a self-employed person suffers a major injury while working at their own premises they do not need to notify the enforcing authority immediately. However, they or someone acting for them must report the injury within 10 days.

Recording

In the case of an accident at work, the following details must be recorded:

- Date.
- Time.
- Name.
- Occupation.
- Nature of injury.
- Place of accident.
- Brief description of the event.

Copies of F2508 or suitable alternative records must be kept for at least 3 years. They may be held electronically provided they are printable.

Defences

A person must prove that he was not aware of the event and that he had taken all reasonable steps to have such events brought to his notice.

MAJOR INJURIES (RIDDOR 1995 - SCHEDULE 1)

The list of major injuries includes:

- Any fracture, other than the finger or thumbs or toes.
- Any amputation.
- Dislocation of the shoulder, hip, knee or spine.
- Permanent or temporary loss of sight.
- Chemical, hot metal or penetrating eye injury.
- Electrical shock, electrical burn leading to unconsciousness or resuscitation or admittance to hospital for more than 24 hours.
- Loss of consciousness caused by asphyxia or exposure to a harmful substance or biological agent.
- Acute illness or loss of consciousness requiring medical attention due to any entry of substance by inhalation, ingestion or through the skin.
- Acute illness where there is a reason to believe that this resulted from exposure to a biological agent or its toxins or infected material.
- Any other injury leading to hypothermia, heat-induced illness or unconsciousness requiring resuscitation, hospitalisation greater than 24 hours.

DISEASES (RIDDOR 1995 - SCHEDULE 3)

Conditions due to physical agents and the physical demands of work, e.g.

- Inflammation, ulceration or malignant disease of the skin due to ionising radiation.
- Decompression illness.
- Subcutaneous cellulitis of the hand (beat hand).
- Carpal tunnel syndrome.
- Hand-arm vibration syndrome.

Conditions due to chemicals and other substances e.g.

- Arsenic poisoning.
- Ethylene Oxide poisoning.
- Cancer of a bronchus or lung.
- Folliculitis.
- Acne.
- Pneumoconiosis.
- Asbestosis.
- Occupational dermatitis.

Infections due to biological agents, e.g.

- Anthrax.
- Hepatitis.
- Legionellosis.
- Leptospirosis.
- Tetanus.

DANGEROUS OCCURRENCES (RIDDOR 1995 - SCHEDULE 2)

Dangerous occurrences are events that have the potential to cause death or serious injury and so must be reported whether anyone is injured or not. Examples of dangerous occurrences which might take place in general workplaces that must be reported are:

- The failure of any load bearing part of any lift, hoist, crane or derrick etc.
- The failure of any pressurised closed vessel.
- The failure of any freight container in any of its load bearing parts.
- Any unintentional incident in which plant or equipment either:
    - Comes into contact with an uninsulated overhead electric line, or
    - Causes an electrical discharge from such an electric line by coming into close proximity to it.
- Electrical short-circuit or overload attended by fire or explosion which results in the stoppage of the plant involved for more than 24 hours.

Schedule 2 contains requirements to report specific dangerous occurrences for the following workplaces:

- Mines.
- Quarries.
- Transport systems.
- Offshore.

Note: This information is a brief summary only. For full details consult HSE document L73 A Guide to RIDDOR 95.

When notifying and reporting the responsible person is at liberty to use the Incident Contact Centre (ICC), instead of contacting the relevant enforcing authority direct. The ICC can be contacted by telephone; this will satisfy the notification requirement of RIDDOR 1995. The ICC will also fill the appropriate report form in and send a copy for the responsible person's record. In addition, they will send the report to the correct enforcing authority, dealing with the reporting requirement of RIDDOR 1995.

An alternative to contacting the ICC by telephone is to report by accessing the ICC website, www.riddor.gov.uk. This method satisfies RIDDOR 1995 requirements for reporting.

INTERNAL REPORTING AND RECORDING SYSTEMS

Relevant report forms

A number of report forms are utilised to identify and inform that accidents and ill-health have occurred, these include:

- Accident book, in the form of BI 510. This accident book has been revised to take into account the Data Protection Act (DPA) 1998. Completed accident records should be detached from the book, passed to the nominated person and stored securely, for example in a lockable cabinet.
- First aid treatment reports.
- Medical treatment reports.
- Medical (doctor) reports of ill-health.
- Sickness absence reports.
- Event (accident) reports.
- Event (near miss) reports.
- Maintenance/repair reports.
- Insurance reports.
- Reporting Injuries, Diseases and Dangerous Occurrences Regulations (RIDDOR) 1995 reports - F2508, F2508A.

Investigation report forms

Investigation report forms vary in design, layout and content. Many organisations recognise that a different report form may be necessary for first line managers' initial investigations (a level 1 report) and those done by other managers and health and safety professionals (a level 2 report). The main difference is the section relating to causes of the accident. The version used by other managers and professionals often has more analysis in this area and causes greater investigation of underlying causes. In the same way, reports prepared by an investigation team would not tend to be on a pre-printed format, but would be designed around agreed headings and the content/extent of the report would depend on the matter being investigated and findings (a level 3 report).

Common structure of a report tends to determine:

- What happened - the loss.
- How it happened - the event.
- Why it happened - the causes.
- Recommendations - remedial (and preventive) action.

The report is usually supported by drawings, photographs and statements as appendices.

Reporting routes

Reporting of an accident or ill-health may be by a number of means and includes:

- Person suffering harm.
- Person causing loss.
- Person discovering loss.

Person suffering harm

This person is often the source of first reporting of less serious events. The reporting system must make available to them the means to make a report. They have a right to report in an 'accident book' BI 510 (or equivalent) any event that may cause them to claim Social Security benefit. This might be fulfilled by using: a copy of the BI 510 book or first aid/medical treatment documents/event report forms that are adapted to contain the same data. These reports should be under the control of a responsible person who would then initiate an investigation which would usually require the completion of an event (e.g. accident) report.

Person causing loss

This person would be expected to bring the loss to the attention of a line manager who would fill in the appropriate event (e.g. accident) report and initiate an investigation to complete the remainder of the report that the person reporting the loss may not be able to do.

Person discovering the loss

If this person is not the manager responsible for the location in which the loss took place they would have to bring the loss to the attention of a line manager, as above. If the person is the line manager they would initiate an investigation and report on the appropriate event form.

Copies and distribution of reports

Reports from first line managers may be copied to the next line manager (middle manager), health and safety professional and employee representative. It is important that the originator retains a copy till action to prevent re-occurrence is complete. This will help to encourage ownership and continued involvement. The copy passed to the next line manager is usually seen as the primary document. The manager confirms/adds to the investigation, retains a copy and passes the report to a central record point. Clearly this may be done in part or whole as a computerised or paper system.

Records held by the line manager/health and safety professional may be held for varying periods depending on their role. Central records should be under the control of the responsible person and are usually maintained in accordance with the organisation's own practices. A minimum period is usually 3 years for accident (in order to respond to civil claims) and 40 years for events resulting in ill-health (in order to deal with the long lived nature of the problem).

Follow-up

This virtually finishes the work of the investigator, but management is still responsible for seeing that the necessary remedial actions are implemented, and monitored to ensure that the causes are satisfactorily controlled. The line manager, health and safety professional and health and safety committee/members will monitor these actions.

Action following a fatal accident

Reporting a death at work following an accident should include informing:

- Enforcing authority.
- The senior manager.
- Health and safety specialist.
- Coroner.

- Next of kin.
- Employee representatives.
- Other employees.
- Insurance company.

Note: This information is a brief summary only. For full details consult HSE document L73 A Guide to RIDDOR 95.

Safety Representatives and Safety Committees Regulations (SRSC) 1977

Law considered in context in Element A5.

Arrangement of Regulations

1) Citation and commencement.
2) Interpretation.
3) Appointment of safety representatives.
4) Functions of safety representatives.
5) Inspections of the workplace.
6) Inspections following notifiable accidents, occurrences and diseases.
7) Inspections of documents and provision of information.
8) Cases where safety representatives need not be employees.
9) Safety committees.
10) Power of Health and Safety Commission to grant exemption.
11) Provision as to industrial tribunals.

Outline of key points

The Safety Representatives and Safety Committees Regulations (SRSC) 1977 are concerned with the appointment by recognised trade unions of safety representatives, the functions of the representatives and the establishment of safety committees.

Representatives are appointed when a recognised trade union notifies the employer in writing. Representatives must have been employed throughout the preceding 2 years or, where this is not reasonably practicable, have had at least 2 years' experience in similar employment.

Similarly, employees cease to be representatives when:

- The employer has be notified in writing by the trade union.
- The representative ceases to be employed.
- He/she resigns.

FUNCTIONS OF TRADE UNION - APPOINTED SAFETY REPRESENTATIVES

The SRSCR grant safety representatives the right to carry out certain functions as outlined below.

Functions are activities that safety representatives are permitted to carry out by legislation, but do not have a 'duty' to perform and therefore are treated as advisory actions. As a consequence the representatives cannot be held accountable for failing to carry out these activities or for the standard of the advice given, when performing their functions. They are, however, still employees and have the same consequent duties as any other employee (for example their duties under HASAWA Ss 7and 8). Their functions as safety representatives are:

a)   To take all reasonably practical steps to keep themselves informed of:

- The legal requirements relating to the health and safety of persons at work, particularly the group or groups of persons they directly represent.
- The particular hazards of the workplace and the measures deemed necessary to eliminate or minimise the risk deriving from these hazards and the health and safety policy of their employer and the organisation and arrangements for fulfilling that policy.

b)   To encourage co-operation between their employer and his employees in promoting and developing essential measures to ensure the health and safety of employees, and in checking the effectiveness of these measures.

c)   To carry out investigations into:

- Hazards and dangerous occurrences (incl. accidents) at the workplace.
- Complaints, by any employee he represents, relating to that employee's health, safety or welfare.

d)   To carry out inspections of the workplace.

e)   To bring to the employer's notice, normally in writing, any unsafe or unhealthy conditions, or unsafe working practices, or unsatisfactory arrangements for welfare at work, which comes to their attention whether during an inspection/investigation or day to day observation.

The report does not imply, that all other conditions and working practices are safe and healthy or that the welfare arrangements are satisfactory in all other respects. Making a written report does not preclude the bringing of such matters to the attention of the employer or his representative by a direct oral approach in the first instance, particularly in situations where speedy remedial action is necessary. It will also be appropriate for minor matters to be the subject of direct discussion, without the need for a formal written approach.

f)   To represent the employees they were appointed to represent in consultation at the workplace with inspectors of the Health and Safety Executive and of any other enforcing authority within the Act.

g)   To receive information from inspectors in accordance with section 28(8) of the 1974 Act.

h)   To attend meetings of safety committees during which he/she attends in his capacity as a safety representative in connection with any of the above conditions.

EMPLOYERS DUTIES

The Regulations require employers to make any known information available to safety representatives which is necessary to enable them to fulfil their functions. This should include:

a)   Information about the plans and performances of the undertaking and any changes proposed, in so far as they affect the health and safety at work of their employees.

b)   Information of a technical nature about hazards to health and safety and precautions deemed necessary to eliminate or minimise them, in respect of machinery, plant, equipment, processes, systems of work and substances in use at work. This should include any relevant information provided by consultants or designers or by the manufacturer, importer or supplier of any article or substance used, or proposed to be used, at work by their employees.

c)   Information which the employer keeps relating to the occurrence of any accidents, dangerous occurrences or notifiable industrial disease and any statistical records relating to such accidents, dangerous occurrences or cases of notifiable industrial disease.

d)   Any other information specifically related to matters affecting the Health and Safety at work of his employees, including the result of any measurements taken by persons acting on his behalf in the course of checking the effectiveness of his health and safety arrangements.

e)   Information on articles or substances which an employer issues to homeworkers.

f)   Any other suitable and relevant reasonable facility to enable the representatives to carry out their functions.

TRAINING

The basis of Trades Union Congress (TUC) policy is that the union appointed safety representative will be trained on TUC approved courses. However, there is much to be gained by the employer approaching the trades unions active in his workplace with the objective of holding joint company/industry based courses. In any event it is prudent for the employer to carry out company/industry orientated training to supplement the wide industry based TUC course. The functions and training of the safety representatives should be carried out during normal working hours. The representative must receive normal earnings, this taking into consideration any bonuses which would have been earned if carrying out their normal work activities.

FUNCTIONS OF HEALTH AND SAFETY COMMITTEES

If two or more appointed safety representatives request in writing the formation of a safety committee, the employer must implement this request within three months. Consultation must take place with the representatives making the request and the appointing trade union. A basic requirement for a successful safety committee is the desire of both employee and management to show honest commitment and a positive approach to a programme of accident prevention and the establishment of a safe and healthy environment and systems of work. For any committee to operate effectively, it is necessary to determine its objectives and functions.

Objectives

a)   The promotion of safety, health and welfare at work by providing a forum for discussion and perhaps a pressure group.

b)   To promote and support normal employee/employer systems for the reporting and control of workplace problems.

Functions

a)   To review accident and occupational health trends.

b)   To review recurring problems revealed by safety audits.

c)   To consider enforcing authority reports and information releases.

d)   To consider reports on matters arising from previous safety committee meetings.

e)   To assist in the development of safety rules and systems of work and procedures.

f)   To review health and safety aspects of future development and changes in procedure.

g)   To review health and safety aspects of purchasing specifications of equipment and materials.

h)   To review renewal/maintenance programmes.

i)   To monitor safety training programmes and standards achieved.

j)   To monitor the effectiveness of safety and health communications within the workplace.

k)   To monitor the effectiveness of the Safety Policy.

This may be summarised as review and recommend on the overall direction of the health and safety programme, on specific aspects of the programme, on difficulties encountered in its implementation and to monitor the programme in both a specific and overall manner.

Composition

The membership and structure of the safety committee should be settled in consultation between management and the trade union representatives concerned. This should be aimed at keeping the total size as compact as possible, compatible with the adequate representation of the interests of management and employees. Management representatives will naturally be appointed by the management. Employee representatives will either be appointed by a recognised Trade Union (HASAWA 2(4)) or, in a non-union company, elected by their colleagues. The committee suggested in HASAWA section 2 (7) will probably be the 'Company Safety Committee.' There is nothing to prevent the formation of 'works' or 'office' committees as required in order to maintain the company safety committee at a reasonable size.

Social Security Administration Act (SSAA) 1992

Law considered in context in Element A2.

Arrangement of Act

PART 1 - CLAIMS FOR AND PAYMENTS AND GENERAL ADMINISTRATION OF BENEFIT

Necessity of claims

Widowhood benefits

Claims and payments regulations

Community charge benefits etc.

Industrial injuries benefit

8)   Notification of accidents, etc.

9)   Medical examination and treatment of claimants.

10)   Obligations of claimants. Disability working allowance.

The social fund

Child benefit

Statutory sick pay

Statutory maternity pay

Emergency payments

PART II - ADJUDICATION

Adjudication in relation to industrial injuries and disablement benefit

44) Declaration that accident is an industrial accident.
45) Disablement questions.
46) Medical appeals and references.
47) Review of medical decisions.
48) Appeal etc. on question of law to Commissioner.

PART III - OVERPAYMENTS AND ADJUSTMENTS OF BENEFIT

PART IV - RECOVERY FROM COMPENSATION PAYMENTS

PART V - INCOME SUPPORT AND THE DUTY TO MAINTAIN

PART VI - ENFORCEMENT

PART VII - PROVISION OF INFORMATION

PART VIII - ARRANGEMENTS FOR HOUSING BENEFIT AND COMMUNITY CHARGE BENEFITS AND RELATED SUBSIDIES

PART IX - ALTERATION OF CONTRIBUTIONS ETC.

PART X - REVIEW AND ALTERATION OF BENEFITS

PART XI - COMPUTATION OF BENEFITS

PART XII - FINANCE

PART XIII - ADVISORY BODIES AND CONSULTATION

PART XIV - SOCIAL SECURITY SYSTEMS OUTSIDE GREAT BRITAIN

PART XV - MISCELLANEOUS

Industrial injuries and diseases

183) Research on industrial injuries, etc.
184) Control of pneumoconiosis.

PART XVI - GENERAL

Subordinate legislation

Supplementary

SCHEDULES

Outline of key points

SECTION 8 - NOTIFICATION OF ACCIDENTS

Regulations may provide -

(a) for requiring the prescribed notice of an accident in respect of which industrial injuries benefit may be payable to be given within the prescribed time by the employed earner to the earner's employer or other prescribed person;

(b) for requiring employers -

(i) To make reports, to such person and in such form and within such time as may be prescribed, of accidents in respect of which industrial injuries benefit may be payable;

(ii) To furnish to the prescribed person any information required for the determination of claims, or of questions arising in connection with claims or awards;

(iii) To take such other steps as may be prescribed to facilitate the giving notice of accidents, the making of claims and the determination of claims and of questions so arising.

SECTION 44 - DECLARATION THAT ACCIDENT IS AN INDUSTRIAL ACCIDENT

(1) Where, in connection with any claim for industrial injuries benefit, it is determined that the relevant accident was or was not an industrial accident, an express declaration of that fact shall be made and recorded and a claimant shall be entitled to have the question whether the relevant accident was an industrial accident determined notwithstanding that his claim is disallowed on other grounds.

Sub-sections 2-5 relate mainly to the administration of this process.

(6) For the purposes of this section, an accident whereby a person suffers personal injury shall be deemed, in relation to him, to be an industrial accident if -

(a) it arises out of and in the course of his employment;

(b) that employment is employed earner's employment for the purposes of Part V of the Contributions and Benefits Act;

(c) payment of benefit is not under section 94(5) of that Act precluded because the accident happened while he was outside Great Britain.

Social Security (Claims and Payments) Regulations (SSCPR) 1979

Law considered in context in Element A2.

Arrangement of Regulations

PART I

General

1) Citation and commencement

2) Interpretation

PART IV

Special provisions relating to industrial injuries benefit only

24) Notice of accidents

25) Obligations of employers

26) Obligations of claimants for, and beneficiaries in receipt of, injury benefit or disablement benefit

PART V

Miscellaneous provisions

31) Breach of regulation

SCHEDULE 4 - PARTICULARS TO BE GIVEN OF ACCIDENTS

Outline of key points

PART IV

REGULATION 24 - NOTICE OF ACCIDENTS

(1) Every employed earner who suffers personal injury by accident in respect of which benefit may be payable shall give notice of such accident either in writing or orally as soon as is practicable after the happening thereof:

Provided that any such notice required to be given by an employed earner may be given by some other person acting on his behalf.

(2) Every such notice shall be given to the employer, or (if there is more than one employer) to one of such employers, or to any foreman or other official under whose supervision the employed earner is employed at the time of the accident, or to any person designated for the purpose by the employer, and shall give the appropriate particulars.

(3) Any entry of the appropriate particulars of an accident made in a book kept for that purpose in accordance with the provisions of regulation 25 shall, if made as soon as practicable after the happening of an accident by the employed earner or by some other person acting on his behalf, be sufficient notice of the accident for the purposes of this regulation.

(4) In this regulation -

"employer" means in relation to any person, the employer of that person at the time of the accident and "employers" shall be construed accordingly; and

"employed earner" means a person who is or is treated as an employed earner for the purposes of industrial injuries benefit.

(5) In this regulation and regulation 25, "appropriate particulars" mean the particulars indicated in Schedule 4 to these regulations.

REGULATION 25 - OBLIGATIONS OF EMPLOYERS

(1) Every employer shall take reasonable steps to investigate the circumstances of every accident of which notice is given to him or to his servant or agent in accordance with the provisions of regulation 24 and, if there appear to him to be any discrepancies between the circumstances found by him as a result of his investigation and the circumstances appearing from the notice so given, he shall record the circumstances so found.

(2) Every employer who is required to do so by the Secretary of State shall furnish to an officer of the Department within such reasonable period as may be required, such information and particulars as shall be required -

(a) of any accident or alleged accident in respect of which benefit may be payable to, or in respect of the death of, a person employed by him at the time of the accident or alleged accident; or

(b) of the nature of and other relevant circumstances relating to any occupation prescribed for the purposes of Chapter V of Part II of the Act in which any person to whom or in respect of whose death benefit may be payable under that chapter was or is alleged to have been employed by him.

(3) Every owner or occupier (being an employer) of any mine or quarry or of any premises to which any of the provisions of the Factories Act 1961(a) applies and every employer by whom 10 or more persons are normally employed at the same time on or about the same premises in connection with a trade or business carried on by the employer shall, subject to the following provisions of this paragraph - (a) keep readily accessible a means (whether in a book or books or by electronic means), in a form approved by the Secretary of State, by which person employed by the employer or some other person acting on his behalf may record the appropriate particulars (as defined in regulation 24) of any accident causing personal injury to that person; and (b) preserve every such record for the period of at least 3 years from the date of its entry.

REGULATION 26 - OBLIGATIONS OF CLAIMANTS FOR, AND BENEFICIARIES IN RECEIPT OF DISABLEMENT BENEFIT

(1) Subject to the following provisions of this regulation, every claimant for, and every beneficiary in receipt of disablement benefit shall comply with every notice given to him by the Secretary of State which requires him either -

(a) to submit himself to a medical examination by a medical practitioner who has experience in the issues specified in regulation 12(1) of the Social Security and Child Support (Decisions and Appeals) Regulations 1999 (b) for the purpose of determining the effects of the relevant accident or the treatment appropriate to the relevant injury or loss of faculty; or

(b) to submit himself to such medical treatment for the said injury or loss of faculty as is considered appropriate in his case by the medical practitioner in charge of the case

(2) Every notice given to a claimant or beneficiary requiring him to submit himself to medical examination shall be given in writing and shall specify the time and place for examination and shall not require the claimant or beneficiary to submit himself to examination before the expiration of the period to 6 days beginning with the date of the notice or such shorter period as may be reasonable in the circumstances

(3) Every claimant and every beneficiary who, in accordance with the foregoing provisions of this regulation, is required to submit himself to a medical examination or to medical treatment -

(a) shall attend at every such place and at every such time as may be required; and

(b) may, in the discretion of the Secretary of State, be paid such traveling and other allowances (including compensation for loss of remunerative time) as the Secretary of State may with the consent of the Minister for the Civil Service determine.

REGULATION 31 - BREACH OF REGULATIONS

If any person contravenes or fails to comply with any requirement of these regulations (not being a requirement to give notice of an accident or a requirement to submit himself to medical treatment or examination) in respect of which no special penalty is provided, he shall for such offence be liable on summary conviction to a penalty not exceeding £200 or, where the offence consists of continuing any such contravention or failure after conviction thereof, £20 for each day on which it is so continued.

SCHEDULE 4 - PARTICULARS TO BE GIVEN OF ACCIDENTS

1) Full name, address and occupation of injured person.
2) Date and time of accident.
3) Place where accident happened.
4) Cause and nature of injury.
5) Name, address and occupation of person giving the notice, if other than the injured person.

Social Security (Industrial Diseases) (Prescribed Diseases) Regulations (SSIDPDR) 1985

Law considered in context in Element A2.

Arrangement of Regulations

PART I

1) Citation, commencement and interpretation.

PART II

2) Prescription of diseases and injuries and occupations for which they are prescribed.
3) Sequela or resulting conditions.
4) Presumption that a disease is due to the nature of employment.

PART III

5) Development of a disease.
6) Date of onset.
7) Workmen's compensation cases.
8) Re-employement of pneumoconiotics and special provisions for benefit (workmen's compensation cases).

PART IV

9) Definition of "relevant diseases".
10) Application of Chapters IV and VI of Part II of the Act.

11)   Presumption that a disease is due to the nature of employment.

PART V

Special provisions as to pneumoconiosis, byssinosis, occupational deafness and certain other diseases.

PART VI

Transitional provisions and revocations

Outline of key points

The Social Security (Industrial Injuries) (Prescribed Diseases) Regulations (SSIIPDR) 1985 list those diseases that are prescribed for the purpose of payment of disablement benefit.

A prescribed disease is defined in the Social Security Act (SSA) 1975 as:

- A disease that ought to be treated, with regard to its causes, incidence and other relevant considerations, as a risk of occupation and not a risk common to everyone.
- Such that, in the absence of special circumstances, the attribution of particular cases to the nature of the employment can be established with reasonable certainty.

Schedule 1 to the regulations classifies prescribed injuries or diseases as:

- Conditions due to physical agents - such as cataract from an occupation involving frequent or prolonged exposure to radiation from re-hot or whit-hot material.
- Conditions due to biological agents - infection by leptospira from an occupation involving work in places liable to be infested with rats, field mice, or voles; work at dog kennels or handling of dogs; contact with bovine animals or pigs or their meat products.
- Conditions due to chemical agents - Anaemia with a haemoglobin concentration of 9g/dL or less, and a blood film showing punctuate basophilia from an occupation involving the use or handling of, or exposure to the fumes, dust or vapour of, lead.
- Miscellaneous conditions - Diffuse mesothelioma (primary neoplasm of the mesothelium of the pleura or of the pericardium or of the peritoneum) from an occupation involving exposure to asbestos at a level above that commonly found in the environment at large.

Some of the prescribed diseases carry a specification of how much harm has occurred, e.g. a 50dB reduction in hearing in both ears, this level of harm is required before benefit is payable. These regulations were amended in 2006, the amendment regulations are shown here to illustrate that change does take place over time and the typical scope of the change.

Social Security (Industrial Injuries) (Prescribed Diseases) Amendment Regulations (SSIIPDAR) 2006

Arrangement of Regulations

1)   Citation, commencement and interpretation.

2)   Amendment of the principal regulations.

3)   Amendment of Schedule 1 of the principal regulations.

4)   Transitional provision.

Outline of key points

These Regulations amend the Social Security (Industrial Injuries) (Prescribed Diseases) Regulations 1985 (S.I. 1985/967), which prescribe diseases for which industrial injuries benefit is payable.

Regulation 2(1) makes a consequential amendment to the definition of "primary carcinoma of the lung".

Regulation 2(2) provides, on a claim for disablement pension in respect of prescribed diseases D8 and D8A, that entitlement may arise from the first day a person suffers from a loss of faculty due to that disease and prescribes lung impairment caused by primary carcinoma of the lung as a loss of faculty from which the resulting disabilities are to be taken as amounting to 100% disablement.

Regulation 3(2) amends prescribed disease C24 in Part I of Schedule 1 by substituting diseases C24 and C24A. Where due to exposure to vinyl chloride monomer, angiosarcoma of the liver, osteolysis of the finger-tips, sclerodermatous thickening of the skin of the hand, liver fibrosis and Raynaud's phenomenon are each prescribed independently. Only work involving exposure to vinyl chloride monomer in the manufacture of polyvinyl chloride before 1st January 1984 is prescribed in relation to Raynaud's phenomenon.

Regulation 3(3) amends prescribed disease D8 in Part I of Schedule 1 by substituting diseases D8 and D8A. The disease previously prescribed as D8 has been replaced with primary carcinoma of the lung where there is accompanying evidence of asbestosis and primary carcinoma of the lung. New occupations involving exposure to asbestos are prescribed in relation to primary carcinoma of the lung.

Regulation 3(4) amends prescribed disease D9 in Part I of Schedule 1 so that the obliteration of the costophrenic angle is used in the diagnosis of the prescribed disease.

Regulation 4 makes transitional provision so that the amendments made to Schedule 1 by regulation 3(2) and (4) do not apply to claims made before these Regulations come into force.

Index